Handbook of Coatings for Concrete

Handbook of Coatings for Concrete

edited by
Dr R.Bassi and Professor S.K.Roy

Whittles Publishing

Typeset by
Whittles Publishing Services

Published by
Whittles Publishing,
Roseleigh House,
Latheronwheel,
Caithness, KW5 6DW,
Scotland, UK

© 2002 Whittles Publishing

ISBN 1-870325-82-6

Printed by Bookcraft, Midsomer Norton, UK

Contents

Preface

Brian Goldie
Protective Coatings Europe

This handbook provides detailed information on the use of coatings to protect concrete from atmospheric exposure and has been written by experts in the field in Europe and the Far East and edited by two well known names in concrete coatings research.

It reviews the present state of knowledge of the different generic types of coatings commonly used, highlights specific needs in the protection of concrete, discusses the standardised testing carried out and has a useful section on typical case histories. Each chapter is illustrated by clear diagrams and photographs where necessary and there is a useful bibliography at the end of each chapter.

The handbook starts with a comprehensive introductory chapter to set the scene; why coat concrete, with what and how should it be carried out. The following chapters of the book essentially take the points made here and expand on them. Firstly the types of coatings typically used are described, but before this, the second chapter gives an overview of paint technology, so that those readers not familiar with this subject will be able to understand the concepts discussed. For each generic coating type, an easily understood description of the chemistry is given followed by the properties and performance of the coatings and finally typical uses.

Acrylic and cementitious coatings form a very important segment of the concrete protection market and three chapters are devoted to these coatings. In addition, the other widely-used generic resin systems, epoxy and polyurethane, are also given very detailed coverage.

The handbook then turns to some specific problems with concrete and how coatings can be used to overcome these. Chapters focus on the protection of rebars in reinforced concrete structures, anti-carbonation coatings, and crack-bridging by coatings. There are also chapters dealing with the aesthetic properties of coatings, including biological growth, its evaluation, and the use of biocides.

How to select the correct coating, and the range of international test procedures needed are covered in one chapter as is the very important topic of surface preparation. This topic is covered to some extent in the previous chapters on the generic resins, but is given a more detailed treatment, since even when the best coating system is selected, if the surface has not been prepared properly, the desired performance will not be achieved.

There is a very topical chapter on solvents in coatings and the need to reduce their emission to the atmosphere (the VOC regulations). A description of the problem plus a look at how industry is tackling this and some future trends are discussed.

The final chapter describes some selected case studies of the successful use of coatings to protect concrete from atmospheric exposure. These illustrate some of the topics covered in the book.

Whilst the protection of concrete against atmospheric attack is a major use of coatings, it is not the only reason concrete would be coated. Concrete is a major structural material and is used in a variety of environments from which it must be protected. It is not possible in one book to be totally comprehensive in coverage of the use of coatings to protect concrete and readers should consult other specialised textbooks or the coatings manufacturers for advice on situations not described. To aid the reader, the Appendix lists contact details for a selection of coating manufacturers specialising in supplying coatings for concrete in Europe and N. America.

Standards and Codes of Practice
Every effort has been made to quote the correct and appropriate code/standard in the text. However, with the proliferation of of national and international standards in draft and final forms, readers are advised to check for the most up-to-date version in their sphere of activity.

Contributors

Dr. R. Bassi	Projects Manager Building Research Establishment Bucknalls Lane Garston Watford, WD2 7JR, UK
Dr. S. Beinborn	formerly Technical Services Manager Vantico Polymer Specialities Ernst Scheringstrasse 14 PO Box 1620 D-59180 Bergkamen GERMANY
Dr. Razmik Boodaghians	formerly Vinamul Uk Ltd. Business Outreach Officer Research & Business Development Office South Bank University Borough Road London, SE1 0AA, UK
Mr. J. Boxall	formerly Projects Manager Building Research Establishment Bucknalls Lane Garston Watford, WD2 7JR, UK
Dr. Peter Chan	General Manager Polymer Coating Technologies of Singapore Pte Ltd. 16 Joo Koon Crescent SINGAPORE 629019

S.K. Chew	Assistant General Manager Nippon Paint (Singapore) Pte Limited 1 First Lok Yang Road, Jurong SINGAPORE 629728
Dr. D. Crump	Projects Manager Building Research Establishment Bucknalls Lane Garston Watford, WD2 7JR, UK
Mr. S.P. Darwen	Technical Sales Vantico Polymer Specialities Duxford Cambridge
Mr. H. Davies	Building Research Establishment Bucknalls Lane Garston Watford, WD2 7JR, UK
Dr. M. Decter	formerly with Fosroc Coleshill Road TAMWORTH Staffordshire, B78 3TL, UK
Mr. M.A. Gatrell	Research and Development Chemist Liquid Plastics Limited Astral House P.O. Box 7 Miller Street Preston, PR1 1EA, UK
Mr. J. Gillatt	Group Product Manager – Biocides Thor Specialities (UK) Limited Earl Road Cheadle Hulme Cheshire, SK8 6QP, UK
Mr. M. Greenhalgh	Avecia Ltd. Research Department P.O. Box 42 Hexagon House Blackley Manchester, M9 8ZS, UK

Dr. C.A. Hunter	BRE Environment Building Research Establishment Bucknalls Lane Garston Watford, WD25 9XX, UK
Dr. S.A. Hurley	Technical Manager and Principal Chemist Taywood Engineering 345 Ruislip Road Southall Middlesex, UB1 2QX, UK
Mr. John Midwood	Carrs Paint Limited Westminster Works Alvechurch Road West Heath Birmingham, B31 3PG, UK
Mr. M. Murray	(formerly Bulding Research Establishment) Greenwich Council Strategic Development & Planning Office Peggy Middleton House 50 Woolwich New Road London, SE18 6HQ, UK
Mr. J.A. Phipps	Mott MacDonald Spring Bank House 33 Stamford Street Altrincham Cheshire, WA14 1ES, UK (Now with EQE International, The Beacons, Warrington Road, Birchwood, Cheshire. WA3 6WJ)
Professor S.K. Roy	Graduate Programme of the Civil Engineering Department Petra Christian University Surabaya INDONESIA

Mr. M. B. Squirrell

Business Development Manager
MBT Feb
19 Broad Ground Road
Lakeside
Redditch
Worcestershire. B98 8YP

Mr. V. F. Stadelmann

Rohm & Haas France S.A.
Quartier les Lucioles
371, Rue L. Van Beethoven
Sophia Antipolis
F-06560 Valbonne
FRANCE

Mr. Haydn Thomas

Product Manager
H. Haeffner & Co. Limited
St. Maur
Beaufort Square
Chepstow, NP16 5EP, UK

Mr. M.G. Wilson

Liquid Plastics Limited
P.O. Box 7
London Road
Preston, PR1 4AJ, UK

Mr. A.P.J.Yates

Projects Manager
Building Research Establishment
Bucknalls Lane
Garston
Watford, WD2 7JR, UK

1 Coated concrete – why, what and how

S.K.Roy

1.1 Introduction

The durability of concrete depends on its quality; good quality concrete is inherently durable. The durability can be increased by proper choice of materials, proportioning, placing and curing. Usually concrete with higher strength and lower permeability is more durable. Another way of enhancing the durability of concrete is by applying a coating. Concrete coatings can provide decoration, cleanability, dust reduction, water-proofing, improved surface release properties, enhanced slip resistance, protection against reinforcement corrosion (reduction of carbonation and chloride ingress), as well as resistance to chemical attack. Coatings can also protect concrete from damage caused by frost, abrasion, mechanical stress, salt penetration, water, and from solar heat. For good performance of coated concrete, the characteristics of the concrete have to be taken into consideration for selection of the correct surface preparation prior to the application of the right coating for a given environment. In this chapter, some of the characteristics of concrete are given first; various ways in which concrete can degrade are then discussed, followed by a section on surface preparation and coating application. Various coatings available for concrete, as well as some tests commonly carried out on coated concrete, are also given.

1.2 Characteristics of concrete

For the purpose of coating, concrete is non-homogeneous. Because of variations in cement or sand and coarse aggregate, admixtures, mixing, vibration, weather conditions and so on, the ideal homogeneity is lost in the actual concrete. The proportions of the ingredients used control the workability of the mix, strength, density, curing characteristics, etc. Proper curing is necessary for making strong and durable concrete. During curing hydration of cement occurs and water must be present.

Concrete should not be coated when true water is present in it. Usually two months curing of concrete at temperatures over 21°C is considered adequate for most types of coating although recommendations range from one month to six months.

Cementitious materials can be of various types e.g. five ASTM types of Portland cements, (standard, reduced heat of hydration and increased sulphate resistance, high early strength, low heat of hydration, sulphate resistant), calcium aluminate cement, magnesium oxychlorides, pozzolonas, granulated blast furnace slag, pulverized fly ash, etc. Admixtures, added just before or during mixing of concrete, can influence workability, settlement, segregation, pumpability, slump rate and curing. The coating system used should be compatible with the admixtures present in the concrete.

Sodium silicate, magnesium fluorosilicate, zinc fluorosilicate, lead fluorosilicate, etc. which are used to improve surface hardness, impermeability to liquids and resistance to mild chemical attack, make acid etching of the harder surface difficult and cause poor adhesion of many coatings.

Form release agents (used to release formwork from the concrete), as well as curing compounds (used to prevent loss of water from freshly placed concrete), should be compatible with the coating system; if they are incompatible, they must be removed during the surface preparation. Oils are often used for form release. Some of the oil goes into the concrete surface and unless the oil is removed by blasting, the coating will have poor adhesion. For concrete surfaces which will be coated, instead of oil, non-migrating birch coatings should be used for the forms.

Another characteristic which affects the selection of surface preparation before coating application is how the surface is finished. A steel trowelled finish (smooth, slick surface), a broom finish (rough surface) and a poured-in-place concrete surface (air pockets) each require different surface preparation. Laitance (fine cement powder) which is found on all poured concrete work has a poor bond to the body of the concrete and poor strength. Laitance must be removed by acid etching or blasting to get adequate bonding of the coating to sound concrete. Air pockets can be reduced by proper vibration and placing techniques but they are present in the surface of all concrete. Some air pockets are filled with loose cement, which has no strength, and coatings applied over it will have poor adhesion. Air pockets can be filled by sacking, grouting, or applying a surfacer to the concrete and the material used to fill in the pockets must be compatible with the coating system to be used.

1.3   Deterioration of concrete

In this section, the deterioration of concrete by alkali-silica reaction (ASR), leaching, thermal and moisture movements, carbonation, and chloride ingress are described and the ways in which coatings can prevent or reduce each of these degradations are discussed.

1.3.1   Alkali-silica reaction (ASR)

In the presence of moisture, concrete can deteriorate by an alkali-silica reaction (ASR) if the aggregates are reactive. Some aggregates used in making concrete contain a reactive form of silica which reacts with the sodium and potassium hydroxides released from the cement and causes deterioration of the concrete. As a result of this reaction an alkali silicate gel is formed and this gel sets up expansive forces which cause deterioration; cracks appear in a random pattern and a soft viscous gel oozes out through the cracks and pores. This gel hardens and turns whitish on exposure to air. The reactivity of aggregates is due to the presence of opaline silica, microcrystalline silica, chalcedony, tridymite, crystoballite, certain cryptocrystalline volcanic rocks such as rhyolites and andesites, some zeolites, and certain metamorphic schists. For ASR to occur, there must be present a high alkali level in the cement (more than 0.6%), reactive constituents in the aggregates, and water. If any one of these three factors is missing, no ASR can occur (Roy *et al.*, 1997). Hence waterproofing coatings on concrete can prevent its deterioration by ASR.

1.3.2   Concrete deterioration by leaching

A major cause of deterioration of concrete is the presence of water (Roy, 1994). Large quantities of water entering the concrete through the pores can cause leaching in which lime in the concrete is leached out and redeposited on the surface where it undergoes a chemical reaction and forms sheets of calcite and stalactites hanging down from overhangs or from the underside of the slabs or concrete structural elements. When soft water comes into contact with the concrete, the concentration of dissolved calcium salts is very low whereas that in concrete is many orders of magnitude higher. Because of the large disparity in concentration, the dissolution rate is very high and rapid attack can take place. Concrete constituents have higher solubility in acidic waters and, as a result, more materials can dissolve in them. Water containing carbon dioxide can form insoluble calcium carbonate and can cause rapid degradation of concrete. Carbonic acid is a stronger acid than silicic acid and, since a weaker acid can be displaced from its combination by a stronger one, water containing carbon dioxide can also decompose calcium silicates, aluminates, hydrosilicates and aluminate hydrates in concrete. As a result of leaching, concrete loses strength. Seepage accompanied by freeze-thaw cycles and formation of ice can result in spalling, chipping, exfoliation of concrete surfaces or rendered cementitous finishes. The alternate freezing and thawing of water within the concrete can cause deterioration. Leaching can be prevented by treating concrete with a waterproofing coating.

1.3.3   Concrete deterioration by thermal and moisture changes

When exposed to sun and rain, concrete experiences changes in temperature and moisture content. One kind of moisture change is due to changes in season. Temperature also changes from day to night. As a matter of fact, micro changes in temperature are taking place almost continuously. A sudden change in temperature can be brought about by abrupt rain during a hot sunny day. Changes of temperature or moisture content in concrete bring about movement (Roy *et al.*, 1999).

A rise in temperature or wetting causes expansion; a drop in temperature or drying is associated with shrinkage. When movement is prevented or restrained, stress develops. Cyclic stressing or straining can cause deterioration of concrete. Again waterproofing, as well as heat reflecting coatings, can reduce concrete deterioration due to movement.

1.3.4   Carbonation of concrete

Carbon dioxide in the air can reduce the alkalinity of the concrete surrounding the rebar and causes corrosion of steel reinforcement. When the alkaline materials in the concrete react with atmospheric carbon dioxide, they are converted to carbonates. The pore water in concrete has a pH of about 12.6 and at this pH steel is passive. However, when the pH drops to about 11 due to carbonation, passivity is lost and corrosion starts. Carbonation starts from the surface and proceeds inwards. The rate of carbonation depends on atmospheric parameters (e.g. humidity, concentration of carbon dioxide) as well as on concrete quality (e.g. permeability). The carbonation rate is generally considered to be diffusion controlled.

Carbonation occurs very rapidly in the humidity range of 50% to 80%. It should be understood that carbonation is not a reaction of gaseous carbon dioxide with solid lime; it is a reaction of carbon dioxide dissolved in a moisture film on the surface of the pores with alkali in solution. Below 50% humidity there is no moisture film on the surface of the pores and carbonation is slow. Above 80% humidity the pores are completely saturated; the carbon dioxide has to dissolve in the pore water, diffuse through the pores, reach the concrete beyond the carbonation front, and then react. As a result, when pores are not saturated but only have a layer of moisture on their walls, carbon dioxide can rapidly diffuse through the pores and react on the moist pore wall surfaces. This makes carbonation fastest in the humidity range of 50% to 80%. The carbonation rate depends on the concentration of carbon dioxide. The normal concentration of carbon dioxide in air is about 300 ppm but this concentration can be much higher in garages, underpasses, and some enclosed places such as a grain silo. Moreover, the atmospheric carbon dioxide level is going up with time and is predicted to reach a level of 600 ppm in 100 years. This means that a reinforced concrete structure designed and built this year for a service life of 100 years will suffer from enhanced corrosion of reinforcing steel due to the increase in the carbon dioxide level and the actual life will be greatly reduced. According to BS8110, a structure with 30 mm cover of a high strength concrete should last forever from the corrosion point of view at the present CO_2 level of 300 ppm. If the CO_2 level reached 600 ppm, the same concrete would have a much shorter life.

Once corrosion starts in carbonated concrete, the corrosion rate depends on the permeability of the concrete and the availability of moisture and oxygen from the environment. Thus corrosion of reinforcement due to carbonation involves a period of initiation (time from casting of concrete to onset of corrosion) and propagation (progress of corrosion at a variable rate). While making a condition survey of a concrete structure, it is important to make a distinction between the initiation and propagation phases. The carbonation depth and chloride level at different depths can be determined during service. In this way areas becoming vulnerable can be identified and treated before costly damage occurs.

Carbonation depths and compressive strengths of reinforced concrete buildings can be measured easily. The average carbonation depth, d, is related to the age of the building by the relationship $d = K\sqrt{age}$, where K is the carbonation constant. Much work has been reported by various authors on carbonation of concrete and mortars both in terms of laboratory testing (Roy *et al.*, 1996a) and surface of concrete structures (Brown, 1991). A number of mathematical models have been put forward as a result of testing which are then used in service life prediction of concrete structures (Tuutti, 1980). Most of the reported data on carbonation of building surfaces have, however, been limited to temperate climates. For example, North America and Europe are covered well, with a reasonable body of data for the Middle East but little published information is available for tropical climates where the structures are subjected to high temperatures, abundant sunshine, high relative humidity, and frequent and heavy rain (Roy *et al.*, 1996a,b). If we consider carbonation to be simply a diffusion process, then the carbonation depth d is related to the exposure time (age of building) t, by the equation $d = K\sqrt{t}$ (Roy, 1994). The K values of 5.5–8.6 mm/(year)$^{1/2}$ measured in tropical climates are generally higher than those 1–3 mm/(year)$^{1/2}$ reported for temperate climates (Roy, 1994; Roy *et al.*, 1996b; Roy *et al.*, 1997). The difference can be partly attributed to significantly higher mean daily temperatures in tropical climates compared to temperate climates. As pointed out by Brown (1991), there appeared to be three primary factors determining the depth of carbonation, these being age, exposure and quality of concrete. Brown suggested that a relationship existed between carbonation depth, age and strength (S), which had the form $D = K(t)^{1/2}/S$, i.e. carbonation depth decreases with increase in strength. Anti-carbonation coatings are now available to protect concrete from carbonation.

1.3.5 Chloride induced corrosion

Chloride ions replace some of the oxygen in the passive film on the reinforcement steel, making it more conductive and soluble. The film loses its protective character, being unable to maintain the high potential difference across it, and the measurement of the potential at the steel surface gives a value close to that of an iron electrode. The breakdown of the passive film is localized and creates macro galvanic cells with the local active areas as anodes and the remaining areas as cathodes. The rate of dissolution of iron depends on the concentration of chlorides, the solubility of oxygen, the cathode/anode ratio, and the electrical resistivity of concrete between the cells (Roy, *et al.*, 1993; Roy *et al.*, 1996c).

The Building Research Establishment (Digest 263 and 264, 1982) assesses the corrosion risk due to chlorides as : low (0–0.4% chloride), medium (0.4 to 1.0% chloride), and high (above 1% chloride). The US Federal Highway Administration restricts chlorides to 0.20%. The present British code for reinforced concrete limits total chloride content of the mix to 0.4% and precludes the addition of calcium chloride. Concrete coatings can act as barriers to the ingress of chloride and hence provide protection from chloride induced corrosion.

1.3.6 Deterioration by sulphate attack

Another common form of concrete deterioration is related to the presence of sulphates in the soil or ground water in which the concrete is buried, or in the aggregates.

The intensity and the rate of sulphate attack depend on a number of factors such as the type of sulphates (magnesium sulphate is the most vigorous), its concentration and the continuity of its supply. Permeability and the presence of cracks also affect the severity of attack. Sulphate solutions react with calcium hydroxides and calcium aluminates of hydrated cement in concrete to form calcium sulphate and calcium sulphoaluminate compounds; the volume of these compounds is greater than the volume of reactants from which they are formed. This increase in volume within hardened concrete contributes towards the breakdown of concrete. Coatings can stop or reduce the supply of sulphate to the concrete and hence prevent its breaking down due to sulphate attack.

1.3.7 Cracking of concrete

A crack occurs in a material when the tensile stress applied to that material exceeds its tensile strength. It is thus not uncommon to find cracks occurring in concrete structures as concrete has a low tensile strength. Tensile stress is built up when a tendency to change in size is wholly or partially restrained. Such restraint is present in slabs in the form of subgrade friction and is provided in structural members by adjacent members to which they are connected. In large masses of concrete, drying or cooling of the surface causes the attempted reduction in size of the surface layers to be restrained by the interior.

In addition to low tensile strength, concrete also undergoes large volume changes. Concrete swells as it becomes wet and shrinks as it dries. Any extreme change in temperature also causes concrete to undergo large volume changes. Cracking in concrete can also be due to chemical attack, expansion of the reinforcement due to corrosion, inadequate structural support, differential movements with other adjacent materials, momentary loading such as that due to vibrations from traffic, machinery, etc., soil movements, externally applied loads such as that from wind, a new extension above the structure, etc.

Specifically, concrete suffers from cracking due to shrinkage (plastic, hydration, drying, carbonation), differential settlement, differential movement, alkali-silica reaction, unsound concrete, sulphate attack, inadequate structural support, and reinforcement corrosion (Roy and Chew, 1992). Whatever the reason for the cracks, for the purpose of repair they are classified as active (still undergoing increase in dimension), or inactive (not likely to change in dimension). Narrow cracks can be repaired by brushing in dry cement and spraying water over them. Epoxy injection is considered best to repair large inactive cracks. When an inactive crack does not pass through the concrete member, epoxy mortar can be used instead of just epoxy and hardener. Active cracks are expected to show further movement and hence they are sealed with an elastomeric sealant; acrylic sealants are normally used but other sealants can also be employed. The crack-bridging capacity of the coating is a very important property to be considered when selecting a coating for concrete having surface cracks.

1.4. Surface preparation

As mentioned earlier, surface preparation depends on a number of factors such as
1. type, placement, curing, finishing, age and condition of the concrete;
2. coating system to be used; and
3. exposure condition.

Surface preparation requires
1. removal of oils, grease, incompatible curing compounds, laitance, efflorescence, etc., (ASTM, D4258, 1999);
2. treatment of air pockets, corners, expansion joints, etc.; and
3. acid etching (ASTM, D4260, 1999), blasting (wet or dry) (ASTM, D4259, 1999), wire brushing, roughening by impact tools, power grinding, removal of chemical contamination, etc.

Surface preparation ensures that the prepared surface is suitable for application of the coating and that the bond between the concrete and the coating is going to be strong. Improper surface preparation is rated as one of the most frequent causes of failure of concrete coatings. Before the selection of the proper surface preparation method, the views of the coating manufacturer should be seriously considered. A mock-up test can also be conducted with a selected preparation method.

1.5 Application of coatings

Coatings are usually applied by brush, roller, trowel, or spray gun (conventional or airless). For a given paint to be applied by conventional spray gun, the size of the fluid nozzle, the pressure setting of the air compressing regulator, and percentage setting of the air and the paint regulator should be as specified by the paint manufacturer.

For airless spray application, the minimum working pressure on paint for a given spray tip size and spray tip angle should be specified by the paint manufacturer and followed by the applicator.

For a multi-coat system, the coating sequence, the film thickness ranges for each coat, and the maximum and minimum drying times for each coat in a given environment (temperature and humidity) should be specified and then followed during application. The environmental conditions during application and curing are important. The application work should be carried out by a well-qualified painter. Improper curing before being placed in service can also cause the failure of the coating.

1.6 Coatings for concrete

Various materials available for coating concrete including silicones, silanes, cementitious coatings, thin film urethanes, epoxy polyesters, latexes, chlorinated rubbers, epoxies, epoxy phenolics, aggregate filled epoxies and thick filled elastomers (urethane, polysulphide) (NACE, 1991). Each of these coatings can be recommended for a specific set of service conditions which are listed as water repellency, cleanability, aesthetic, concrete dusting, mild chemical, severe chemical, moderate physical and severe physical.

Various coatings for concrete are recommended for different exposure conditions. Tables 1.1 amd 1.2 are adapted from Foscante and Kline (1998).

To repair concrete for service in aggressive environments, an elastomeric membrane coated with inorganic cement can be mechanically attached to the substrate with studs or the repair concrete can be attached to the old deteriorated surface with a concrete adhesive (Roy *et al.*, 1997).

1.7 Tests and Standards

A liquid concrete coating is usually tested for viscosity, fineness of grind, drying time, specific gravity, pigment volume concentration, coverage capacity, non-volatile matter, brushing properties, etc. A hardened coating can be tested for adhesion, thickness, colour, gloss, wet scrub resistance, opacity, alkali resistance, fastness to light, etc. (Aldinger, 1991) In all major countries, these tests are covered in national standards, e.g. ASTM Standard E96, Singapore Standard SS5, and so on.

Table 1.1 *Different coating systems for various exposures..*

Exposure condition	Coating System
Atmospheric	Acrylic latex, high performance epoxy or urethane, silicate or hydrophobic sealers
Atmospheric plus mechanical stress	Elastomeric polyurethane, glass or sand filled epoxy/polyester
Immersed	Coal tar epoxy, one or two coats of high performance epoxy, polyurethane or other elastomeric lining, vinyl or other thermoplastic lining, glass or sand filled polyester/epoxy

Flooring is addressed as a separate classification as given in Table 1.2.

Table 1.2 *Recommended coatings for concrete flooring in terms of severity of exposure conditions.*

Exposure condition	Coating system
Severe service	Membrane with acid brick and mortar, polymeric sheet lining
Heavy duty service	Sand filled epoxy surfacer, polyester surfacer, elastomeric polyurethane for crack bridging
Moderate service	Epoxy with polyurethane topcoat, durable epoxy high build, polyurethane sealer with polyurethane topcoats
Light service	Silicate or hydrophobic sealer, polyurethane sealer

There are a number of artificial and natural weathering tests used by both the paint manufacturers in the development of new paint formulations and by paint manufacturers and paint users in assessing the suitability of a paint for a particular application and in determining its durability under the particular, or similar, environmental conditions. Artificial (accelerated) weathering tests involve exposing the paint for a fixed period in a weathering apparatus to ultraviolet radiation, elevated temperatures and condensation. The exposed samples can then be evaluated for chalking, checking and colour change. Chalking refers to a surface deposit of powder formed by the disintegration of the binder due to exposure to UV light and moisture. Chalking can be gauged by wiping the exposed surface of the paint with a black velvet cloth and comparing with photographic samples as per ASTM Standard D659-86. Checks are slight breaks in the paint film which do not penetrate into the substrate. Checking can be measured by examining at 25 times magnification and comparing with photographic samples as per ASTM D660-88. Colour change is a gradual decrease in colour intensity in the paint due to the use of pigments with insufficient lightfastness. The colour change can be measured by visual inspection under artificial lighting (fluorescent illumination) and comparing with photographic samples as per Singapore Standard SS: Part E3-76.

Natural weathering tests can also be carried out to assess the durability of paints. Test panels of the paint on the cementitious substrate can be affixed to racks and exposed at the site. At selected intervals, the samples are assessed for chalking, checking and colour change as described above. In addition, the samples can be assessed for algae growth. Singapore has a standard method of testing algicidal coatings (SS345-90, Appendix B). In this test, the test paint is applied to the interior of a plastic petri dish and, after UV ageing, is inoculated with a broth culture of algae *Trentepohlia odorata* and incubated for 12 hours per day at 1000–1400 lux. After eight weeks the intensity of algae growth is visually assessed.

Field survey of actual paint works can be carried out to assess their performance. Evaluation of chalking, flaking, discolouration, algae and mould growth, dust and soot deposit, etc. should be carried out. Samples can be evaluated for a given defect using photographic standards and a 0-10 rating scale. Generally a particular defect would be considered to be present if more than 5% of the total surface area tested appears to have that defect (Roy *et al.*, 1996d).

Anti-carbonation coatings are tested for resistance to carbon-dioxide diffusion and water vapour diffusion. For testing carbon-dioxide diffusion resistance, tiles can be coated, conditioned, and sealed in a circular steel rig such that the coated and the uncoated faces are exposed. Carbon dioxide containing 15% oxygen is passed over the coated face at a given pressure and flow rate, and helium gas is passed over the opposite face at the same pressure and flow rate. From the steady state flow of gas and the percentages of carbon dioxide and oxygen in the helium stream, diffusion coefficients of carbon dioxide and oxygen can be calculated using Fick's Law of Diffusion.

For testing water vapour transmission, a coated and conditioned tile is sealed in a test dish using a water vapour impermeable sealant. The coated face is exposed to a dry atmosphere (relative humidity = 0) and the uncoated face is exposed to a wet atmosphere (relative humidity =100). The test dish is weighed daily and the water vapour permeability is calculated as gm/mm/m²/24 hours at room temperature. The diffusion coefficient for water vapour is obtained using Fick's Law of Diffusion. This test, as well as the carbon dioxide diffusion test, is covered by ASTM e-96-80. The water vapour diffusion resistance, expressed as an equivalent air layer, should be less than 4 m and the carbon dioxide diffusion resistance, expressed as an equivalent air layer, should be more than 200 m for a good anti-carbonation coating.

Solar reflective paints are tested for reflectivity, emissivity, and absorptivity (Whiteley, 1981). The energy of the solar spectrum is distributed as: infrared,55%; visible, 40%; ultraviolet, 5%. A solar reflective paint, such as aluminium paint, is highly reflective from UV to IR and a specular reflectance of about 65% can be measured with a reflectance meter. For most non-metallic surfaces, regardless of colour, the emissivity (causing loss of heat by radiation) is about the same. Single component water-based solar reflective high build systems with solar absorption (measured as per ASTM 903) as low as 0.16 are available in the market.

References

Aldinger, T.I. (1991) Technical specifications for concrete coating work. *Materials Performance,* June 1991, 36–41.

American Society for Testing and Materials (1999) *ASTM D4258. Practice for surface cleaning concrete for coating.* ASTM, Philadelphia.

American Society for Testing and Materials (1999) *ASTM D4261. Practice for surface cleaning concrete unit masonry for coatings.* ASTM, Philadelphia.

American Society for Testing and Materials (1999) *ASTM D4260. Practice for acid etching concrete.* ASTM, Philadelphia.

American Society for Testing and Materials (1999) *ASTM D4259. Practice for abrading concrete.* ASTM, Philadelphia.

Brown, J.H. (1991) Carbonation – the effect of exposure and concrete quality field survey results from some 400 structures. *Durability of Building Materials and Components,* J.M. Baker et al.(Eds.), E.&F.N. Spoon, London, 294–253.

BRE (1982) Digest 263, 264

Foscante, R.E. and Kline, H.H. (1988) Coating concrete – An overview. *Materials Performance,* September 1988, 34–35.

NACE (1991) Coatings for concrete. *NACE Standard RP0591-91, Section 7,* NACE.

Roy, S.K., Liam, K.C. and Northwood, D.O. (1993) Chloride ingress in concrete as measured by field exposure tests in the atmospheric, tidal and submerged zones of a tropical marine environment. *Cement and Concrete Research,* **23**(6), 1289–1306.

Roy, S.K. (1994) Leaching of concrete – its cause, effect and remedy. *ISI-UTM International Convention,* Kuala Lumpur, Malaysia, January, 08.07-1– 08.07-6.

Roy, S.K., Northwood, D.O. and Poh, K.B. (1996a) Effect of plastering on the carbonation of a 19 year old reinforced building. *Construction and Building Materials,* **10**(4), 262–272.

Roy, S.K., Northwood, D.O. and Poh, K.B.(1996b) The carbonation of concrete structures in the tropical environment of Singapore and a comparison with published data for temperate climates. *Magazine of Concrete Research,* **48** (177), 293–300.

Roy, S.K., Poh, K.B. and Northwood, D.O. (1996c) Studies on durability of concrete in Singapore: Chloride ingress and leaching. *Durability of Concrete Materials and Components, 19-23 May 1996, Stockholm, Sweden,* C. Sjostrom (Ed), 1002–1009.

Roy, S.K., Lee, B.T. and Northwood, D.O. (1996d) The evaluation of paint performance for exterior applications in Singapore's tropical environment. *Building and Environment,* **31**(5), 477–486.

Roy, S.K. and Chew, M.Y.L. (1992) Mechanism and remedies of concrete cracking. *Building Review Journal,* **7**(4), 114–119.

Roy, S.K., Poh, K.B. and Northwood, D.O. (1997) Identifying the alkali reactivity of concrete aggregates – Tests on autoclaved concrete samples. *ACI International Conference on High Performance Concrete: Design and Materials and Recent Advances in Concrete Technology, Kuala Lumpur, Malaysia, December 1977,* V.M. Malhotra (Ed.),193–207.

Roy, S.K., Poh, K.B. and Northwood, D.O. (1999) Durability of concrete – Accelerated carbonation and weathering studies. *Building and Environment,* **34**(5), 597–606.

Tuutti, K. (1980) Service life of structures with regard to corrosion of embedded steel. *Performance of Concrete in Marine Environment Sp.65,* American Concrete Institute, Detroit, 223–236.

Whiteley, P. (1901) Solar reflective paints. *Information Paper No. 26/81,* Building Research Establishment, UK.

2 Basic paint technology

J.Boxall

2.1 Introduction

Paints are surface coatings that are designed to fulfil a protective and/or decorative function for the substrate. While inorganic paints are known, organic coatings predominate in paint technology.

The formulation of paint in respect of its major components, the resinous binder and the pigments, is largely dictated by the intended application, i.e. by the combined requirements of the substrate and the service environment. Thus, paint systems for metals, timber, masonry, etc. may differ markedly from each other, and coatings designed primarily to protect can be formulated on different principles from those that apply to coatings whose function is largely cosmetic.

The major components of a paint formulation are the binder (including any added plasticizer), the pigments (as well as any extender material), a solvent or blend of solvents, and various other substances which may be added at relatively low levels but have a marked effect on the paint. Amongst these auxiliary additives can be included thickeners, dryers, anti-skin agents, surface-active agents, biocides, fungicides and numerous others.

2.2 Paint formulation

2.2.1 Polymers

The polymeric or resin binder of paint is the film-forming component of the formulation; without it, continuous coatings would not be possible. However, a large variety of polymers (resins) and polymer-precursors (materials that will undergo reaction to form a resin) are used in paints.

Paint binders can be subdivided into two broad categories: convertible and non-convertible types. The former are materials that are used in an unpolymerized or partially polymerized state and which, following application to the substrate, undergo reaction (polymerization) to form a solid film. Non-convertible paints are based on polymerized binders dispersed or dissolved in a medium which evaporates after the coating has been applied, to leave a coherent film on the substrate surface.

Some examples of convertible binders to be considered here include alkyd, amino, epoxy, phenolic, polyurethane and silicone resins. Non-convertible binders include chlorinated rubber, acrylic and vinyl resins.

Convertible coatings

Oils

The use of oils in paint formulation was widespread throughout historical times and until the mid-20th century. More recently, however, with the introduction of more sophisticated polymers, their use has declined markedly. They are extensively used, however, as modifying components in the preparation of oil-modified alkyd resins, which form one of the most widely used classes of binder in modern paint technology.

Alkyd resins

Alkyd resins are essentially polyesters and as such are susceptible to degradation by strong acids and alkalis. This limits their use to situations where such exposure will not be experienced. However, oil and fatty-acid-modified alkyds possess, with respect to general performance, the attributes of ease of application and tolerance to adverse application conditions, which render them especially suited to the formulation of general purpose paint systems for the construction industry. Alkyd resins can also be copolymerized with other resin precursors. Thus interaction with isocyanates will yield urethane alkyds, and various other copolymers.

Epoxy resins

Epoxy resins are produced by condensation polymerization between epichlorhydrin and diphenylol-propane (bis-phenol A), usually in the presence of sodium hydroxide and under reflux. The reaction conditions and the proportions of the two constituents determine the properties of the final product.

The epoxy resins undergo cross-linkage during curing. This converts them from linear thermoplastic materials to three-dimensional thermosetting resins. This reaction is slow, even with heat, but a number of reagents, particularly tertiary amines, accelerate ring opening and promote cross-linkage without heating. Since epoxy resins will undergo cross-linkage in the presence of amines, polyamines and amine adducts at room temperature, they are referred to as cold curing materials. The two components need to be packaged separately and mixed just prior to use.

Epoxy resins may be blended with other polymers such as acrylic, amino and phenolic resins and, after cure, the cross-linked material possesses the characteristics of both precursors. Copolymers of epoxy resins with the fatty acids in vegetable oils yield the epoxy esters, and the characteristics of films formed from these binders are determined by the fatty acid and the oil length. Epoxy esters are similar to alkyd resins but, since the ester linkages are in side chains and not in the backbone of the resins as in alkyds, the epoxy esters have greater chemical resistance.

Polyurethane resins

Polyurethane resins are polymers formed by the reaction of isocyanates with hydroxy compounds. Polyurethane resin binders fall into two broad categories, single-pack and two-pack. Three types of single-pack system are known; air curing, moisture curing and the heat curing or stoving. The two-pack systems are cold curing; that is, they can polymerize at low temperature in the presence of a catalyst.

Moisture curing polyurethane systems consist of prepolymers having isocyanate termination to the main chain. The isocyanates terminal group will react with atmospheric moisture and so initiate a series of reactions which result in polymerization and film formation. The final films are hard and flexible with high chemical and abrasion resistance.

The heat curing systems also consist of prepolymers, but differ in that the isocyanate terminations are blocked by reacting them with phenol. The system remains blocked or non-reactive until heated, when the phenol is lost and then cross-linking occurs. The resultant films have excellent physical and chemical properties and the overall system has high storage stability.

The air curing single-pack urethane systems are known as urethane-alkyds (or uralkyds). These binders are akin to the conventional alkyds. The type and amount of oil used to prepare the uralkyd determine the film properties and the films are characterized by good resistance to water, mild corrosives and abrasion.

The two-pack urethane systems are based either on an isocyanate-polyol prepolymer or an isocyanate adduct-polyol combination. The isocyanate-polyol system comprises an isocyanate-terminated prepolymer in one pack and a catalyst, such as a tertiary amine, in the other pack. When mixed, the components react at low temperature but often stoving is employed to accelerate the cure rate, resulting in fairly densely cross-linked resins. The films have excellent properties and the pot life of the mixed components is quite long. The isocyanate adduct system has a non-volatile isocyanate as one component. The second component is a polyester or polyether containing free hydroxyl groups. When mixed, the two components tend to react with atmospheric water vapour or adsorbed moisture on the substrate (and so leads to softer films). A slight excess of this second component is incorporated, although too high a level leads to film brittleness. The resultant films again have high resistance to chemicals and abrasion, excellent physical properties and good durability.

Silicone resins
Silicone resins differ from the majority of other paint polymers in that they have an inorganic backbone, i.e. alternating atoms of silicon and oxygen. Organic groups are attached to the silicon atoms and in fact three types of silicone polymer exist, namely rubbers, fluids and resins, of which only resins are of importance in paint technology. It should be noted that these silicon-oxygen polymers have the generic name of siloxanes, but are commonly known as silicones. Silicone resin can be blended or copolymerized with other resins such as alkyds and polyurethane to yield films of enhanced durability, water repellence and temperature resistance.

Non-convertible coatings

Chlorinated rubber
Natural rubber is not used in paint technology but its derivatives, notably chlorinated rubbers, (and, to a lesser extent, isomerized rubber), are important.

Chlorinated rubbers may be used as paint binders, where they form films by solvent evaporation from solution in aromatic hydrocarbons; fairly high plasticizer levels are required to provide film flexibility. The materials are also blended with many other resins to confer specific properties upon the binder.

Chlorinated rubber binders are primarily used for coatings required to provide high resistance to chemicals and/or corrosion.

Vinyl resins

Vinyl resins are polymers derived from monosubstituted ethanes, i.e. ethylene with one hydrogen replaced by the hydroxyl, chloride, acetate or another group. Of these, polyvinyl chloride (PVC) and polyvinyl acetate (PVA) have the greatest importance in paint technology, although other vinyl resins, particularly various copolymers, are also used as binders.

Acrylic resins

Acrylic resins are polyvinylidene compounds; the best known is polymethylmethacrylate or PMMA. The resins are derived from the esters of acrylic and methacrylic acid which are polymerized by a vinyl-type process.

Acrylic resins are hard and rigid thermoplastic polymers that form somewhat inflexible films but which have good optical properties and excellent chemical resistance. They are attacked, however, by concentrated acids and oxidizing agents. Film flexibility can be enhanced by copolymerization. Acrylic coatings are commonly based on dispersions of the resin in solvents or water.

2.2.2 Miscellaneous binders

Two other binders are important in paint technology although they are not strictly classified as polymers, namely bitumens (USA: asphalts) and inorganic silicates.

Bitumen

Bitmens, used in bituminous paints, are naturally occurring or distilled crude or petroleum oil residues. The grade of bitumen, i.e. its colour and properties, depends on both the source and distillation conditions. When dissolved in hydrocarbon solvents, bitumens form surface coatings by solvent evaporation. The coatings have good resistance to aqueous media, to chemicals, to moderate concentration of non-oxidizing acids and to bases at ordinary temperatures. Blending of bitumen with media that contain drying oil results in paints with compromise properties, that is, rapid drying with good protective characteristics for the substrate under moderate-to-severe exposure conditions. The so-called coal-tar/epoxy-resin coatings are obtained by blending bitumens with epoxy resins, which improves the epoxy resin binder's properties of impermeability to water and resistance to chemicals.

Inorganic silicates

Inorganic silicates are prepared by fusion of sand and silica with sodium and/or potassium carbonate, the fused mass then being digested in water. Zinc dust-inorganic silicate coatings have exceptional durability, temperature resistance and corrosion resistance, but they may be attacked by acids and strong bases. Organic-inorganic silicates consist of zinc dust mixed with ethyl orthosilicate which is combined with the inorganic silicate system. Both single- and two-pack formulations have been developed. The coating properties are superior to those of the inorganic silicates and they have a longer pot life.

2.3   Pigments

Pigments are particulate solids that are dispersed in paints to confer certain characteristics upon them. These characteristics include colour, opacity, durability and mechanical strength.

Pigments fall into two principal groups, namely pigments and extenders:
1. Pigments are primarily required to confer colour and opacity upon the binder but may also have to fulfil other functions such as providing corrosion inhibiting characteristics. They may be subdivided into two main chemical classes, inorganic and organic, which differ markedly in their characteristics and uses. Both types are widely used in surface coatings, although organic pigments tend to find their major application in decorative (as opposed to protective) formulations.
2. Extenders are materials that have virtually no colouring or opacifying function. They are incorporated in the formulation to modify the properties of the paint.

2.3.1   General considerations

Most pigments (here taken to cover both pigments and extenders as defined above) are crystalline and the crystal form often affects the characteristics of the pigment. The size and shape of the pigment particles are an important consideration since they affect the agglomeration or packing within the paint binder or matrix. Particle size also affects the final film gloss, settling of the pigment during storage and wetting by the binder. Other factors such as colour, tint strength, colourfastness and opacity are inherent characteristics of the pigment. Density is another important factor, affecting not only settling but also the volume of pigment for a given weight addition.

Pigments have to be dispersed in the binder and, in order to achieve the desired effect, they must remain in suspension or be easily dispersed again should settling occur. Since paints are manufactured by mechanically incorporating the pigments into the binder, not only the physical characteristics mentioned above are important, but also the texture and the mechanical strength of the pigment particles. Thus a large number of factors must be taken into consideration when selecting pigments for paints.

2.3.2   Pigment volume concentration

In practice, many physical properties of coatings are found to vary in a well-defined fashion with the volume concentration of the pigmentation in the resin component of the dried film. This parameter is known as the pigment volume concentration (P.V.C.) and is defined in the equation below. Knowledge of the P.V.C. of a formulation will enable the interpretation of the test data, as many physical properties of coatings are dependent on compositional changes.

$$P.V.C. = \frac{\text{volume of pigments and extenders}}{\text{volume of pigment and extenders } + \text{ volume of solid binder}} \times \frac{100}{1} (\%)$$

2.3.3 Critical pigment volume concentration (C.P.V.C.)

Many coating properties, especially associated with porosity, such as permeability and blistering, tensile strength and abrasion resistance, are found to exhibit sudden marked changes when a particular volume concentration of pigment in the film is exceeded (Figure 2.1). This formulation point is the critical pigment volume concentration and is a characteristic of pigmented coatings.

The C.P.V.C. of any coating represents the point at which there is insufficient binder to wet the pigment particles. At formulation points below the C.P.V.C. there is a surfeit of binder so that the particles are firmly held in the matrix, while above the C.P.V.C. there is insufficient binder to wet the pigments which are therefore loosely held in the film. For this reason, it follows that high performance or exterior coatings in general are not formulated above their C.P.V.C. since many physical properties would be adversely affected.

2.4   Solvents

Solvents are volatile liquids added to paints to dissolve the binder (the resin component) and/or to modify the paint viscosity. Thus not only must a solvent dissolve the resin but the resulting solution should have a viscosity that is in accord with the proposed storage and application modes of the liquid paint. Consequently, the solvent must have an evaporation rate that permits the paint to deposit a film possessing the required characteristics.

The above selection criteria are valid for solvents used for convertible binders. In non-convertible coatings, solvents have a more complex function in that they determine, wholly or in part, the coating application characteristics as well as the drying time and the properties of the final film. Consequently, complex blends of two or more solvents are often used, the blend comprising a solvent for the binder together with a diluent. The diluent may not be a true solvent for the binder but will aid its dissolution in the primary (or true) solvent and modify the properties of the solvent blend.

2.4.1   Water-borne coatings

Due to environmental pressures, health and safety concerns and legislation, paint manufacturers have developed coatings where the solvent is primarily water.

A polymer can be made soluble in water if the monomer used in its preparation has

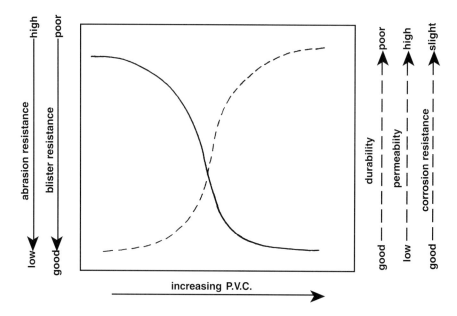

Figure 2.1 *Influence of pigment volume concentration (P.V.C.) on paint performance.*

water-soluble groups such as hydroxyl or carboxyl groups. Aqueous binders can be classified into two main groups:

- dispersion of water-insoluble high molecular polymers; or
- low molecular weight resins that have been modified to become water-dilutable or water-emulsifiable.

There is now a wide range of water-borne coatings, such as one component, two component and stoving systems based on resins such as epoxies, alkyd epoxy esters, acrylic and acrylic-copolymers.

Early types of water-borne coatings had inferior properties to conventional, solvent-borne coatings, though improvements in resin technology and formulation practice have produced coatings of equal or superior performance.

2.5 Plasticizers

Plasticizers are organic additives that are used to increase the film flexibility of paints; particularly those based on binders that otherwise would yield brittle films.

Plasticizers affect many properties of the paint film, including tensile strength, toughness, extensibility, permeability and adhesion. All of these properties are affected to different degrees, often in a complex manner, by plasticization but the detailed effects vary with the polymer and plasticizer types. In general, the plasticizer reduces the tensile strength while increasing the extensibility. Permeability may remain largely unchanged up to a certain critical plasticizer level; thereafter it can increase sharply. Film toughness and adhesion normally increase with the plasticizer level up to a peak value, thereafter decreasing again. The desired effects on the mechanical properties of the film may adversely influence other properties and this consideration often dictates the optimum level of plasticizer that may be added to the formulation.

2.6   Driers

Driers, or drying accelerators, are oil-soluble metal salts of an organic acid added to oxidation curing systems, such as alkyd resins, to increase the curing (drying) rate of the applied film.

2.7   Bioactive additives

Most coatings are susceptible to attack by microorganisms such as fungi and bacteria. Apart from the obvious impairment of appearance, paint coatings may suffer degradation by microorganisms. Bioactive additives are required to prevent this attack.

Biocides or anti-bacterial agents are incorporated within water-borne emulsion paints to prevent bacterial (and fungal) attack on the thickener. Biocides function by interfering with bacterium metabolism, thereby preventing enzyme synthesis, enzymes (rather than the bacteria themselves) being the active agent in paint degradation.

Fungal growth will contribute to the degradation of a paint coating but more commonly it impairs its appearance. In certain circumstances, there may be an associated health hazard, as in kitchens, dairies and breweries. Fungicides are toxic agents that are included in paint formulations to inhibit the colonization and proliferation of fungi.

2.8   Viscosity modifiers and anti-settling agents

Paint formulations may yield liquid paints that are too fluid. With a liquid of low viscosity, the flow may be excessive for some purposes, although high flow may be advantageous in other circumstances. Thus low viscosity is desirable in sealers, but not in high-build coatings and brush-applied paints. Settlement of pigments in storage, particularly if they are dense, occurs readily in low viscosity paints, and heavy settlement can cause problems in redispersing the pigment. These problems of flow and pigment settlement can be offset by adjusting the paint viscosity. In the case of pigments, further adjustments can be made to the formulation to counteract settlement.

Viscosity can be increased by means of thickening agents which increase the viscosity (i.e. decrease flow) without introducing thixotropy.

2.9 Pigment-dispersing agents

Paint formulations require an even dispersion of pigments and extenders throughout the liquid medium. During paint manufacture, this involves dispersion of the pigments and extenders in the liquid medium to break down agglomerates and uniformly wet all the particles. For this to occur, the medium must displace any moisture, occluded gases and fine debris on the particle surfaces; how readily this process is effected is thus of practical importance. While most (but not all) pigments and extenders are olephilic, that is, they are wetted by solvent-soluble media, only a proportion are hydrophilic or wetted by water; for example, many organic pigments are hydrophobic or water-repellent.

Pigment-dispersing agents, or surface-active agents, are used to facilitate pigment and extender dispersion where wetting by the medium is poor or even non-existent. They are often used routinely even when there is good wetting, to ensure good dispersion.

3 Acrylic and styrene/acrylic polymers

Victor F. Stadelmann

3.1 Introduction

Acrylic polymers have the following chemical structure:

```
- CH₂ - CR - CH₂ - CR - CH₂ - CR - CH₂ -
         |           |           |
       C = O       C = O       C = O
         |           |           |
       O - R1      O - R1      O - R1
```

If R is a methyl (CH_3) group, the term methacrylic polymer is also frequently used. Polymethacrylates are harder than the corresponding polyacrylates. Depending upon the group R1, the polymer will be harder or softer. A pure methyl methacrylate polymer will be hard, with a glass transition temperature of about 105°C, while a pure butyl acrylate polymer will be soft (glass transition temperature, Tg, about –55 °C). Combinations of different (meth-) acrylic monomers can result in polymers with any desired hardness, from soft and tacky to hard and tough.

Styrene acrylic polymers show a general structure as follows:

```
- CH₂ - CR - CH₂ - CR - CH₂ - CR - CH₂ -
         |           |           |
       C = O         C         C = O
         |         // \          |
       O - R1      C   C       O - R1
                   |   ||
                   C   C
                   \\ /
                    C
```

The fact that styrene contains double bonds make styrene acrylic polymers less stable than pure acrylics against degradation by ultraviolet light. This may not be of concern for certain applications, but it may be critical for others. Styrene contributes to an increased hydrophobicity; most of the (meth-)acrylic monomers are less hydrophobic than styrene. The (meth-)acrylic polymers are less sensitive to alkaline hydrolysis than vinyl acetate polymers.

Many of the parameters in the polymerization process can be varied (in addition to the variety of monomer units available). It is often very critical to discuss these products in generic terms. Emulsion polymerization allows the production of acrylic polymers at well controlled molecular mass. The use of solvent-based acrylic and styrene/acrylic polymers has dropped considerably over the past years, not only due to environmental considerations, but also because emulsion polymerization allows a much better control over a variety of parameters. Very high molecular mass (order 10^6 and higher) is favourable for properties such as durability and toughness, while low molecular mass (order 10^4) may be preferred for a high tack (as needed for certain adhesives). Differences in molecular mass explain that polymers with an identical overall monomer composition can have completely different performance properties.

An explanation for the effect of molecular mass can be found in the analysis of the torsional modulus as a function of temperature (Figure 3.1). Any polymer is hard and brittle at low temperature. As the temperature increases, the polymer becomes tough and flexible. Pure acrylic polymers can be made to be flexible at temperatures even below minus 50 °C. After a further temperature raise, the polymer softens and becomes plastic. With an increased molecular mass, the leg with tough and flexible behaviour covers a higher temperature range. The modulus of a fully cross-linked polymer will essentially not change until the decomposition temperature of the polymer is reached.

3.2   Physical properties of acrylic coatings

Some of the key properties required for efficient exterior concrete protection are :
* a proper balance of water vapour permeance and carbon dioxide barrier;
* a high degree of alkali resistance;

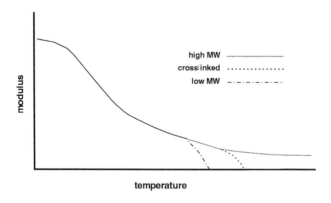

Figure 3.1   *Torsional modulus of polymers.*

- appropriate adhesion characteristics;
- barrier properties against liquid water;
- barrier against penetration of chloride ions;
- retention of properties on ageing; and
- long durability.

3.2.1 Hard and soft acrylic polymers

It has been established that the harder the polymer, the higher its barrier properties against carbon dioxide become. Harder polymers, however, may not be sufficiently flexible at low temperatures (when the concrete has the greatest risk of cracking due to thermal movement). Softer polymers may lack dirt pick-up resistance. Technology has advanced such that soft acrylic polymers can be produced that have excellent dirt pick-up resistance. The surface of the coating cross-links under the effect of natural day-light, which means an increase in surface toughness and thereby resulting in a dirt resistance comparable to that of paint made from a much harder polymer.

Historically, when low temperature flexibility was needed, styrene/acrylic polymers with glass transition temperatures of around 15 °C were softened by the addition of an external plasticizer. While the fresh formulated coatings were actually flexible even at –10 °C, the plasticizer migrated upon ageing and the coatings became more and more brittle at low temperature. These coatings were susceptible to early dirt pick-up.

Figure 3.2 *A building in the Paris area coated with a coloured flexible acrylic coating that protects from the ingress of water.*

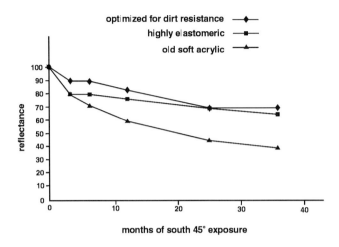

Figure 3.3 *Dirt pick-up resistance graphs.*

They also had low elastomeric properties at elevated temperatures. The current surface cross-linking technology eliminates these deficiencies.

3.2.2 Alkali resistance

Acrylic and styrene/acrylic polymers have a very good resistance to mild alkalis. However, they should in general not be applied directly to "green" concrete. For consistently excellent long term performance properties, the concrete should be allowed to cure for at least one month prior to the application of the coating. Exceptions are concrete curing membranes, which, also based on acrylic or styrene/acrylic polymers, are applied on top of freshly cast (and still wet) concrete and effectively slow down the evaporation of water. Such curing membranes can stay in place and serve as basecoats for pigmented or clear finishes. There are acrylic modified cement mortar based resurfacing compounds available (see further below), which can be top-coated with an acrylic coating within only about three days.

3.2.3 Adhesion to substrate

Acrylics and styrene/acrylic emulsion polymers have inherently good adhesion to even old concrete surfaces. They are not designed, though, to reinforce old spalling concrete. If old concrete is unsound, any loose material must first be removed, e.g. by power washing, and it may need resurfacing. Ultrafine emulsion polymers penetrate deeper into any substrate than conventional emulsion polymers however, they will still not achieve the penetration depth of short chain solvent-based acrylics and styrene/acrylics. Solvent-based penetrating primers are appropriate if a deep penetration is

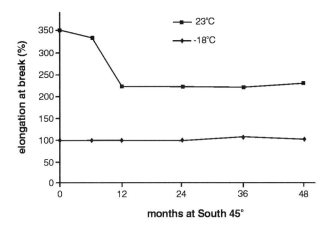

Figure 3.4 *Elongation after natural ageing (acrylic coating at P.V.C. 43%).*

required for consolidating an old substrate, provided that they do not create a water vapour barrier.

3.2.4 Carbon dioxide and water vapour permeability

Pure acrylic emulsion polymers have a favorable balance of water vapour permeability and carbon dioxide diffusion resistance as shown in Table 3.1

Under the applied test conditions, a diffusion equivalent air layer R CO_2 of at least 50 meters is considered to give adequate protection to concrete against carbonation. In order for a coating to be breathable, R H_2O should be less than two meters. Both of these conditions are fulfilled for high performance acrylic paints, whether they are crack-bridging or not. The acrylic paint will protect dimensionally stable concrete structures perfectly well against carbonation. However, if the concrete and the paint develop cracks, carbon dioxide can pass through the cracks and cause carbonation. The crack-bridging coating will remain intact and prevent carbonation. Since the substrate crack width that can be tolerated for a coating without breaking itself is proportional to the applied film thickness, the coverage rate specified by its manufacturer must be respected.

3.2.5 Chloride resistance

Properly formulated and properly applied, acrylic emulsion based coatings can also protect structural concrete from the ingress of chloride ions which would promote the corrosion of steel rebars. An acrylic paint that is conceived to be used in combination with a primer for protecting concrete from chloride ion penetration and which is applied without the primer can result in an adverse effect: the chloride ion content can become worse than that in unprotected concrete! (see Figure 3.5.)

Table 3.1 *Diffusion resistance coefficients μ and diffusion equivalent air layers as determined by Klopfer/Engelfried (Dortmund University).*

	Typical thickness (mm)	μCO_2	μH_2O
Standard concrete	30	500	70
Cement mortar	10	70	20
Acrylic modified cement mortar	10	1220	250
High quality acrylic paint (35% PVC)	0.1	2 400 000	470
Crackbridging acrylic coating (35% PVC)	0.4	289 000	2550

	Thickness (mm)	$R\ CO_2(m)$	$R\ H_2O(m)$
Standard concrete	30	15	2.1
Cement mortar	10	0.7	0.2
Acrylic modified cement mortar	10	12.20	2.5
High quality acrylic paint (35% P.V.C.)	0.1	240	0.05
Crack-bridging acrylic coating (35% P.V.C.)	0.4	115	1.02

The specific paint acts as a selective permeable membrane: chloride ions can pass from the highly concentrated solution into the concrete, but they cannot diffuse back through the acrylic paint. A thick (about 350 μm) crack-bridging, elastomeric coating can provide excellent chloride barrier properties. This specific coating will also remain

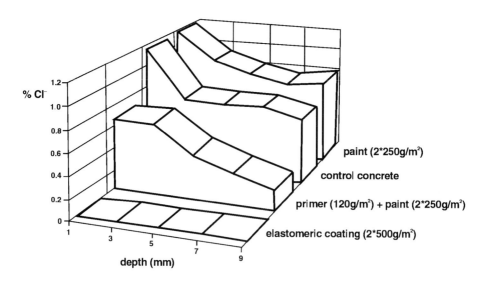

Figure 3.5 *Chloride ingress (three months immersion at 40 °C).*

Figure 3.6 *Coliseum, Virginia coated with an elastomeric acrylic coating.*

Figure 3.7 *Concrete floor coated with an acrylic sealer.*

intact, even if a crack of up to about 1 mm develops in the concrete substrate (see Figure 3.6).

Clear or lightly pigmented aqueous acrylic sealers can successfully protect concrete floors e.g. in warehouses and garages from dusting and being stained by engine oils (Figure 3.7).

3.3 Cementitious coatings

Acrylic polymer emulsions or spray-dried acrylic powders (which are easily re-emulsified in the presence of water) are also successfully used for modifying Portland cement based compositions. While the hydration of Portland cement normally requires a four-week humid cure in order to develop its strength properties, specially designed acrylic polymers allow the hydration to take place under low ambient humidity. In addition, the acrylic polymer contributes to some flexibility of cementitious mortars, without any loss of the compressive strength inherent in Portland cement. The excellent alkali resistance of (styrene/)acrylics ensures that these properties are also maintained under wet conditions. Combining these interesting performance characteristics makes it possible to obtain thin cementitious coatings that have good adhesion, toughness, abrasion resistance, chloride ion barrier properties, low porosity (which means increased cohesion) and a high flexibility, relative to unmodified cement mortars (Table 3.2). Vinyl acetate based modifiers may give similar properties under dry conditions; their sensitivity to alkaline hydrolysis limits their use to applications that exclude temporary or constantly wet areas. As mentioned earlier, the acrylic polymer emulsion may be added to a dry mix of sand/cement/fillers or it may be part (in powdered form) of a dry mix, to which only water needs to be added prior to use. Since the acrylic powder needs

Table 3.2 *Unmodified versus acrylic modified cement mortars.*

Properties	Unit	Standard	Unmodified control	Primal E-330S 15% on cement
Set time	hours	EN 196	3.5	7
Thin section cohesion	-	Rohm & Haas	poor	excellent
Compressive strength	MPa	EN 196	40 [1]	39
Flexural strength	MPa	EN 196	4.1	10.8
Tensile strength	MPa	ASTM C-190	1.6	4.2
Impact strength	N.m	ASTM D-2794	0.7	1.8
Shearbond Adhesion	MPa	Rohm & Haas	0.3	4.4
Abrasion resistance (weight loss)	%	ASTM D-4060	23.8	1.2
Strain	%	UEATC	0.02	0.5
Acid resistance (10% citric acid)	-	Rohm & Haas	abrades readily	unaffected

[1] Wet cure conditions 23°C – 100% RH

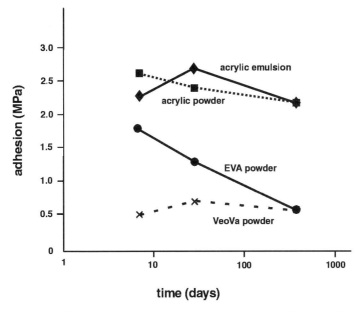

Figure 3.8 *Effect of natural exterior exposure on the adhesion of modified cementitious coatings.*

to be re-emulsified, the mixing time may be somewhat longer than for an unmodified cement mortar.

In all applications as cement modifiers, the polymer/cement ratio is a key factor that determines the final properties. Standard modification levels range from 5 to 15% solid polymer on cement, while highly flexible cementitious coatings may need up to 100% polymer on cement.

Figure 3.8 illustrates that the acrylic polymer, both in the form of aqueous emulsion and as redispersible powder, maintains the high adhesion values of a cementitious coating even after several years of natural weathering.

3.4   Typical acrylic formulations

The excellent resistance of pure acrylic polymers against degradation from ultraviolet light have made them excellent candidates for the factory coating of concrete roof tiles, both as pigmented paints or clear varnishes. These acrylic coatings protect the tiles from the ingress of rainwater, which otherwise could result in deterioration by freezing/thawing, and concrete deterioration caused by acid rain. They also maintain the long term aesthetics by preventing dirt pick-up, efflorescence and reducing the growth of microorganisms.

High performance acrylic coatings over concrete can last a long time without any failures, provided that they are properly formulated and applied. A thorough surface preparation, which largely depends upon the type of coating to be applied, may be the determinant for the long term success of the job. While solvent-based acrylics or styrene/acrylics should never be applied to wet substrates, aqueous systems will not dry within a reasonable time under high humidity conditions. Following the coating manufacturers' instructions is the key to achieving the long term durability that high quality acrylics and styrene/acrylics can provide.

The following tables provide typical formulations and mixes for diverse uses.

Table 3.3 *A typical compositional example for an elastomeric acrylic coating for concrete protection.*

Materials	Parts by weight (kg)
Formulation ELW-91-49-1	
Water	110.00
Orotan®731 (25 %)	13.60
Triton CF-10	2.83
Nopco NXZ	4.25
Acrysol®RM-8	21.25
Propylene glycol	24.08
Tioxide TR-92	120.60
Durcal 5	396.60
Butyl carbitol	17.00
Skane®M-8	5.67
Nopco NXZ	4.25
Primal®EC-2848P	565.40
Acrysol®ASE-60	7.08
Water	74.99
TOTAL	**1367.60**

Table 3.4 *A typical formulation of a clear acrylic concrete floor sealer.*

Formulation CS-91-15	
	kg
Water	63.86
Fluorad FC-120	0.024
Nopco NXZ or SWS-211	0.036
Butyl carbitol	4.80
Ethylene glycol	2.00
Dibutyl phthalate	2.40
Tributoxyethyl phosphate	0.30
Kathon LX (1.5%)	0.07
Primal®WL-91K	36.14
TOTAL	**109.73**

Table 3.5 *A typical acrylic concrete curing membrane.*

	kg
Primal®CS-3800	44.5
Water	52.0
Dowanol PPH	3.3
Defoamer	0.2
Fluorad FC-120	0.04
TOTAL	**100.04**

Table 3.6 *A typical high quality, semi-flexible decorative paint for concrete or masonry.*

Materials	Parts by weight (kg)
Formulation EM-49-50/OP	
Water	154.6
Orotan®731 (25 %)	19.5
Dowanol DPnB	32.7
Byk-033	5.7
Acrysol TT-615	2.2
Aq. Ammonia	2.8
Kathon LXE	2.8
Skane®M-8	4.3
Triton CF-10	1.4
Celite 281	27.6
Tiona RCL-535	357.3
Durcal 10	99.0
Micro Mica W1	51.1
Primal®LT-2949	390.5
Ropaque®OP-96	86.6
Acrysol® RM-2020	49.7
Water	111.2
TOTAL	**1399.0**

Table 3.7 *A typical dry-mix of an acrylic modified, highly resistant cementitious floor topcoat.*

Formulation (SLS-06-B)	
	kg
Drycryl® DP-2904	3.0
TRG Fondu cement	20.0
Sand (0.125 to 0.5 mm)	50.0
Durcal 2	20.0
Gypsum	5.0
Peramin SMF 30	1.0
Hydrated lime	1.0
Tartaric acid	0.35
Lithium carbonate	0.1
Culminal MHPC 500 PF	0.08
TOTAL	**100.53**

Mix 100 parts with 23 parts of water for about 1 minute.

Table 3.8 *Flexible cementitious waterproofing membrane.*

	kg
Dry part:	
Cement (42.5 MPa)	80
Fondu cement	20
Polestar 501	20
Sand (0.05 to 0.2 mm)	87.5
Wollastonite FW 200	62.5
Talc AT-1	10
TOTAL	**300**
Liquid component:	
Primal®FM-2727	100
Agitan 301	3
Water premixed with	25
KTPP	2.5
TOTAL	**130.5**

Mix 50 parts of liquid component with 100 parts of dry mix for 2 minutes.

Table 3.9 *Example of a cementitious powder paint for exterior application.*

Formulation CPP-06-A	kg
Drycryl®DP-2904	5.0
Sand (0.2 mm)	60.0
White cement	25.0
Hydrated lime	5.0
Tiona RCL-376	3.0
Peramin SMF 10	0.5
Esacol ED	0.3
Cecavon MG 52	0.2
TOTAL	**99.0**

Add 30 parts of water to 100 parts of dry mix and mix for 1 minute.
Let mix slake for 5 minutes and mix for an additional 30 seconds.

Table 3.10 *A clear varnish for concrete roof tiles (factory applied).*

	kg
Primal® AC-357	935.0
Texanol	63.1
Drew L-108	0.4
TOTAL	**998.5**

Table 3.11 *A black factory-applied roof tile coating.*

Formulation TF 153/72	kg
Water	162.0
Natrosol 250 HHR	0.9
Ammonia (25%)	0.5
Orotan 731	9.0
Byk 022	2.5
Bayferrox 380M	80.3
Micro Mica W1	120.6
Durcal 5	496.9
Primal® E-822K	430.6
Texanol	10.7
Water	41.5
Slip-Aid SL-300	18.5
Acrysol® RM-8 (at 10% a.i.)	1.8
TOTAL	**1000.0**

Table 3.12 *A cementitious rendering.*

Formulation ERS-06-A	kg
Drycryl® DP-2904	0.2
White cement	20.0
Hydrated lime	4.0
Sand (0.125–0.5 mm)	75.0
Cecavon MG 52	0.5
Culminal C 8564	0.2
Hostapur OSB	0.1
TOTAL	**100.00**

Add 25 parts of water to 100 parts of dry mix and mix for 1 minute.
Let mix slake for 5 minutes and mix for an additional 30 seconds

Table 3.13 *An example of a solvent-based acrylic penetrating primer.*

Formulation PP-66-1	kg
Xylene	5.0
Solvesso 100	20.0
Paraloid® B-66 (100%)	15.0
Innipol 002	1.0
Plasticizer Cereclor 54DP	6.5
Tioxide RCR-2	18.0
Microdol 1	11.0
Celite 499	4.0
Aerosil 200	1.0
Micro Mica W1	7.0
Solvesso 100	5.5
TOTAL	**94.0**

Table 3.14 *An example of an acrylic emulsion-based (unpigmented) primer.*

	kg
Primal®CS-4000	32.00
Nopco NXZ	0.22
Butyl Cellosolve	2.31
Water	65.43
Fluorad FC-120	0.04
TOTAL	**100.00**

4 Cement-based and fibre-reinforced coatings

Mike Squirrell

4.1 Definition

For the purposes of this section, coatings refer to fluid products applied by brush or spray, which, when cured, form a 'coat' typically 0.5–1 mm in thickness per layer. Whilst all rely in some part on the hydration of cement to convert from the 'fluid' to the 'solid' state, most will also contain polymers to impart specific physical properties. Microfibres will be included in some formulations, whereas fibre meshes may be used in others as a form of reinforcement.

4.2 Uses

The primary objective of this chapter is to provide information on the protection of concrete. In some instances, concrete will require protection against physical or chemical attack, whilst in other circumstances, it may be the embedded reinforcement which requires protection against corrosion. To cover the subject fully, it is necessary to consider not only the obvious structures, such as commercial properties and bridges, but also less obvious, sometimes hidden, structures, such as reservoirs. Some examples are given in Table 4.1.

4.3 Description

In their most basic form, cement-based coatings are a simple blend of cement, usually OPC, and graded fine sand. More sophisticated products, designed for specific properties, will still contain cement and graded fine sand, but will also contain additives in order to waterproof, control open time (pot life), setting time and water retention (to aid curing) and to improve thixotropy, density and plasticity.

Fibres based on polyethylene, polypropylene, alkaline resistant glass and acrylates are most commonly used for controlling cracking due to shrinkage and increasing thixotropy. Less common are natural organic fibres and coated carbon fibres. Reinforcing meshes are based on alkaline resisting glass, polypropylene and nylon. Strands are approximately 1 mm in diameter, with mesh opening sizes of 3–5 mm.

Polymers play an important function in cement coatings, improving all physical

Table 4.1 *Matching structures with desired protection.*

Structure	Protection required
Inland exposed Commercial, industrial buildings	Waterproofing CO_2 resistance
Coastal exposed Commercial, industrial buildings	Waterproofing CO_2 resistance Chloride resistance
Bridge and highway structures	Waterproofing CO_2 resistance Chloride resistance
Foundations	Waterproofing Sulphate resistance
Reservoir roofs Roofs	Waterproofing CO_2 resistance Sulphate resistance
Reservoirs internal	Soft acidic water Waterproofing

properties, including adhesion, flexibility, plasticity and water retention. 'Soft' polymers go further than improving flexibility and impart true elastomeric properties, but caution is required as some coatings lose this capability with time or through immersion in water.

Polymers are supplied in liquid form or, more recently, as spray dried powders, which are incorporated in the formulation to produce one component products. They may be based on vinylacetate, ethylene vinylacetate, styrene butadiene rubber, styrene acrylic or pure acrylics.

4.4 Performance

The performance of coatings based on cement and polymers varies quite considerably, depending upon formulation and polymer type. Some types of polymer, by design, re-emulsify (such as polyvinyl alcohol) and are not suitable for coatings.

The powder component of proprietary products will be formulated to maximize the efficiency of the polymer type, which may be in liquid form or, increasingly, in powder form. Such is the expertise of some formulators that coatings can be developed for specific functions, whilst others have good all-round performance.

Performance can be judged on the functionality of the coating and its durability.

Functions	**Durability**
Waterproofing	Adhesion
CO_2 resistance	Water vapour permeability
Chloride resistance	Freeze-thaw resistance
Re-alkalization	E-modulus

Other characteristics which may require evaluation include dynamic crack- bridging and fire resistance.

Performance is important for the functionality of the product. However, another important requirement is often the aesthetics. Because of their cement base and method of application, notably a stiff brush, it is unlikely that most coatings of this type will have much appeal. It is possible to achieve reasonable aesthetics by using white cement, pigmenting and spray application, but the uniformity of texture and colour will never be up to the standard of paints or acrylic type coatings. There is, of course, always an option to overcoat with a cosmetic coating. It should be noted that compatibility of overcoats should always be confirmed. As a rule, solvented paints should not be used over polymer modified coatings.

4.5 Benefits

With so many modern resin-based systems available, what does an 'old fashioned' cement-based material have to offer? In a word, durability. The physical compatibility with concrete, in terms of expansion/contraction, E-modulus and permeability provide a material capable of lasting the lifetime of the structure, when properly applied.

4.6 Coverage versus usage

Coverage rates quoted in manufacturers' literature are factual, based on measured wet densities, e.g.:

Mixed coating weight: 2250 kg/m^3
thus @ 1 mm thickness, 1 m^2 = 2250/1000 = 2.25 kg/m^2 of mixed material.
If the water to solids ratio is 0.20: 2.25 kg × 0.20 = 0.45 kg of water
Mixed material = 2.25 kg/m^2
Less water = 0.45

Coating powder required = 1.80 kg/m^2

It is necessary for the contractor, at this stage, to assess the coverage versus the usage. The calculation shows that 1.80 kg of powder will cover 1 m^2 at an *average* of 1 mm on a perfectly flat surface. The specification is most likely to be for a *minimum* of 1 mm on a less than flat surface. The surface texture will be different on every project. It is not, therefore, possible to predict accurately what the exact usage rate will be.

Surface texture or profile will have a significant effect on the achievable usage rate, more so with thinner coatings. Estimations must allow for surface texture and wastage. Unlike solvented coatings, there is no significant volume or thickness loss during drying of the coatings.

4.7 Application

Coatings based on cement should not be applied when the temperature is below 5 °C or expected to fall below 5 °C within 24 hours.

4.7.1 Substrate condition

The condition of the substrate is a key factor in any coating application. Cement-based coatings can last the design life of the structure, but only if the preparation is correct. There is great emphasis on this point, as it is the most common cause of premature coating failure.

The essential conditions of the substrate can be defined as follows:

Structurally sound

High strength rigid coatings will require a minimum substrate cohesive strength of 1.5 N/mm^2. If the substrate strength is insufficient, it is possible for the stresses produced during drying/curing of the coating to cause a structural failure within the substrate. If in doubt, the surface should be tested with a 'pull-off test' after preparation.

Clean, free of all previous coatings or contaminants which affect adhesion

It may appear obvious that a coating will not bond to its host structure if there is a layer of dirt, dust or algae in between. However, this is often overlooked. Not so obvious, but equally important, are contaminants such as oil, clear impregnating waterproofing treatments and lithium-based surface hardeners. Previous coatings, even if well adhered to the substrate, are more likely to work as a bond breaker than an adhesion promoter for cement-based coatings.

Mechanically keyed

As with the two previous sections, this section also is concerned with adhesion. Adhesion between cementitious products is a physical function of the smaller particles within the 'wet' mix penetrating the pores, voids and interstices and hardening, thus mechanically interlocking with the surface. Polymers assist in this function by lubricating the fine particles, producing dense, compact material at the interface.

Dampened

It is important to saturate the prepared surface with clean water to satisfy the 'suction'. Cement requires approximately 17% moisture for complete hydration. If water is sucked out of the coating by the substrate, there is insufficient left for hydration, resulting in reduced physical properties. Whilst hard dense concrete will require minimal dampening, absorbent concrete may require saturating more than once. There should not be standing water at the time of application, as this will form a thin film interfering with the adhesion between coating and substrate.

4.8 Mixing

With all proprietary products, it is essential to follow the instructions given by the manufacturers. Cement-based products are always supplied in powder form and will require the addition of liquid at the job site. The liquid may be water only or a liquid polymer, which may or may not require diluting. Some polymers may be used at different dilution rates, dependent upon the intended use of the coating or the ambient conditions.

Most products based on cement will have performance data generated at standard liquid demands. Abuse of the liquid content can seriously damage their health.

It is unusual for a coating to be mixed with too little water as this will produce a material which is, at best, difficult to apply, causing severe wrist strain and reducing coverage, neither of which are of benefit to the contractor. Conversely, too much liquid will ease the application and stretch the coverage with two major drawbacks:

1. the coating will be thinner than the designed thickness; and
2. excessive liquid increases the water/cement ratio, reducing all the desired physical properties.

Some manufacturers will offer a range of liquid, i.e., 4.5–5.0 l/25 kg, with the aim of producing a mixed material of uniform consistency. Several factors, apart from the quantity of liquid, can affect the consistency, including ambient or material temperature, variation in some of the products' constituent parts (whilst remaining within specification), excess material in the containers, efficiency of the mixing equipment. In general, if the consistency is correct, the coating thickness will be correct.

Polymers have a notable effect on consistency and there are differences between polymers added in liquid form and those included as freeze dried powders. When mixing, liquid and powder polymers have opposite effects. Liquid polymer products are mixed to the desired consistency and, when left to stand for approximately 10 minutes, will stiffen as the oven-dried fine sands and fillers slowly absorb water. Most of the original consistency can be regained by re-mixing. However, a small quantity of additional liquid may be required.

With one-component powder polymer products, mixing to the desired consistency, allowing to stand for 10 minutes and re-mixing, may well produce a material which is 'wetter' than desired, as the polymer slowly re-emulsifies and the plasticizing effect is initiated.

4.8.1 Basic rules of mixing

Liquid or no polymers: mix to the *desired* consistency. Allow to stand and re-mix, adding more liquid as required.

Powder polymers: mix to a *stiff* consistency, allow to stand, re-mix adding more liquid as required.

4.9 Methods of application

The method of application must be capable of spreading the material evenly, at a controlled thickness, whilst achieving good adhesion (some skill on the part of the operative is useful). The most common application technique employs a brush or broom. Given sufficient area, a spray is a viable option, and a squeegee is occasionally used on horizontal surfaces.

4.9.1 Brush or broom

Applicators will have severe problems unless they select the correct type of brush or broom. Standard paint brushes or brooms are not satisfactory, as they have insufficient rigidity to apply products with any pressure. Manufacturers will usually supply the correct brushes for their products. It is essential to use the manufacturer's own brush or 'similar approved' type.

Brush application to vertical surfaces has more kinship to plastering than painting with emulsion. The action is one of 'laying on' the material with upward vertical strokes, brushing well into the surface and 'levelling' off, finishing with brush strokes in one direction for a uniform appearance.

The performance and durability of the coating will depend upon coating thickness. It is, therefore, important to check the minimum (and maximum) depth of coating at regular intervals.

Much the same methodology is used for broom application. Again, it is essential to force the material into the substrate by vigorous brushing. The broom should not simply be used as a spreader for a material tipped on to a surface. The work should be planned to maintain a wet edge.

4.9.2 Spray application

For spray application, it is necessary for the applicator to have not only product knowledge, but a good understanding of the equipment involved. Spray application is basically the combination of two separate functions:

1. pumping: transportation of the mixed material to the point of application; and
2. spraying: distribution of the material on to the surface.

Suitable pumps

It is necessary to determine the correct pump for the product and for the site conditions.

Product considerations include:
- Aggregate size
- Rheology

- Viscosity
- Rate of application

Site condition considerations include:

- Power source available
- Accessibility

The following types of pumps are generally suitable for cementitious coatings:

Rotor-Stator powered by 110v, 440v or air
Peristaltic powered by 110v, 440v
Pneumatic powered by air

Rotor-Stator pumps are the most widely available. Electric powered machines are more controllable than air powered, boasting variable speed and a reverse gear, whilst air models are restricted to a range of speeds and the slowest speed may be too fast for coatings. Application rate is largely determined by the coating thickness and operative's ability. The thinner the coating, the slower the pump rate requirement. In the absence of historical data, it is possible to calculate guideline pump rate requirements based on some assumptions, i.e.:

Assume coating thickness: 1 mm (1 mm $\times$ 1 m^2 = 1 l)
Operative's capability: 3 m^2/min = 3 l/min pump rate

It should be noted that pump output ratings quoted by manufacturers are often for pumping water. The rate will be slower for more viscous materials.

Peristaltic pumps offer a distinct advantage in so far as there are no moving parts in contact with material. However, they are hard to find, particularly on hire fleets. They require electricity for power. Note that electrically powered units will require an air supply for spraying.

Pneumatic or pressure pots are air powered and have the advantage of no moving parts being in contact with the material – in fact they have no moving parts at all. One disadvantage is that, being a 'sealed' system, it is necessary to stop the application to replenish the 'pot'. Again, this type of equipment is not readily available.

A point to consider at this stage is mixing. Should it be estimated that the pumping and therefore application rate is 3 l/minute, then approximately 6 kg of mixed material will be required each minute. This would mean mixing a pre-bagged 25 kg unit every 5 minutes. It should thus be considered whether the mixing can keep up with the pump.

Spraying

There are many configurations of spray gun, but not all are suitable for all products. Standard unmodified materials are compatible with most guns, whilst heavily polymer or fibre-modified materials are 'selective'. The following general rules apply.

High polymer content
It is necessary for the air to be introduced quite close to the nozzle exit. If the air under pressure and travelling at speed is in contact with the polymer for too long, drying can occur before the material reaches the substrate or even in the gun, which will cause blockages.

High or long fibre content
'Straight through' guns, with no offsets or bends, have fewer problems with blockages. Slow tapers at the nozzle are best avoided. Most guns will have a range of nozzle aperture sizes. The smaller the aperture, the finer or smoother the surface finish. Surface finish will be affected by both the aperture size and air pressure.

The vital link between the pump and spray gun is the delivery hose; 35 mm or 25 mm diameters are usually available. The smaller size is preferable for coatings, primarily because less material is required to fill it. It is also easier to manoeuvre and less arduous for the operative. Some hoses have male fittings at both ends, allowing the hose to be reversed in the event of a blockage.

Site conditions
It is necessary to assess if the access will allow for a small mobile pump unit, which can be manoeuvred along scaffolding, or if a static, more powerful pump with long hoses, is more suitable. As coatings require a very low output and the cost per kilogram of product is relatively high, smaller, more mobile units have greater benefits.

Spray application
The spray head is held at right angles 30–60 cm from the surface and moved slowly in a circular motion until sufficient thickness is built up. The work should be planned to maintain a wet edge. It is important to check the minimum (and maximum) depth of coating at regular intervals.

4.10   Curing

Until sufficiently set, coatings must be protected from rain and temperatures below 5 °C. In hot or windy conditions, applications should be protected by fog spraying with clean water once set or covered with wet hessian. Covering with polythene is not a good idea in sunny conditions as it can produce very high temperatures at the surface.

4.11   Conclusion

Reading back, one could be left with the impression that the application of cement-based coatings is an exact science. This is not the case. The care and attention required is similar to other types of protective coatings. Whilst the skill of the operative has positive benefits in achieving the maximum aesthetic effect, diligence is the main attribute required to obtain the maximum durable performance.

5 Cross-linking acrylic cement mixture

R. Boodaghians

5.1 Introduction

Water-borne polymer dispersions are an increasingly important class of materials for improving the properties of cement mortars. Industry's demand for more durable mortars made from cement has resulted in the development of a variety of polymer types such as acrylic copolymers, vinyl-acrylics, styrene acrylic and styrene butadiene. The use of polymers as cement admixtures is to obtain enhanced mechanical properties, provide chemical resistance and reduce difficulties with shrinkage on drying. Other benefits derived from the use of such polymer modifiers may include improved workability, reduced water sensitivity and air entrainment.

This chapter describes the properties of a new cross-linkable water-based acrylic binder that has been developed which exhibits significant improvements in performance over standard polymer admixtures.

5.2 Polymer design and function

The progress made with the development and introduction of water-based polymer dispersions into cement composites is still dominated by their ability to deliver a higher degree of performance and durability for the finished product. Conventional latex admixtures rely on physical entanglement and the polymer film formation characteristics of the binder to reduce the number of microcracks which appear in the hardened cement paste. The latter is generally considered to posses an agglomerated structure of calcium silicate hydrates and calcium hydroxide bound together by weak van der Waals forces. In such a structure the polymer film interactions seem to bridge the microgaps and prevent further propagation. This in turn promotes the development of a stronger cement hydrate aggregate bond, leading to improved mechanical properties of the cured cement mortar and concrete. In spite of the enhanced performance profiles achieved with interactions through conventional latex modified cement mortars, these cannot be as effective as chemical cross-linking for highly demanding application areas.

5.2.1 Reaction mechanism

It is generally speculated that a cement polymer mixture can go through four major steps involving a progressive phasing network in establishing its cured structure (Schwiete *et al.*, 1969; Wagner and Grenley, 1978; Ohama, 1995).

Immediately after mixing the system contains unhydrated cement particles and water. Polymer particles are dispersed in the water phase. These particles gradually start to deposit on unhydrated cement particles and cement gel. The latter is formed as the hydration product of cement particles which in turn releases calcium hydroxide into the water phase. Calcium silicate may also be formed as a result of a reaction between calcium hydroxide and the silica found on the surface of the aggregates. In the third phase polymer particles start to flocculate due to a reduction in the capillary water and form a close-packed layer surrounding the mixtures of cement gel and the unhydrated cement particles. Finally, polymer particles coalesce to form a continuous polymer film binding the hydrates together via an interpenetrating polymer network.

Overall, the presence of polymer is expected to improve the general resistance properties of the modified cement mixture. Adding a compatible cross-linking functionality to certain polymers can give distinctive advantages, such as rapid early cure and strength development, good compressive strength and very good resistance to the effects of most aggressive chemicals. It is also believed that a cross-linked membrane-like polymer network engulfing the hydrated cement particles and aggregates can contribute considerably towards resistance against chloride ion penetration, moisture transmission, carbonation and oxygen diffusion.

5.3   New binder

An ambient cross-linking acrylic copolymer has a glass transition temperature of less than 1 °C with a non-volatile content of 55%, a monodisperse particle size distribution with a mean of 0.3 μ, pH of 5 and viscosity of less than 1 poise (Brookfield 2/20 at 25 °C). The cross-linking reaction is activated by the high pH conditions found in cement and mortar formulations. The polymer dispersion is stabilized with a unique surfactant system which offers good compatibility in a cementitious environment. It also helps with the control of foam, colour development and the rheology of the mix.

5.4   Application test results

The following test results were obtained from a mix of 3 parts sharp sand to 1 part Portland cement with varying levels of the new cross-linking polymer dispersion. The application performance study included an acrylic polymer recommended by the industry for such use. The amount of latex added varied from 5 to 20% solid polymer on cement weight. The evaluation work also considered a blank sample without any polymer. Wherever applicable, tests have been performed in accordance with the relevant British Standards methods.

5.4.1   Workability

Concrete mixtures modified by polymer dispersions give better workability than those without any polymer. It has been suggested that the presence of certain polymers in cement mixtures gives rise to an increased level of air entrainment by the cement matrix. This in turn can cause reductions in flexural and compressive strengths due to an increase in the porosity of the structure. Figure 5.1 shows a typical density profile for a series of the cement mixtures. As can be seen, the cement mixtures with the new cross-linking polymer are able to sustain their density in comparison to both the blank and the acrylated samples.

5.4.2   Compressive strength

The thermoplastic nature of most water-borne polymer dispersions can lead to a reduced compressive strength for a given polymer modified cement mixture.

Figure 5.2 shows a measure of compressive strength development as a function of time for a latex modified cement mixture containing 10% solid polymer on cement weight. Also shown are the measured figures for the wet and dry cured blank samples. As can be seen, the strength obtained with the new cross-linking system is comparable to that measured for the blank samples possible to achieve under ideal conditions. Therefore, it is believed that the cross-linking functionality of the new polymer contributes to the increased performance level observed in comparison to similar non-reactive polymer systems.

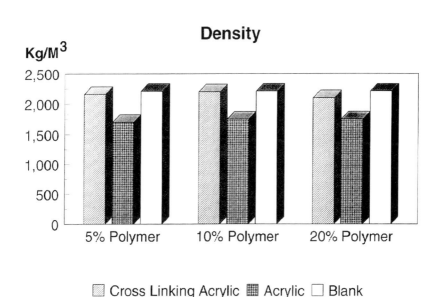

Figure 5.1   *Typical density profiles.*

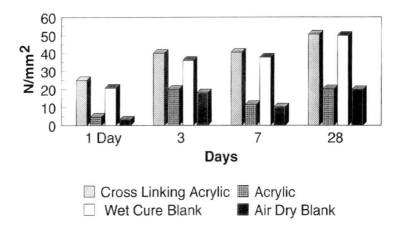

Figure 5.2 *Compressive strength.*

5.4.3 Flexural strength

Figure 5.3 compares flexural strength of the new cross-linking acrylic polymer with that of an industry accepted acrylic system under similar test conditions with respect to time. It can be seen that the alkaline cross-linkable acrylic system gives a high strength with significantly faster development of the early strength in relation to the final strength measured after 28 days.

5.4.4 Adhesive bond strength

A polymer modified cement mixture is expected to show better adhesion properties to a given substrate. The development of adhesive bond strength may depend on the nature of the substrate and its porosity as well as the polymer cement ratio. For example, adhesion of fresh concrete may be poor due to shrinkage characteristics at early ages of curing, but this becomes a less significant factor to consider after a longer curing period.

The results in Figure 5.4 show that the new binder promotes the development of higher bond strength than the industry norm under similar test conditions. It is very important to note that the cement mixture modified with the cross-linkable polymer tested under wet conditions is still producing as high an adhesive bond strength as that of the standard acrylic in dry conditions.

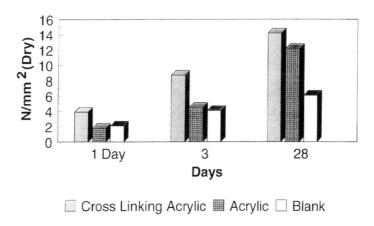

Figure 5.3 *Rapid strength deveopment.*

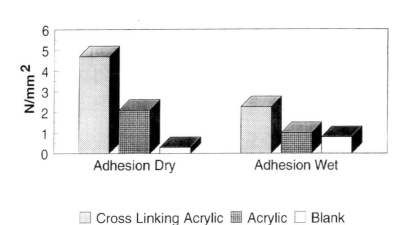

Figure 5.4 *Adhesion.*

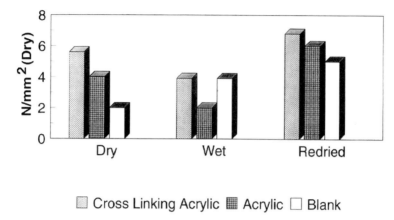

Figure 5.5 *Tensile strength.*

5.4.5 Tensile strength

Tensile strength is usually improved with latex-modified mortar which contributes to the enhanced binding network within the mortar matrix including the aggregates.

Figure 5.5 demonstrates the dry and wet performance with the new binder in comparison to a non cross-linking acrylic binder. Once again, the cross-linking mechanism with the new binder reflects further improvements in the tensile strength, its performance under wet conditions being equal to that obtained for an ordinary acrylic binder under dry conditions.

The increase seen with the redried samples may be due to an improved hydration process under water soak conditions.

5.4.6 Abrasion resistance

The ability of a polymer modified concrete surface to withstand abrasion may depend on the nature and the type of the polymer and its cement ratio. In an attempt to measure this property under the given wear conditions defined as a footpath in moderate traffic, the results shown in Table 5.1 have been obtained.

Footpaths in moderate traffic areas are expected to have an abrasion index of 1.2 at 28 days. As can be seen, the modified system with the new binder reaches this level of performance after 1 day. The performance rating of 2.4 achieved after 7 days can be favourably compared to a value of 1.5 expected of high foot traffic areas such as pedestrian malls.

Table 5.1 *A modified flooring system utilizing the new cross-linking polymer at 10% dry weight on cement tested after 1 and 7 days (seven days results reported for duplicate samples).*

Test sample / Day	Revolutions	Abrasion index
A, after 1 day	2300	1.02
B, after 7 days	5000	2.40
C, after 7 days	5000	2.43

Table 5.2 *The amount of material worn under wet conditions after 24 hours from a heavy industrial formulation cured over varying periods of time.*

Cure period	Cross linkable system abraded in gm	Blank sample abraded in gm
3 days	11	62
7 days	9	65
28 days	7	24

Results indicate significant performance improvements with the presence of the new binder in a cement mixture.

5.4.7 Water resistance

In general, both the latex modified and the ordinary mortar and cement systems will absorb water through capillary action. This does not seem to present a problem unless rebar corrosion or interstitial salt formation occur in the structure. However, it has been noted in the past that polymer dispersion modified cement and mortars do not necessarily benefit in their compressive strength from such a modification compared to ordinary cement and mortar formulations. Part of the reason for this is thought to be associated with the thermoplastic nature of the polymer and its softening characteristics with the absorption of water. The latter effect has been reduced significantly with the unique structure of the new binder and its alkaline cross-linking capability. The test results shown earlier in Figure 5.2 support this specific behaviour.

5.4.8 Chemical resistance

The chemical resistance of a given mortar and cement formulation in the presence of a polymer dispersion will depend on the type of the polymer, the amount present in the formulation and the nature of the chemicals involved.

Figures 5.6, 5.7 and 5.8 show the flexural strength obtained after an attack by hydrochloric acid, lactic acid and diesel fuel respectively for a series of polymer mod-

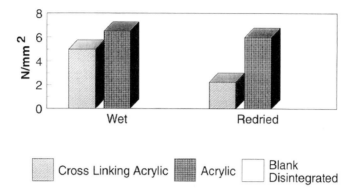

Figure 5.6 *Resistance to hydrochloric acid.*

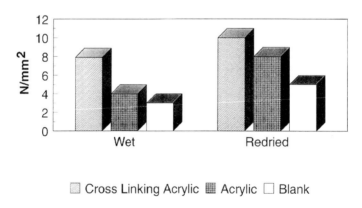

Figure 5.7 *Resistance to lactic acid.*

ified cement samples. In each system, 20% solid polymer on cement weight was used and after 28 days dry cure samples were immersed in the respective chemical for 28 days and tested whilst still wet. Also some samples were further tested after drying for 7 days including overnight at 50 °C. As can be seen, the results for the cross-linking polymer system are significantly better than the non cross-linking system. It is interest-

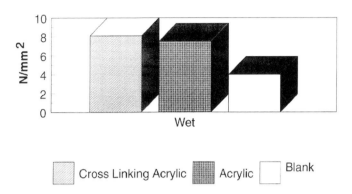

Figure 5.8 *Resistance to diesel fuel.*

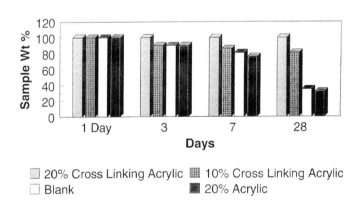

Figure 5.9 *Sulphuric acid resistance.*

ing to note that the blank sample disintegrated when hydrochloric acid was the attacking chemical.

Overall, the results of the reduction seen in strength properties under chemical attack compare favourably with the initial improvements gained in strength under normal conditions.

Figure 5.9 shows the effect of etching with 10% sulphuric acid solution over a 28-day immersion period. Test samples were measured for weight loss versus time imThe cement sample modified with a commercially recommended acrylic polymer was only evaluated at maximum loading of 20% solid polymer on cement weight due to very significant weight losses at lower levels. As can be seen, the performance progressively improved with polymer loading for the modified cement samples with the cross-linking latex with an optimum occurring at about 20% polymer loading. At this equivalent loading, the cement samples modified with the commercial acrylic latex showed poor results especially at 28 days. The blank sample showed a very large weight loss between 7 and 28 days. This reduction was comparable to that of the commercial acrylic polymer within experimental error.

5.5   Conclusions

The above application test results clearly indicate the significant improvements achieved with the ambient cross-linking chemistry built into the polymer design. The reaction by which this process takes place is simple and practical since the triggering mechanism uses the alkalinity of the cement matrix. This means that cross-linking occurs during or soon after film formation, as curing takes place for the cement matrix, rather than before. Extensive cross-linking before film formation may reduce the effectiveness of the polymer film in binding the cement hydrates together. This in turn may reduce the magnitude of the expected benefits associated with the cross-linking approach. The degree of cross-linking is also controlled by the level of the active component of the cross-linking functionality. Low cross-linking may not produce the degree of performance improvement desired. On the other hand, high cross-linking may cause polymer film embrittlement. These factors have been considered during the design of the polymer dispersion in order to obtain the balanced performance desired by the end user. For example, the new binder increases the rate of early flexural strength development without any loss of final strength achieved by the cured cement. This property is advantageous in flooring systems as well as in the industrial production of cement-based products, leading to an early use of the finished product.

The excellent properties obtained with the new cross-linking binder for mechanical resistance, adhesive, bond strength and workability make it suitable for use in self levelling cementitious overlay formulations. Traditionally, epoxy and polyester-based resins have been used in such applications for their hard wearing surface characteristics.

The use of water-based and low environmental impact products with improved performance properties as viable alternatives to solvent-based or conventional water-borne products with high volatile organic content is growing (Boodaghians, 1996). The water-borne nature and the glass transition temperature characteristics of the polymer make the new binder an environmentally friendly product. The latter property allows good polymer film integration within the cement matrix without the need of any coalescing agents, even at low ambient temperatures. The application performance obtained with the new binder under wet conditions may allow concrete repairs to take place in adverse weather conditions. These features are particularly important in marine applications. Preliminary test results obtained from the exposure of concrete compositions modified with the new binder to the marine environment have been very encouraging. There are clear indications that resistance to chloride ion permeation can be markedly improved.

The application test results discussed in this chapter show that ambient temperature cross-linking functionality built into a water-borne polymer backbone requiring a simple and practice triggering mechanism can significantly improve the overall performance properties of polymer modified concrete and mortars. Comparison of several key resistance properties of polymer-modified concrete and mortars with a conventional acrylic binder indicates that the hydrophobic all acrylic polymer composition, in conjunction with the cross linking functionality, provides a significant advance over current polymer dispersion technology.

References

Boodaghians, R. (1996) Water-borne polymer dispersions for coalescent-free coating formulations. *Pitture e Vernic*, **72**(2), 18–21.

Ohama, Y. (1995) *Handbook of polymer modified concrete and mortars*. Noyes.

Schwiete, H.E., Ludwig, W. and Aachen, G.S. (1969) The influence of plastic dispersions on the properties of cement mortars. *Betonstein Zeitung*, **35**(1).

Wagner, H.B. and Grenley, D.G. (1978) Polymer modified concrete. *Journal of Applied Polymer Science*, **22**(3).

Acknowledgement

My special thanks to Mr Colin Fuller for his help in the preparation of this paper. I would also like to thank Dr Tony Lawson for the polymer synthesis and Mr Ian Nelson for the application testing.

6 Use of epoxy resin systems in concrete protection

S.Beinborn and S.P.Darwen

6.1 Introduction

Epoxy systems have been used in the protection and repair of concrete for many years, and the technology behind these systems is improving continuously in response to changes in environmental legislation and in customer performance requirements. Epoxy resins and curing agents are used in the protection of concrete as coatings, self levelling floors and screed floors, in the repair of concrete structures as crack injection products , and patch repair systems and also as bonding agents in segmental construction, bedding mortars and bolt anchoring. The use of epoxy systems in the protection and repair of concrete has become synonymous with structural longevity and high performance, high specification construction and repair. As an illustration of this, it is interesting to consider the usage of epoxy systems in concrete repair and protection per capita across Europe (Figure 6.1).

There is a fairly clear correlation in the above data between the rate of use of epoxy systems in civil engineering applications and those regions known to have strong regulations and high performance specifications for the materials used in their construction industries.

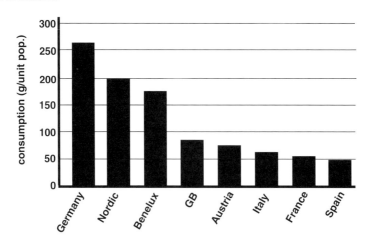

Figure 6.1 *Epoxy consumption for civil engineering; a European perspective.*

This chapter examines the chemistry of the epoxy resin cold cure systems typically used in concrete protection and considers the properties which make these materials particularly useful for these applications. Finally, examples will be given of on-site experience with a number of different systems in repair and coating applications.

6.2 Chemistry

6.2.1 Epoxy resins

Epoxy resins contain one or more reactive epoxy groups. The most technically and commercially important epoxy resins are produced by condensation of epichlorohydrin and bisphenol-A (and/or bisphenol-F). The resulting glycidyl ethers vary in molecular mass depending on the equivalents of epichlorohydrin and bisphenol-A (or bisphenol-F) used in the condensation reaction. Relatively low molecular weight liquid epoxy resins are available from this reaction and are used in solvent-free systems; there are many so-called liquid bis-A epoxy resins[1] (see end of chapter for key to products) available in the market which have a molecular mass of approximately 380. Higher condensate, solid[2] or 'advanced' resins of molecular mass 760 or greater are useful in the coatings industry, but are more commonly used in the protection of steel structures for the marine and heavy duty markets. Epoxy functional novolac resins[3] are also available with a range of functionalities and viscosities, these resins are mainly used where very high chemical resistance is required.

In addition to the above resinous materials, another class of epoxy functional materials is extremely useful in the protection and repair of concrete. These are the reactive diluents which are used to modify the above epoxy resins and produce systems with viscosities appropriate for on-site ambient temperatures. These materials are manufactured via the condensation reaction of epichlorohydrin with alcohols and glycols. The most commonly used of these reactive diluents are the C_{12-14} glycidyl ether[4] derived from coconut oil alcohols and sometimes simply referred to as alkyl glycidyl ether and hexanediol diglycidyl ether.[5] Alkyl glycidyl ether combines good viscosity reducing properties with surface tension modification of the epoxy base which helps to improve the wetting of pigments and fillers and the general 'trowelability' of screed flooring systems and mortars. Hexanediol diglycidyl ether has good viscosity reducing capability and helps to maintain the chemical resistance of the epoxy resin base.

Currently, the workhorse epoxy resin for use in most civil engineering applications is a mixed bisphenol-A/bisphenol-F epoxy resin modified with the above mentioned alkyl glycidyl ether.[6]

6.2.2 Reactions of epoxy resins

The epoxy functional group is capable of undergoing numerous reactions, which normally involve the addition of a co-reactant to the epoxy group with concomitant hydroxyl group formation. Crucially no by-products are eliminated during this reaction. The most important reactions of epoxy resins for cold cure surface protection of con-

Table 6.1 *Amine types used in the cold curing of epoxy resins.*

Type	Example
Aliphatic polyamine	Dipropylene triamine
Cycloaliphatic polyamine	Isophorone diamine
Aromatic polyamine	Diaminodiphenylmethane
Araliphatic polyamine	m-xylene diamine
Polyaminoamides	Condensation, tall oil fatty acid and tetraethylenepentamine
Mannich bases	Condensation, phenol, formaldehyde and trimethylhexamethylene diamine

crete are those involving the addition of amines and mercaptans to low viscosity liquid epoxy resins in solvent-free systems.

There are numerous different classes of amines which may be used to cure epoxy resins, some of which are illustrated in Table 6.1.

In order to optimize the properties of the polymer resulting from the reaction of the above amines with an epoxy resin, two conditions must be met:

• ideally there should be a 1:1 reaction of epoxy groups with active hydrogen, (i.e. N–H or S–H) in order to form a polymer; and

• the addition reaction should be able to proceed as close to 100% as possible.

The reaction between active hydrogen (N–H or S–H) and epoxy groups will continue at a given ambient temperature until the Tg of the developing polymer is at, or above, the ambient temperature. At this point polymerization will cease as mobility within the polymer network becomes negligible and reaction stops. Unfortunately, for most of the above amines, this point is reached at a relatively low conversion of active hydrogen, and so the resulting polymer has low cross-link density and a high content of free amine and epoxy groups. This usually means that the majority of the amine types have to be modified in order to become useful curing agents under cold cure conditions. The exceptions to this are the polyaminoamides and the Mannich bases, as they have internal plasticization which allows the reaction to proceed, although these amine types are also often modified in commercial curing agents. For heat curing, modification is not always necessary, as the post cure temperature will be above the initial curing temperature; this maintains mobility in the amine-epoxy mixture and ensures the progress of the reaction.

Modified amines as described above are capable of reacting with epoxy resins to high conversions down to 10 °C or even 5 °C, although the rate of reaction becomes sluggish at these ambient temperatures. Under cold curing conditions, it is often necessary to speed up the amine-epoxy reaction this may be achieved in a number of ways:

• use of highly reactive, basic amines;
• use of tertiary amines; or
• use of certain organic acids.

The main problems found on site in the use of epoxy systems are caused by the effects of water and/or water plus carbon dioxide on the curing polymer. These problems are manifest as surface defects on curing films, lower than expected chemical resistance and mechanical strength and/or poor adhesion to wet surfaces. The key factor in each of the above cases is the unwanted irreversible reaction between water and carbon dioxide in the form of carbonic acid with the amine species, as shown below.

$$CO_2/H_2O$$

$$R–NH_2 \longrightarrow RNH_3^+ \quad HCO_3^-$$

Interaction of 'carbonic acid' with amine to give amine bicarbonate

Unfortunately this reaction is faster than the more desirable amine-epoxy reaction, particularly at low temperatures, and especially so if the amine is very basic. The simplest consideration of the effects of this side-reaction tells us that it will consume reactive amine, and so cause a non-equivalence of N–H groups to epoxy groups, leading to an incompletely cured polymer. The other effects of this side-reaction are the surface defects mentioned above. Formulating skill and expertise are required to minimize the risks from this and other competing reactions and to optimize the properties of epoxy systems to make them commercially useful. This expertise is provided by commercial curing agent suppliers.

The work of curing agent and epoxy resin producers to provide an optimum epoxy binder can be undone in the final coating or repair formulation if the choice of pigments and filler is not carried out with care, and this is where the skill of the formulator is vital. For example, in the formulation of systems where pedestrian or vehicular traffic is expected, fillers should be chosen for their hardness which is imparted to the coating to improve scratch and abrasion resistance. In this case, quartz or silica sands and flour are particularly useful and soft fillers such as dolomite or other high carbonate containing fillers should be avoided in spite of their low cost. In fact, soft fillers of this type will compromise scratch resistance, dirt pick-up and chemical resistance, particularly to acids in floor coatings and bund linings.

In high chemical resistance applications, inert fillers such as barytes should be used along with appropriate wetting agents to help wet out the surface of pigments and fillers. If the surface of the pigments and fillers in the formulation is not sufficiently coated with binder in the final cured system, this will become a prime site for chemical attack, as spillages are absorbed into the filler particles and begin to attack the binder structure over a period of time Having chosen the correct pigments and fillers, it is essential that they be dry and stored in a dry atmosphere, as moisture absorbed on to the surface of pigments and fillers is incorporated into the epoxy resin and, through interaction with the curing components, compromises the properties of the finished system.

The choice of additives for a particular formulated system will to some degree be specific to that particular combination of epoxy resin, curing agent, pigment and fillers. It is therefore dangerous to assume that, for a particular formulated epoxy base, curing agents of similar type and loading will give the same quality of cured properties. It may be the case that some systems will work in this way but many will not and some reformulating is often necessary in order to accommodate an alternative curing agent to the one the system was designed around.

6.3 Properties of epoxy resins

As the associated technology has progressed, epoxy systems for use in concrete protection, repair and bonding have become suitable for a wide variety of applications. Low viscosity solvent-free systems are now commonplace, water-based systems are firmly established in the market, flexible products are available and even some of the main performance problem areas, such as adhesion to wet concrete, have been successfully addressed.

6.3.1 Standard mechanical properties

The typical properties obtained with industry standard epoxy resin-curing agent combinations for application in solvent-free coatings, self-levelling floors and screed floors are given in Table 6.2.

This combination of properties demonstrates the durability of epoxy resin systems. This durability makes these types of system ideal for use in concrete protection in solvent-free coatings and self levelling or screed floors.

Table 6.2 *Typical mechanical properties of industry standard epoxy/curing agent combinations after 7 days cure at ambient temperature.*

Epoxy resin	Curing agent	E-modulus MPa	Compressive strength , MPa	Flexural strength, MPa
Modified bis-A/F[6]	Formulated cyclo[7]	18,000	106	37
Modified bis-A/F[6]	Accelerated cyclo[8]	15,450	114	37

6.3.2 Flexibility

Variations on the theme of concrete protection include coatings for concrete where movement and cracking are to be expected and it is imperative that the integrity of the protective coating be maintained over a limited range of substrate movement. Examples would include car park decking, bund linings and waterproof membranes. These cases require a flexible system, although too much flexibility can cause problems by masking building defects and excessive movement. Recently European standards have been proposed for the measurement of both dynamic and static crack-bridging of com-

Figure 6.2 *Absorption of cracking energy in a multi-layer epoxy concrete protection system.*

mercial formulations for use in these applications, and this type of standard is essential to ensure that commercial systems are 'fit for purpose'. Flexible curing agents[9] can be used in epoxy systems for application in these cases either as single or multi-layer systems, as shown in Figure 6.2.

The multi-layer approach is particularly suitable where chemical resistance is an issue since the chemical resistance of flexible epoxy systems is often lower than standard epoxy systems. In the multi-layer case, the flexible layer is further protected by a topcoat with higher chemical resistance.

6.3.3 Chemical resistance

The chemical resistance of a particular epoxy resin-curing agent combination will in large part be determined by the nature of the curing agent. Full details of specific combinations are available from most curing agent suppliers along with formulating advice in choosing the particular combination which is best suited to the particular chemical resistance spectrum required.

In general it is safe to say that the use of more reactive basic amines (or their derivatives) as curing agents will give lower chemical resistance against acids, whilst slower reacting amine types tend to have poorer chemical resistance to solvents. This is, of course, very generalized and only considers amine availability in the polymer and the relative cross-link density of the polymer. Nonetheless it is a reasonable rule of thumb when beginning to choose a system for particular chemical resistance.

Table 6.3 *Range of performance properties available with different curing agent types (all data with modified liquid epoxy resin after 7 days cure at RT).*

Curing agent	Gel-time, mins@25°C	Comp. strength, MPa	Flexural strength, MPa	[Acid]/ [Solvent] resistance*	Elongation, %
Araliphatic[10]	15	119	33	[m] / [p]	~5
Cycloaliphatic[7]	38	106	37	[m] / [m]	~5
Aromatic[11]	25	94	31	[g] / [g]	~5
Polyaminoamide[12]	110	77	29	[m] / [p]	10
Flexibilised[9]	45	17	12	[p] / [p]	122

* g = good, m = moderate, p = poor

Table 6.3 will give some impression of the diversity of properties available with different curing agent choices.

6.4   Typical applications

6.4.1   Concrete sealing in adverse conditions

This first example involves the sealing of concrete staging leading down into the sea, located in northern Spain. The main problems in this case were the necessity of achieving good adhesion to wet concrete coupled with the likelihood of curing under salt water (Figure 6.3).

The reason for the application of the coating was to protect from dirt pick-up and to prolong the life of the concrete by sealing and hence slow natural deterioration through ingress of chloride ions and attack by atmospheric acidity. The substrate was cleaned by jet washing in order to remove dirt and particularly salt from the surface pores of the concrete. This, of course, ensured that the concrete was thoroughly saturated with water. A primer coat[13] was applied and immediately overcoated with a pigmented coat of the same binder. This system then in effect cured under salt water since on site there was a six hour application window between tides and the system was not fully cured as the tide came in.

This protection job was carried out in March 1995 and has been in service with little or no sign of deterioration, in spite of the adverse conditions under which the coating was applied.

6.4.2   Concrete protection in swimming pool construction

This example illustrates the versatility of epoxy systems as in this case epoxy products were used for all parts of the pool lining from priming to tile jointing. This job was carried out for a well-known holiday park chain at a new site in Germany. The pool shape was cast in concrete and then primed with a low viscosity solvent-free epoxy

Figure 6.3 *Concrete shelving by the sea protected by coating with an epoxy system developed specifically for adhesion to difficult substrates.*

primer[14] to strengthen the concrete and to act as a tie-coat for subsequent layers. This particular primer can be overcoated wet on wet, thus saving time and money. Following priming, two coats of a flexible waterproof membrane[15] were then applied in order to protect the concrete from any leakage of chlorinated water which can cause serious damage to concrete substrates.

Following the application of the waterproofing systems, the tiling was carried out using an epoxy resin-based water wipeable tile bedding and jointing system.[16]

Work on this project was carried out during the course of 1994, and the pool has been in service since completion. No problems have been reported with this facility at the time of writing (*see* Figures 6.4 and 6.5).

6.4.3   Bolt anchoring in bridge construction

Severe vibrational stresses on the bonded area both from vehicular traffic and the operation of the swing bridge mechanism during retraction and replacement of the bridge deck were expected in this application. It was therefore decided that the best approach to this job would involve the use of a flexible epoxy bonding system[17] to fix the bolt housings into the concrete base in order that this vibrational energy be dissipated in the bond and not transmitted to the rigid concrete base (*see* Figures 6.6 and 6.7).

Figure 6.4 *View of pool section primed and coated with waterproof membrane.*

Figure 6.5 *Finished pool area with water wipeable epoxy tile jointing and bedding.*

Figure 6.6 *A view of bridge construction over the Eider River in Germany.*

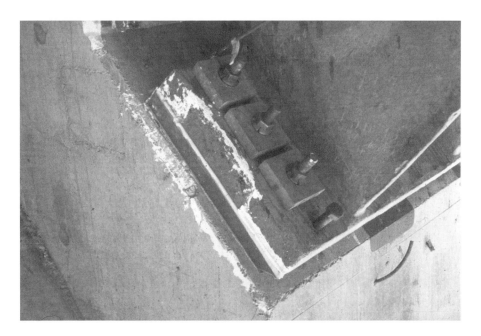

Figure 6.7 *Detail of bolt fixings using a flexibile epoxy system.*

6.5 Future developments

As with any technology there are always improvements to be made and work continues with epoxy systems to produce more user friendly, higher performance systems.

One of the major current concerns in the field of epoxy systems is the types of plasticizer which are used in the formulation of epoxy curing agents, and the effect of these materials on the final cured polymer. For instance, in certain parts of Europe, particularly Scandinavia and Germany, there is concern over the use of nonyl phenol in common curing agents for epoxy systems because of the toxicological aspects of this material. Work is being carried out by curing agent suppliers to improve the toxicological rating of their products and some advances have already been made in eliminating the use of suspect materials such as nonyl phenol from curing agent formulations without any deterioration in the system performance.

Another approach to toxicological concerns is to consider water-based epoxy products where no solvents or plasticizers are used. With this type of technology, the struggle has always been to match performance to existing solvent-based or solvent-free systems, in particular in drying speed and corrosion resistance. These issues have been addressed and the latest water-based epoxy systems are capable of drying speeds and corrosion resistance much closer to the traditional type of epoxy binder system. Furthermore, water-based curing agents and resins have been designed which allow their use in thicker layer coating systems for concrete as a form of self-levelling floor.

Developments and trends in construction have led to increasingly tougher demands on the materials used in this industry. The main reason for this is the pressure on time during construction projects with drying out times for concrete being continually squeezed. Additionally, preparation of steel by hydroblasting is now more and more favoured on waste toxicology grounds. The main problem resulting from these two effects is that adhesion to the resulting substrates is increasingly problematic; indeed, there is a general consensus that the levels of moisture in new concrete is one of the main causes of flooring failures. New products have been and are being developed which are able to be applied in these conditions and give the level of performance normally expected of epoxy systems.

Cost is always an issue in deciding which type of system is used in the protection and repair of concrete, and this has to be balanced with the performance level which is required of the system. Often this has meant some compromise in the performance of the system which is eventually applied. Whilst there have always been cost/performance epoxy systems on the market, performance levels have often been disappointing and the tolerance to application conditions inconsistent. Newer, low cost systems have been developed which provide much higher levels of consistency and performance than was previously possible within the cost/performance product end of the market.

6.6 Conclusion

Epoxy technology, and in particular curing agent technology, has developed a great deal from the early days, as have the applications for which this polymer binder is suitable. Epoxy systems correctly formulated and applied provide constructions which will stand the test of time and require less servicing and renovation than when traditional building techniques are used. As was suggested at the beginning of this chapter, infrastructure is the foundation of any nation, and in Europe at least, it seems to be the case that those countries with sound infrastructure are those with the highest usage of epoxy per capita in construction and repair. The technically active suppliers in the epoxy market will ensure that epoxy resin technology continues to advance in order to meet the ever increasing demands of the market, and to provide ever wider scope for the use of this versatile binder system.

Bibliography

Ellis, B. (ed). (1993) *Chemistry and Technology of Epoxy Resins*, Blackie Academic & Professional.

Oldring, Dr. P. (ed.) (1997) *Surface Coatings Technology*, vol. II, 'Waterborne and Solvent Based Epoxies and their End User Applications', John Wiley & Sons.

Lee, H. and Neville, K. (1967) *Handbook of Epoxy Resins*, McGraw-Hill.

Various *Surface Protection I & II*, Vantico PolymerSpecialities.

Reference products

1: Araldite GY 250
2: Araldite GT 7071
3: Araldite GY 1180
4: Araldite DY-E
5: Araldite DY-H
6: Araldite GY 783
7: Aradur 46
8: Aradur 46S
9: Aradur 76
10: Aradur 16
11: Aradur 81
12: Aradur 370
13: Aradur 450/Araldite GY 793
14: Aradur 50/Araldite GY 764
15: Aradur 76/Araldite GY 783
16: Araldite GY 891/Aradur 891

7 Polyurethanes

M.G.Wilson

7.1 Introduction

There can be no more versatile class of polymer than polyurethanes. They are used in many different forms and in a wide variety of market sectors. This chapter discusses the different types of polyurethanes available; the chemistry of polyurethanes which lead to their widely varying properties and potential end uses. In particular, of course, the fitness for purpose of polyurethane coatings on concrete will be discussed and these will be exampled by some specific case histories. Finally, and necessarily, a short section considers health and safety, and environmental issues.

It was in 1937 that Dr Otto Bayer (I.G. Farben Industries) made the first ever polyurethane elastomer by reacting toluene di-isocyanate with polyols. Since then, engineers and scientists alike have utilized the almost unique ability of polyurethanes to be manipulated both chemically, to produce an almost infinite variety of properties, and mechanically, to allow the use of many different manufacturing techniques and the production of widely differing forms. As well as this, polyurethanes are used in numerous market sectors and, with continued advances in the technology of formulations and preparation, there can be no doubt that their use will continue to increase in the foreseeable future.

7.2 Forms/uses of polyurethanes

Whilst this chapter is primarily concerned with the use of polyurethanes as coatings for concrete, it would be remiss not to mention briefly some of the other variety of forms and uses of polyurethanes available today.

7.2.1 Foams

Foams are available in both flexible and rigid forms and are made by forming gas bubbles within the mixture as it polymerizes and hardens.

There are three main types of foam available, these being low density flexible foams, low density rigid foams and high density flexible foams (microcellular elastomers). These foam materials may be manufactured continuously and 'cut into size' or may be manufactured in-mould as single items. The main use for the flexible foams is in soft furnishings whilst, due to their exceptional thermal insulation properties, closed cell rigid foams find wide use in refrigeration units and for thermal insulation of buildings, and may even be spray applied onto concrete in some instances.

7.2.2   Solid polyurethane elastomers

Several methods may be employed to produce solid polyurethane elastomers. These include reaction injection moulding (RIM) (also used for foams), injection moulding of thermoplastic polyurethanes, and casting of thermosets. Amongst the end uses are automotive parts, shoe soles, cable sheathing, tyres and fibres.

7.2.3   Adhesives, binders, coatings, paints

Strictly speaking, these are also solid urethane elastomers. In this instance, however, they are classified differently as they may be applied by alternative methods. These may include brushing, spraying, rollering, trowelling. They are also characterized by being relatively thin film applications.

Their uses are self-explanatory; however, they are also widely diverse. Adhesives, for example, may be used for bonding plastics, rubbers and metals. Coatings and paint may be applied on metal aircraft wings, plastic vehicle body parts and indeed, pertinently, onto concrete structures.

7.3   Background chemistry

It would be impossible to discuss the use of polyurethane coatings on concrete without discussing in at least some detail the chemistry of the many available systems. The reason for this being that an understanding of the basic chemistry and the terms used to describe different generic types can lead to making a better choice of product for any particular application.

As already mentioned, the ability to produce products with a nearly infinite variety of properties necessarily means that there is much to discuss in this section. It is intended as guidance only and it is hoped that whilst being technical in nature it is understandable and beneficial to all.

The basic reaction to form a polyurethane is one which occurs between a di- or poly-isocyanate and a polyol.

$$\text{OCN} - R^1 - \text{NCO} + \text{HO} - R - \text{OH} \longrightarrow \left[\begin{array}{c} \text{C} - \text{N} - R^1 - \text{N} - \text{C} - \text{O} - R - \text{O} \\ \underset{\text{O}}{\|} \ \underset{\text{H}}{|} \qquad \underset{\text{H}}{|} \ \underset{\text{O}}{\|} \end{array} \right]_n$$

di-isocyanate   *diol*   *polyurethane*

Other reactions which are equally important occur between a di-isocyanate and other active hydrogen containing species, for example amines and water.

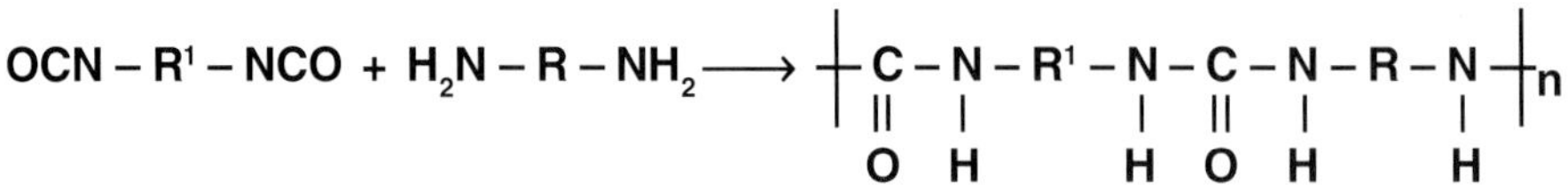

OCN – R¹ – NCO + H2N – R – NH2
C – N – R¹ – N – C – N – R – N
O H H O H H
n

di-isocyanate *amine* *polyurea*

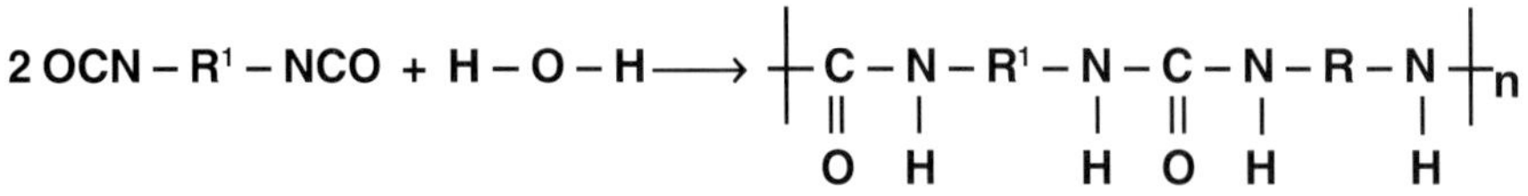

2 OCN – R¹ – NCO + H – O – H
C – N – R¹ – N – C – N – R – N
O H H O H H
n

di-isocyanate *water* *polyurea* $+ CO_2$

Whilst these two reactions do not form polyurethane linkages, the latter will in particular be shown to be vital with regard to making a choice of which system to use and also how correct application is vital.

7.3.1 Di-isocyanate monomers

The single most important building block of polyurethanes is a di-isocyanate monomer. Several different types are commercially available, including the two discussed below.

Aromatic di-isocyanates

MDI
methylene diphenyl di-isocyanate

OCN
CH2
NCO

TDI
toluene di-isocyanate

CH3
NCO
NCO

2,4-TDI

CH3
OCN
NCO

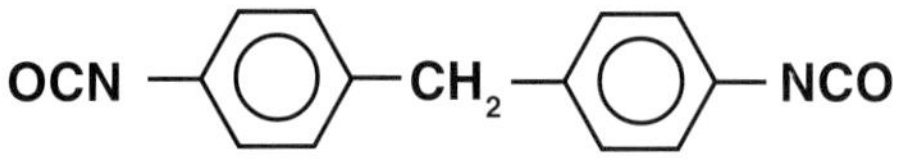

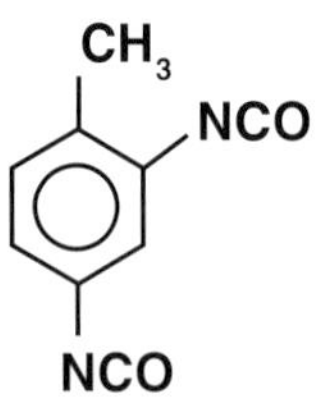

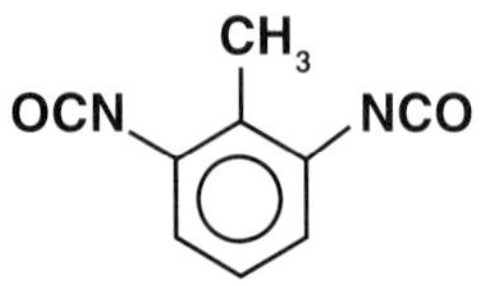

2,6-TDI

Aliphatic di-isocyanates

HDI
hexamethylene di-isocyanate

$$OCN - (CH_2)_6 - NCO$$

IPDI
isophorone di-isocyanate

m-TMXDI
meta-tetramethylxylene di-isocyanate

Isocyanate m-TMXDI is classified as an aliphatic isocyanate as the isocyanate groups are pendant to an aliphatic structure rather than the aromatic ring.

There are, of course, other commercially available monomeric di-isocyanates; however, those mentioned above will be sufficient to discuss the rôle they have to play with regard to formulating polyurethanes and, in particular, the application of polyurethanes in specific environments. Table 7.1 indicates polyurethane properties as affected by isocyanate.

Table 7.1 *The effects of isocyanate on polyurethane properties.*

	Chemical resistance	Weathering resistance	Flexibility	Hardness	Abrasion resistance	Heat resistance	Water resistance
Aliphatic	Good	Excellent	Good	Good	Good	Good	V. good
Aromatic	Excellent	Poor*	Fair	Excellent	Excellent	V. good	Excellent

* Aromatic isocyanates are classed as giving poor weathering resistance as they will discolour very significantly when exposed to UV light. If colour is not a concern or if they are formulated for example with black pigments, they can show extremely good durability externally.

This comparison of properties of aromatic and aliphatic isocyanates is only a guide and there is no doubt that the particular isocyanate used and its co-reactants will have a considerable effect on the performance.

The main difference between the two classes of di-isocyanate is that the aliphatic isocyanates can form colour-stable products, whereas aromatic isocyanates can not. If one were, for example, choosing an exterior architectural coating where good colour stability was important, then an aliphatic system would be required. If, however, the requirement was for an internal flooring system with no exposure to UV light, then it would be satisfactory to choose an aromatic base.

There may, of course, be other considerations so, for example, if a high degree of chemical resistance was important and colour was of secondary concern, an aromatic system might be preferred even in an external environment.

7.3.2   Prepolymers/adducts/trimers and dimers

With the exception of MDI, which in any case is not normally used in pure form, all isocyanate monomers are classified as toxic. This, therefore, precludes their use in this form in most coating applications. So called 'crude' MDI, which is a combination of MDI and higher molecular weight oligomers has very low volatility and, therefore, represents a reduced hazard. All other isocyanates, and MDI included, are however usually pre-reacted to form higher molecular weight, lower volatility and hence safer intermediates.

Prepolymers

One of the most common methods of increasing molecular weight is to pre-react the di-isocyanate with a polyol in such a way that the 'prepolymer' still has pendant isocyanate groups and, therefore, remains reactive.

$$OCN - R^1 - NCO \ + \ HO - R - OH$$

di-isocyanate   *polyol*

$$\downarrow$$

$$OCN - R^1 - \underset{H}{\overset{\overset{\textstyle O}{\|}}{N - C}} - O - R - O - \underset{H}{\overset{\overset{\textstyle O}{\|}}{C - N}} - R^1 - NCO$$

polyurethane prepolymer

This reaction, using a di-isocyanate in approximately a 2:1 excess with a polyol in controlled conditions, produces an isocyanate functional prepolymer which due to its very low volatility is significantly safer to handle than the original monomer. These prepolymers remain liquid in their own right, or in solution and, due to the retained isocyanate functionality, can react when combined with further polyol or water to form a solid polyurethane.

In a similar way, the di-isocyanate monomer may be reacted with a diamine to form a polyurea prepolymer. If this is then reacted with a polyol, it would form a polyurea urethane, though commonly the urea term would be dropped.

Adducts

Adducts are generally formed in exactly the same way as prepolymers though they are usually characterized by the use of lower molecular weight polyols.

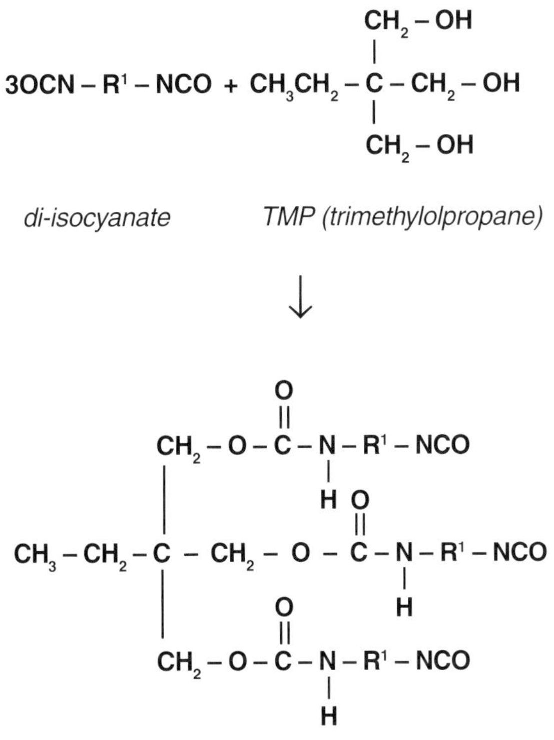

$$
3OCN - R^1 - NCO \; + \; CH_3CH_2 - C \underset{\underset{CH_2 - OH}{|}}{\overset{\overset{CH_2 - OH}{|}}{-}} CH_2 - OH
$$

di-isocyanate   *TMP (trimethylolpropane)*

↓

$$
CH_3 - CH_2 - C \Big\langle
\begin{array}{l}
CH_2 - O - \overset{\overset{O}{||}}{C} - \underset{\underset{H}{|}}{N} - R^1 - NCO \\
CH_2 - O - \overset{\overset{O}{||}}{C} - \underset{\underset{H}{|}}{N} - R^1 - NCO \\
CH_2 - O - \overset{\overset{O}{||}}{C} - \underset{\underset{H}{|}}{N} - R^1 - NCO
\end{array}
$$

di-isocyanate/TMP adduct

Water can also be used to react with the di-isocyanate to form what is known as a biuret adduct. These relatively low molecular weight adducts are nonetheless still of a low order of volatility and hence have reduced potential toxicity in comparison to the monomer. Because both adducts are relatively low molecular weight and tri-functional in nature, they are used to introduce hardness into systems.

Trimers and dimers

The third way to increase molecular weight is to trimerize or dimerize the di-isocyanates.

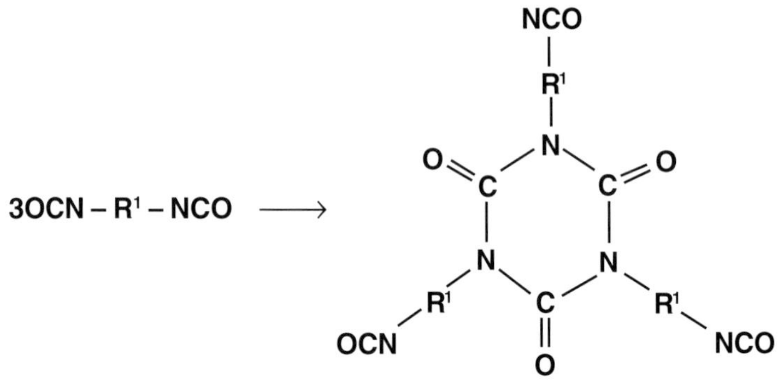

$$3OCN - R^1 - NCO \longrightarrow$$

trimer (isocyanate)

$$2OCN - R^1 - NCO \longrightarrow OCN - R^1 - N \qquad N - R^1 - NCO$$

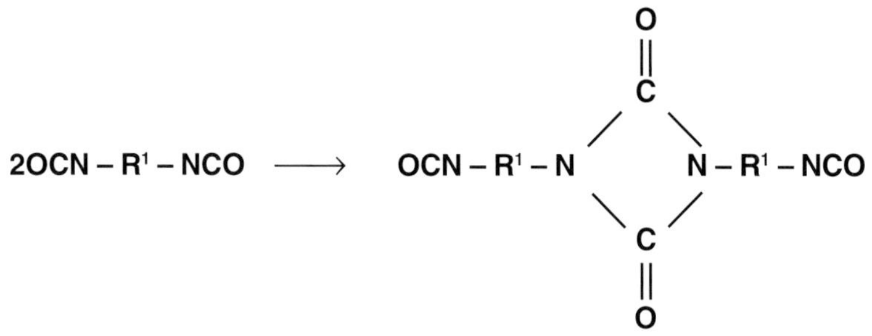

dimer (uretdione)

As with the adducts, these homopolymers may be added to introduce hardness into the polyurethane.

7.3.3 Polyols/co-reactants

As previously mentioned, the normal route to produce a polyurethane is to react a di- (or poly) isocyanate with a polyol. As with isocyanates, polyols are available in an extremely wide range of forms, functionalities and molecular weights. Naturally, the choice of polyol, or polyols, also has an extremely important part to play in the performance of polyurethane products. Some of the more common types are outlined below.

Polyester polyols

$$HO - R \left[O - \overset{\overset{\displaystyle O}{\|}}{C} - R \right]_n OH$$

ester link

Polyether polyols

$$HO - R \left[O - R \right]_n OH$$

ether (alkoxy) link

Polycarbonate polyols

$$HO - R \left[O - \overset{\overset{\displaystyle O}{\|}}{C} - O - R \right]_n OH$$

carbonate link

Polyacrylate polyols

$$HO - R \left[CH = CR^1 - \overset{\overset{\displaystyle O}{\|}}{C} - O - R \right]_n OH$$

acrylate link

Whilst other types of polyols are used in the formation of polyurethane, the four outlined above are by far the most common. They are all available in a wide variety of molecular weights and functionalities and, therefore, even within each group, the performance properties of polyurethanes incorporating them can differ considerably.

As with the isocyanates, it is possible to tabulate the general properties which may be brought to polyurethanes by the inclusion of various polyols.

Table 7.2 *The effects of polyol on polyurethane properties.*

	Chemical resistance	Weathering resistance	Flexibility	Hardness	Abrasion resistance	Heat resistance	Water resistance
Polyester	Fair	Good	Excellent	Fair	Good	Poor	Good
Polyether	Fair	Fair	Excellent	Poor	Poor	Poor	Fair
Polycarbonate	Fair	Good	Excellent	Fair	Good	Fair	Good
Polyacrylate	Good	Excellent	Good	Good	Good	Good	Good

As was mentioned previously, it is difficult to generalize about the properties of particular chained groups within the polymer backbone. For instance, a linear, low functionality, high molecular weight polyester within a polyurethane can give rise to poor saponification (alkali hydrolysis) resistance. A lower molecular weight and high functionality, highly branched polyester can, on the other hand, give good hydrolytic stability when included.

It is worth at this point considering which polyol systems might be best incorporated when used over concrete substrates. In fact all types may be used; however, the choice may well be dependent upon the particular requirement of the application.

For an exterior grade coating, resistance to UV light is obviously important. Just as aromatic isocyanates give rise to instability in UV light, so too do polyether polyurethanes. The ether linkage is easily attacked by UV light and, with an unprotected system, breakdown can be extremely rapid.

Polyester polyurethanes show excellent resistance to UV light and might, therefore, be considered to be the better choice. Normally, however, softer and more flexible products are often required for concrete protection. A polyester system manufactured with such properties would be made using higher molecular weight, low functionality linear polyester polyols. These have been shown to have poor saponification resistance. This would naturally make them unsuitable for use over a potentially highly alkaline concrete substrate.

Polycarbonate polyurethanes generally sit between polyethers and polyesters with regard to UV and saponification resistance. Polycarbonates have better UV resistance than polyethers though not as good as polyesters. On the other hand, the polycarbonate backbone confers better saponification resistance than polyesters, though not as good as polyethers.

Polyacrylate systems in general show excellent exterior durability. Their UV stability is very good and resistance to saponification is generally better than a polyester system.

Taking the above on face value, it would seem not to be a wise choice to use a polyether polyurethane for exterior applications due to its poor resistance to UV radiation. On the other hand, the inclusion of pigments in a coating formulation and the further inclusion of UV absorbers and light stabilizers can render them sufficiently durable for the majority of external applications. Polyesters, as stated, are unstable to saponification. It is not possible to include additives which would improve resistance and, therefore, the better choice for an exterior system may well be the polyether. Better options still would be the use of either polycarbonate polyurethanes or polyacrylate polyurethane which would give better overall durability than the polyether or polyester systems.

Of course, only two properties have been considered during this discourse and the selection of the correct system must take other things into consideration. For instance, chemical resistance would be a major criterion for a bund lining, whilst hardness and solvent resistance may be more important for an anti-graffiti coating. Another major consideration may well be price, with polyacrylates and polycarbonates being significantly more expensive than polyesters, with polyether systems enabling the cheapest polyurethane products. A further consideration may be VOC (volatile organic content). In order to make systems at a suitable viscosity for application, significantly more solvent is required for polyacrylates, with reducing quantities required for polycarbonates, polyesters and polyethers.

Without going into too much detail here, it can be seen that the choice of polyol within a polyurethane system can have a significant effect on many properties. It is important for the formulator to understand these effects; however, it is also useful for the end user to understand these effects and terms so that a better, more informed choice of product can be made.

7.4   Polyurethane systems (formulation)

The basic starting point for the formulator of polyurethane coatings is an isocyanate terminated prepolymer prepared as described from monomeric di-isocyanates and polyols. To this may be added other prepolymers, adducts, dimers and trimers to modify the potential properties depending upon requirements.

These blends of isocyanate reactive species are then cross-linked to form solid polyurethanes by further reaction with active hydrogen containing chemicals such as polyols or water.

7.4.1   Two component polyol/poly-isocyanate systems

Probably the most common type of polyurethane available for coating purposes are two-component systems. In these systems, the polyol (or blend of polyols) is kept in a separate container from the poly-isocyanate prepolymer blend until ready for use. In this instance, the pigments, plasticizer, catalyst, UV absorbers, etc., are pre-blended into the polyol component. Generally, only solvent is included with the isocyanate component, although plasticizer may also be included to enable a suitable mix ratio.

Invariably the two components will be supplied already packaged in the correct mix ratio. Just prior to application, the two components are mixed and stirred thoroughly. From the moment of mixing, the reaction between polyol and poly-isocyanate is proceeding, leading to a viscosity increase, limited pot life and then inevitable gellation. This same reaction proceeds if the mixed components have been applied to the substrate.

The main reaction is therefore :

$$\text{Polyol} + \text{Poly-isocyanate prepolymer} \rightarrow \text{Polyurethane}$$

Inevitably many of the components included in the formulation, i.e. polyol, solvent, pigments, etc., will contain water. As discussed, water will also react with the poly-isocyanate, so this becomes a competing reaction if the components are not pre-dried. This situation is compounded when the mixed system is applied to the substrate as the isocyanate now also becomes available to react with atmospheric moisture and moisture in the substrate. Thus, the following reaction can also proceed:

$$\text{Poly-isocyanate prepolymer} + H_2O \rightarrow \text{Polyurethane} + CO_2$$

When a two-component system is applied to a substrate and the reaction proceeds, the viscosity increases. This will cause the molecular mobility of the system to reduce, thereby making it more difficult for the isocyanate groups and hydroxyl groups to come into contact and react. This effect makes the reaction of isocyanate with water even more prevalent. The extent to which this reaction occurs is also dependent upon atmospheric conditions, i.e. temperature and, in particular, humidity. The higher the humidity, the greater the reaction of the isocyanate with water.

This can obviously lead to variability in both performance and appearance of the polyurethane system. High humidity can lead to reduced cross-linking between the polyol and poly-isocyanate leading to changed mechanical properties and weathering capabilities. The increased contribution of the isocyanate/water reaction can produce a down-glossing of the finished film and in severe cases bubble and pinhole formation as CO_2 gas is released.

7.4.2   Moisture cure polyurethane systems

The side reaction described in the previous section can, of course, be used in its own right to fully cross-link poly-isocyanates to form a solid film.

$$\text{Poly-isocyanate (polyurethane prepolymer)} + H_2O \rightarrow \text{Polyurethane} + CO_2$$

With this type of system, the isocyanate terminated prepolymers and adducts are blended and into this are added the solvent, pigments and other additives required. This type of product is rather more difficult to manufacture as it often requires pre-drying of the various additives to avoid reaction of water with the isocyanate in the tin with subsequent CO_2 release and viscosity increase. Once correctly formulated, however, they come packaged as a single component system. All that is required is to open the tin and apply the product to the substrate.

As with two-component systems, it is possible to formulate moisture cure systems with wide ranging property profiles depending upon the choice of starting raw materials. There are, however, several limitations associated with moisture cure polyurethanes, not least of which is due to their moisture sensitivity.

Table 7.3 *Cure versus relative humidity (RH). (Moisture cure urethane)*

Relative humidity	Cure
0–20% RH	Very little cure
20–30% RH	Very slow cure
30–45% RH	Slow cure
45–80% RH	Good cure
80–90% RH	Slight gassing
90–100% RH	Severe gassing

More so than with two-component systems, the curing and quality of polyurethane film formation is very much dependent upon atmospheric humidity during application (Table 7.3).

If the relative humidity is too high, the film formation is too rapid to allow release of the CO_2 which is generated. This, therefore, gets trapped in the film. On the other hand, if the humidity is too low, the rate of cure becomes unacceptably slow. Finding the ideal day on which to apply a moisture cure polyurethane system is, therefore, not always easy.

Further, there is a limit to the maximum film build which can be achieved with this type of system. Too high a film build, e.g. >100/200 μ (depending upon formulation), will almost inevitably lead to the formation of bubbles as the CO_2 is unable to escape through the forming skin. The higher the film build, the greater the bubbling.

7.4.3   Moisture triggered, latent hardener/poly-isocyanate systems

There can be no doubt that for the applicator the simplest systems to use are single-pack. With these there is no need to measure out the correct proportions, nor to ensure correct and thorough mixing. Furthermore, there are no limitations on pot-life, as with two-component systems, thereby ensuring little material wastage. That being said, there are limitations on application humidity and application thickness if a correctly cured film with good properties is to be assured. This may cause great difficulty to the contractor who may find that progress is delayed by inclement weather conditions, or simply by having to apply multiple, thin coats.

There are some single-pack systems which get around these problems by the inclusion of a latent hardener, producing a so-called 'moisture triggered' system. The secret of these systems is for the latent hardener to react with atmospheric moisture and for the subsequently activated hardener to then further react with the poly-isocyanate. This can be achieved by introducing an oxazolidine 'hardener' into the system.

Oxazolidines are available in several forms though the most commonly used types of latent hardeners in polyurethane systems are bis-oxazolidines which, when reacted with water, have tetra functionality.

Oxazolidines (preparation)

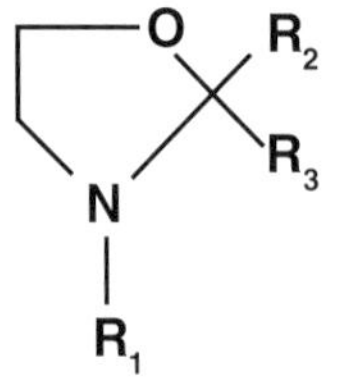

R$_1$ = alkyl group or –ROH
R$_2$ = H or alkyl group
R$_3$ = alkyl group

mono oxazolidine

If R$_1$ is an alcohol group, typically – CH$_2$CH$_2$OH, it is possible to further react this with an OH reactive species to form a bis-oxazolidine, for example, reaction with a di-isocyanate (typically HDI) will produce a urethane bis-oxazolidine.

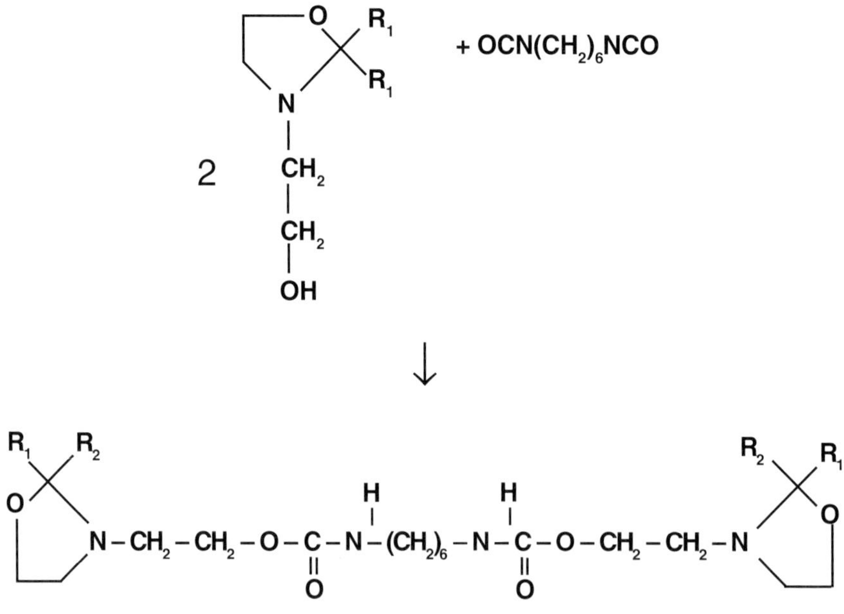

2   + OCN(CH$_2$)$_6$NCO

↓

urethane bis-oxazolidine

It is possible to prepare other types of bis-oxazolidine by choosing different reaction partners. Also available are, therefore, ester bis-oxazolidines and carbonate bis-oxazolidines.

The reaction of oxazolidines with poly-isocyanates is a two stage process with the first stage being reaction with water and the second stage reaction with isocyanate.

Reaction with water

$R_2 = H \rightarrow$ aldehyde
$R_2 = $ alkyl $\rightarrow$ ketone

Reaction with polyisocyanate

Note: There is no production of CO_2

When moisture triggered systems are formulated, all the components are in a single pack. Therefore, poly-isocyanate, pigments, solvents, additives, etc., are all blended together. At this stage, moisture is removed from the system and then the oxazolidine added. Whilst the tin remains sealed the system remains stable. Once exposed to the atmosphere, the reaction can begin.

As the system contains poly-isocyanate, there obviously remains the possibility that this may react directly with atmospheric moisture as can occur with two-pack and single-pack moisture cure systems. If, however, the relative rates of reaction are considered, then it can be seen that this is not likely to be of significance.

		reversible		**Reaction rate**
1.	Oxazolidine + H_2O	$\rightleftharpoons$	activated hardener	Fast
2.	$R - N - H + OCN - R \rightarrow$		urea	Very fast
3.	$R - O - H + OCN - R \rightarrow$		urethane	Medium
4.	$H_2O + OCN - R \quad\rightarrow$		urea	Medium

The first reversible reaction between the oxazolidine and water proceeds quickly to form an hydroxyl and amine functional species. This reaction is reversible; however, as the reaction between the subsequently formed amine and isocyanate is very fast, the first reaction rapidly moves to completion. The formation of urea links in this way, therefore, commences virtually immediately. The reaction rates of the hydroxyl group with poly-isocyanate and water with poly-isocyanate are very similar. Due, however, to the fact that a lot of cross-linking has already occurred through reaction of amine with isocyanate, less isocyanate is in any case available to react with water. The system also rapidly gels; this means that whilst some CO_2 will be released it cannot form discrete bubbles and it simply evolves from the film. This effect becomes more prevalent as it is normal with these systems to use an excess of oxazolidine. This means that the amine isocyanate reaction becomes even more important and leads to even less evolution of CO_2. It does, however, give rise to reduced cross-link density.

The rate of cure of moisture cure systems is very dependent upon the atmospheric relative humidity (Table 7.3). With moisture triggered systems, the humidity will still affect the rate of cure; however, it is nowhere near as significant (Table 7.4). This is because the rate determining step (i.e. slowest reaction) with this system is that between hydroxyl and poly-isocyanate. Furthermore, there is no upper limit for humidity as even with high moisture content bubbling in the film will not occur. In fact oxazolidine moisture triggered systems can quite happily cure under water without problems.

There are some other points worth noting about these moisture triggered systems. Oxazolidines are low viscosity species and their inclusion can significantly reduce solvent requirement. Systems are available today with as little as 5% by weight being solvent. As well as the urethane bis-oxazolidines, it was previously mentioned that ester and carbonate linked oxazolidines are also available. These are of even lower viscosity and can make a significant contribution towards further reduction of VOC.

Oxazolidines can themselves react with isocyanates and, therefore, only the less reactive isocyanates may be used in combination with oxazolidines to form stable products. Therefore, the aliphatic isocyanates IPDI and TMXDI are commonly used with oxazolidine. Aromatic systems are generally not stable with oxazolidine and even HDI has too high a reactivity. All moisture triggered polyurethane systems on the market are therefore aliphatic in nature and eminently suitable for exterior application, provided they are otherwise formulated correctly.

Table 7.4 *Cure versus relative humidity. (Moisture triggered urethane)*

Relative humidity	Cure
0–10%	Little cure
10–20%	Slow
20–30%	Medium
30–100%	Excellent cure

7.4.4   Polyurea systems (polyamine/poly-isocyanate)

It is worth mentioning at this stage the very specialized but increasingly important polyurea systems. These are two-component systems where instead of using polyol to react with poly-isocyanate, polyamines are used. It has already been mentioned that the reaction between amines and isocyanates can proceed extremely rapidly. Such is the speed, with gel times as low as two seconds or less, that these systems cannot be pre-mixed, but require specialized plural component spray equipment to apply them. They are, however, finding a niche in some applications over concrete where their ability to cure extremely rapidly, even under very severe, cold, wet conditions, is utilized.

7.4.5   Water-based single-pack systems

Thus far, only solvent-based (or high solids solvent-based) systems have been discussed. There continues, however, to be increased awareness in both environmental and health and safety issues. Adding to that the simplicity of using only water for clean up, it is not surprising that water-based systems are becoming important.

As with their solvent-based counterparts, an extremely wide variety of properties is achievable when using polyurethane dispersion systems (PUDs). The reason for this is that, whilst more limited, there still remains a very wide choice of basic raw materials to use.

There is no need in this section to look fully at the method of preparation of the PUDs; however, the outline sequence is shown below.

1.   Preparation of isocyanate terminated prepolymer.
2.   Carboxylation   ⎫
3.   Neutralisation   ⎬ introduces hydrophilic sites.
4.   Dispersion in water.
5.   Chain extension — to fully polymerise.

The above is typical of the regime to produce an anionic PUD, though other types and routes are possible. The important things to note are as follows :

As with other polyurethane systems, the first stage is the formation of the isocyanate terminated prepolymer and, at this stage, many of the finished product properties are introduced. The vast majority of PUDs commercially available are based on aliphatic isocyanates as they are less reactive towards water during the production stage. Aromatic systems are, however, available.

Coating systems manufactured from PUDs are made in the same way as other water-based dispersion/emulsion systems. Worthy of note here is that many PUD coating formulations will contain the powerful solvents required for formulation of the product prior to dispersion. For example, N-methylpyrrolidone is often present in relatively large quantities, though some newer, low solvent or solvent-free PUDs are becoming available.

Due to the fact that these are water-based systems, there are of course more severe limitations on their use externally. Inclement or cold weather may preclude their use; however, given good application conditions they can achieve excellent properties. At the moment, they have a relatively low share of the market, particularly as other water-borne emulsion systems, e.g. acrylics, tend to be cheaper; however, there is no doubt they will gain wider use in the future.

7.4.6   Water-based two-component polyurethane systems

Over the last few years, several water-based two-component polyurethane systems have become available. It would seem at first that these are strange systems as reactive poly-isocyanate is mixed into a water-based emulsion containing either a water dispersible polyol or a hydroxyl functional acrylic. That the isocyanate does not react completely with the water is probably due to the fact that it emulsifies and blends with the polyol which tends to protect it. Furthermore, after application of the system, the water begins to evaporate thereby giving an ever increasing hydroxyl : water ratio.

One method of producing a water dispersible polyol is to prepare a hydroxyl terminated polyurethane prepolymer with some carboxyl functionality. These prepolymers may be made in the same way as the previously described isocyanate terminated counterparts. It is, once again, possible due to the diversity of available raw materials to virtually tailor-make a product with the required properties.

There are some limitations to the use of these two-component water-based polyurethane systems. As with their solvent-based or solvent-free counterparts, there is a pot-life limitation. Some reaction will also inevitably occur between isocyanate and water and bubbling can occur, especially if applied in over-thick films.

Whilst for the time being these systems are not commonplace, there would seem no doubt that they will grow in relative importance in years to come. As with the water-based polyurethane dispersion technology, they will probably assume greater importance for internal use which, of course, is not blighted by inclement weather.

7.4.7   Fluorinated polyurethanes

One further class of polyurethane system worthy of mention is that which contains a fluorinated backbone. As with many other fluorinated systems, they are characterized by an extremely high level of durability, whilst also being available with a wide range of different mechanical properties. They can be formulated in many of the earlier described forms, i.e. single-pack, twin-pack, etc., and can often be used where extremes of performance are required. For the time being these systems are extremely expensive and will currently tend to find use in very specialized niche market areas. In time, no doubt, prices will reduce and, due to their sometimes unsurpassed performance, they may assume greater importance in the future.

7.5   Application of polyurethane systems to concrete

Where there is concrete, it is generally feasible to find a polyurethane coating system which can protect it. As previously and repeatedly stated, it is possible to produce polyurethane systems with such a wide variety of different properties that one such system should be able to meet the performance criteria of most specifications.

It is not necessarily true to say that a polyurethane system will always be the best answer to any problem as 'fitness for purpose' covers many different criteria. Amongst these may, for instance, be cost for whilst the polyurethane may fit the bill, it may be that an equally adequate, cheaper alternative is available. However, polyurethane systems very often do provide the best solutions to a particular problem, as is evidenced by their extensive use on concrete in many differing and often very extreme environments.

Whilst other chapters in this book describe in more detail the deterioration and the surface preparation of concrete and some specific application fields, these will also be discussed briefly here. This section will, therefore, describe the methods of preparation of concrete surfaces along with methods of application of the coating systems, as well as ideal application conditions. Thereafter, we shall look more specifically at particular applications and uses and discuss some of the performance criteria required for each and how the chosen polyurethane system may be 'fit for purpose.' Finally, some examples of application of polyurethane systems to concrete will be considered to demonstrate how they have met the specification criteria.

7.5.1 Deterioration of concrete and protection

7.5.2 Surface preparation

Prior to the application of any system to concrete, it is of course vitally important that the surface be properly prepared. The phrase 'ensure that the concrete is clean, dry and sound' is one that is invariably used when describing the preparation of concrete, but what does this mean?

Briefly, 'clean' means that there is no foreign matter, such as dirt, dust, oil or grease. 'Dry' means that no free water is present, or that the water content of the concrete is no greater than the maximum allowable level for a particular coating system (often measured as wood moisture equivalent). 'Sound' means that there is no laitance or weak surface skin (including previous coatings which are loose and flaking) and that the concrete has no other defects such as cracks and holes which may affect the coating's performance.

A typical preparation sequence might be as follows:

Cleaning

Removal of any oil, grease or other dirt or grime which may prevent a coating system being applied. This generally means surface cleaning and may simply be by way of wire brushing, broom, mopping or vacuuming to remove easily dislodged matter. It may also include low/med pressure water washing or steam cleaning. If grease or oil is also present, the use of detergents, is usually required. Flame treatment may also be used to remove grease and oils. It might also be important to use a biocidal treatment to remove fungal and algal species, etc.

Abrading and/or acid etching

If more than just surface cleaning is required, it is possible that other techniques such as grinding, scarifying, scabbling, blasting, high pressure water jetting, or acid etching (e.g. with hydrochloric acid) may be utilized.

It is worth noting that abrasive blasting may also be used after the repair of any defects to provide a roughened surface to promote surface adhesion.

Repair of defects

Repair of cracks, holes or spalls is often vital prior to the application of any coating system. Large cracks and holes may be filled with proprietary repair mortars; smaller cracks will often require a 'v' notch grind prior to filling with mortar. If movement is expected, it is possible to fill these cracks/holes with flexible polymeric sealants and fillers and indeed many polyurethane based versions are available, though other compatible types may also be used under polyurethane coating systems.

7.5.3   Systems application

Having prepared the concrete surface, it is now ready for application of the required coating system. This may include primers and top coats along with other ancillary products such as reinforcing tapes and mats. The actual system utilized will depend upon the demands of the application. The consideration will include substrate condition, end use, climatic/weather conditions, ease of application, durability, aesthetics, health and safety and environmental issues, cost, etc.

The application methods may well be determined by site conditions and/or restrictions, or possibly some methods may be precluded by the actual product or system being applied. Other criteria affecting the method of application may be as listed for system choice. For example, weather restrictions, health and safety considerations and cost may all be important parameters with regard to choice.

The method of application is generally not too great an issue with regard to the end client. It is, however, extremely important to the contractor who should determine the most suitable approach to suit the client's wishes. Of the three main methods available (brush, roller or spray), brush application would generally only be used for small areas of detail work. Roller or spray are suitable for larger areas; however, sometimes there are restrictions on the use of spray applications. Problems associated with overspray, health and safety or even simply accessibility may not allow the use of spray.

Precise details of application methods should, of course, accompany every system available on the market. Whilst there are some systems which are more user friendly than others, the contractor involved should be fully conversant with the actual system being used. Ideally the contractor should be trained (ideally backed up by a Contractor QA Scheme) in all aspects of the use and application of the product being handled and should be able to provide method statements to the end client which should also include the aforementioned substrate preparation.

7.5.4 Polyurethane systems

Whilst the method of application utilized may be determined by the system being applied, the choice of system will very much depend upon the precise end use. There is no single polyurethane product on the market which will meet all needs; however, there are some which are multi-functional and which may be utilized in a great many different fields of application. Very often the final choice of product will to a degree be a compromise between fitness for purpose, durability and cost. That being said there should be no doubt that for the vast majority of requirements a polyurethane system will be available which is eminently suitable.

7.5.5 Primers/sealers

To enable the correct performance of any coating system, it is often necessary to ensure that the concrete surface is sealed and stabilized with a priming system which will also promote adhesion. Whilst they need to be compatible with the polyurethane topcoat, the primers and sealers themselves need not necessarily be polyurethane. The types of primers and sealers used therefore may be extremely varied and may be dictated by the condition of the substrate, and the end use of the system. Most often, of course, manufacturers of polyurethane systems will make recommendations on which primers to use with their own topcoats and will usually also supply them. Whilst it is not possible to discuss every available priming system, the next section will at least outline several generic types and advise on their suitability for particular end uses.

7.6 Substrate condition

It is very often the condition of the substrate which will necessitate the use of a primer or sealer. Whilst the concrete may well have been prepared correctly, in the manner described earlier, it is still possible that the surface remains friable and dusty, or it may be extremely porous. If the polyurethane topcoats are applied directly to such surfaces, several problems can result.

7.6.1 Friable surfaces

Application directly to a very friable/dusty surface can leave a very weak interfacial layer between the bulk substrate and the coating. This will give rise to a very low level of adhesion and under certain conditions, e.g. through excessive vapour drive or osmotic pressure, can lead to blistering and indeed potentially disastrous wholesale delamination of the polyurethanes from the concrete. Sealers, which may be, for instance, relatively dilute moisture cure urethanes, solution acrylics or perhaps low particle size water-based acrylics or epoxy emulsions, can penetrate into the loose friable surface layer and help to consolidate it. This can therefore eliminate the weak interfacial layer and, providing the topcoat will adhere to the sealer, will reduce any potential for delamination.

7.6.2 Porous concrete

In a similar manner, sealers of the same type can be applied to porous concrete substrates. Porous substrates do not necessarily give rise to problems if topcoats are applied directly; however, several potential ones are worth citing.

1. 'Outgassing' as the solvent (or water) from the polyurethane system is absorbed into the substrate can lead to severe pinholing. This effect is often made worse if, during application and curing, the temperature increases and causes the air within the substrate pores to expand and escape through the curing coating.
2. With solvent-based systems, not only the solvent but also the dissolved polyurethane polymer can be absorbed into the substrate. In a pigmented system as the polymer is absorbed, this gives rise to a pigment rich coating surface which will not only exhibit reduced gloss (due to higher pvc) but may detract from the mechanical properties and durability. This is less of a problem if multiple coats are applied.
3. Many water-based polyurethane or polyurethane acrylic dispersion systems contain coalescing solvents to enable correct cure. If the coalescent is hydrophilic, it can be absorbed into the porous concrete along with water and could raise the minimum film forming temperature of the system to above the application temperature. This would give rise to incorrect cure and perhaps to crazing. Again subsequent coats can mask this effect but the overall adhesion and mechanical properties of the system may be compromised.

If sealers are applied to porous concrete, these can assist in blocking the pores and thereby reducing suction to enable the successful application of topcoats.

7.6.3 Efflorescence/laitance

Often the concrete may contain high levels of water soluble salts which can diffuse to the surface. This can occur particularly if the internal substrate is saturated and, whilst the surface may be acceptably dry to apply the topcoat, the water and associated salts can immigrate to the substrate coating interface. While the water can escape through the coating as water vapour, the salts will build up to such an extent that they can cause delamination of the coating from the substrate. With clear polyurethane systems, these salts can be seen as white deposits beneath the coating and, whilst adhesion loss may not occur, it can certainly detract aesthetically.

The answer is to prevent the salts from reaching the concrete surface. As with friable and porous substrates, this can be achieved with the use of sealers which penetrate the surface. In such circumstances a greater dilution of sealer is often required to enable a greater depth of penetration. Also used are hydrophobic sealers, such as silanes or siloxanes (sometimes combined with acrylics), which penetrate deeply into the concrete. These create a hydrophobic layer a long way from the surface and will assist in eliminating the problem. Such hydrophobic/waterproofing primers are often used simply to enhance the waterproofing qualities of the system as a whole or to ensure at least some retention of waterproofing, even if the topcoats are damaged.

7.6.4 Dampness

Substrate dampness alone can be a major problem when it comes to application of polyurethane systems. Whilst the requirement is generally for a dry substrate, it is not always possible to achieve this. It could be therefore that it is not possible to reduce the moisture content below 28% WME (wood moisture equivalent). If this is the case, it is important to use priming systems which can tolerate such moisture content. Specially formulated epoxies or polyurethanes, using blends of hydrophilic solvents which will absorb surface moisture, are generally the best to use.

Some polyurethane topcoats, particularly those formulated with a latent hardener, moisture triggered mechanism are suitable for direct application to concrete with a high moisture content. The solvent blends tend to be hydrophilic and furthermore, the curing reaction uses up substrate moisture without the formation of carbon dioxide and hence no blistering occurs.

7.7 Primer types

The choice of primer or sealer may be critical to the overall success of any application. Generally the recommendation would be to use compatible systems supplied by the manufacturer for the appropriate polyurethane product. The different available primer types have been briefly discussed; however it is worth expanding on them here.

Very often, providing the substrate is sound, there is no need for any primer. Most polyurethane systems, particularly solvent-based, will to a degree penetrate the concrete substrate and afford sufficient physical adhesion. Certainly there are times when the use of an incorrect primer will detract from the overall performance properties.

7.7.1 Diluted topcoat

Very often all that is required as primer is the topcoat in diluted form. The dilution simply reduces the viscosity and allows greater penetration of the substrate. This can help to seal pores and to bind friable surfaces. Care must be taken when diluting and no reactive solvents (e.g. alcohols) must be used as they would severely affect the properties. Ideally it should also be ensured that the solvents are dry, otherwise this could limit pot life.

7.7.2 Moisture cure polyurethanes

Moisture cure polyurethanes can make excellent primers and sealers. Providing they are applied and cured correctly, it is possible to provide an excellent and compatible base for subsequent overcoating of urethane topcoats. The use of moisture cure primers is however limited due to substrate and weather conditions, as described earlier in this chapter. One further potential problem is that unless overcoated quickly (sometimes no greater than 24 hours), the level of adhesion achieved by the topcoat to the primers may be very poor. In addition, the majority of moisture cure urethane primers are aromatic in nature. This type should not be used under clear topcoats as discolouration may occur.

7.7.3 Acrylics

These are suitable for use under most urethane products. Both water-based or solvent-based types are suitable though more often the solution grade would be used. They do not greatly enhance adhesion and therefore find their major use as sealers.

7.7.4 Epoxies

Epoxy systems probably form the most suitable group of primers/sealers. As with acrylics, they are available in both solvent-based and water-based form. The major disadvantages are that these are two-component systems with limited pot life and have poor low temperature curing characteristics. The water-based systems are in particular susceptible to inclement weather; however, given good cure conditions they can act both as sealers and as excellent adhesion promoting primers. In order to maximize adhesion the top coats should ideally be applied within seven days; however, in this respect they are nothing like as limiting as the moisture cure urethanes.

7.7.5 Silanes/siloxanes

When a hydrophilic waterproofing layer is required then silanes or siloxanes are used, either on their own, prior to other primers/sealers, or indeed combined with, for instance, acrylics. Again water-based or solvent-based options are available as indeed are 100% active silanes. If used on their own, the main danger is that they produce a hydrophilic layer which is particularly difficult for water-based polyurethane systems to adhere to. It can also be demonstrated that unless overcoated sufficiently quickly the adhesion of solvent-based urethane systems may also be retarded. Despite these potential problems, provided they are overcoated sufficiently quickly, they can provide a useful addition to the system as a whole especially if efflorescence is likely to be a problem.

7.8 Polyurethane topcoats

Whilst it is always said that a system's performance is only as good as the preparation which precedes it, even the best preparations will be of no benefit if the incorrect polyurethane is chosen as topcoat.

It is useful to consider the requirements of several different end uses and to discuss the suitability of polyurethanes for these purposes. Earlier in this chapter, the potential problems associated with concrete structures were outlined. Whether dealing with roofs, car parks, facades, bridges, or floors, etc., these problems can manifest themselves and the solutions to these problems may be very similar in each set of circumstances. That being said, there are often very specific requirements which necessitate unique solutions.

Earlier in this chapter, the 'ideal coating' was described which would provide the panacea to all potential concrete problems. The various property requirements will now be expanded upon here.

7.8.1 Adhesion to concrete

The ability to adhere well to concrete, whether it be with or without primer, is obviously of major importance for the majority of applications – typically levels of adhesion of the order of 1.5 to 2.5 MPa to ensure no loss of adhesion under normal use. This is perfectly achievable with all urethane types given the correct preparation, including primer if required. Adhesion can be retarded if the moisture content of the concrete is too high and normally it would be required that the WME would be < 20%. Some urethane systems with the inclusion of hydrophilic solvents and particularly moisture triggered systems can accept moisture contents as high as 28% WME, as a part of the curing mechanism will use up some substrate moisture.

7.8.2 Flexibility/crack-bridging

If waterproofing, anti-carbonation or protection from spillage, etc., is required, the polyurethane system applied must have the ability to bridge cracks. Whilst crack-bridging capability is by no means unique to polyurethanes, there is no doubt that the combined strength and flexibility available with some polyurethane systems facilitates this requirement.

Table 7.5 gives data indicating the typical mechanical properties of a multi-functional polyurethane system which gives excellent crack-bridging capability. Whilst crack-bridging can be achieved with an unreinforced system, there is no doubt that the inclusion of reinforcement, such as a non-woven glass fibre matting, will improve this capability.

Table 7.5 *Typical properties of a multi-functional polyurethane system.*

	Unreinforced polyurethane*	Reinforced with 225 g/m² glass fibre mat
Tensile load (1 cm wide strip)	6.55 kg/cm	34.60 kg/cm
Elongation at break	220%	27%
Tear strength	0.33 kg/mm	5.70 kg/mm
Crack-bridging	> 1mm	> 5mm
DFT	800	2000

* Aliphatic moisture triggered polyurethane roofing system

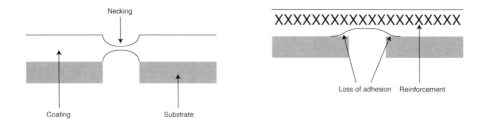

Figure 7.1 *Crack-bridging in reinforced and unreinforced systems.*

It is said that if a crack in structural concrete has opened to greater than 0.3 mm that it constitutes structural failure. The figures in Table 7.5 show that the unreinforced system can more than adequately bridge cracks of that magnitude; however, the reinforced system is still preferred. The reason for this is that an unreinforced system will tend to 'neck' as a crack opens whereas a reinforced system, being so strong, will tend to lose adhesion to the substrate without significant necking (Figure 7.1). This means that the reinforcement helps to spread the load and that the coating is under far less stress and is less liable to fail due to fatigue.

In some instances a hard abrasion-resistant surface may be required. This may, for example, be the case for car park decks. If this is the case, it is likely that a softer polyurethane base coat system may be required below a harder topcoat to provide the required crack-bridging capability.

7.8.3   Anti-carbonation

The main requirements for a coating to confer anti-carbonation properties to concrete are as follows :

CO$_2$ diffusion resistance : $S_D(CO_2) > 50$ metres
Water vapour diffusion resistance : $S_D(CO_2) < 4$ metres

(S_D = diffusion equivalent air layer thickness)

These criteria should be relatively easily met by most correctly formulated polyurethane systems.

If a coating system is required for its protective qualities, film thicknesses of 500 μ to 2–3 mm may be used. This high film build creates a natural barrier to both carbon dioxide and water vapour. As can be seen from Figure 7.2, the inclusion of pigments and extenders creates an even greater barrier to CO$_2$ which will increase the diffusion resistance further. These same pigments and extenders, however, are generally hydrophilic in nature and can promote the permeability of water vapour.

With unpigmented polyurethane systems, it is more difficult to achieve the correct balance. Carbon dioxide can more easily diffuse and the vapour diffusion is retarded by the lack of hydrophilic centres. Clear polyurethane products, which may be used to

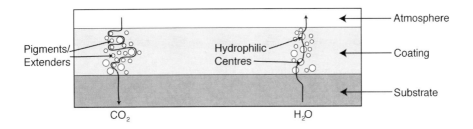

Figure 7.2 *CO_2/H_2O diffusion through pigmented urethane coating.*

maintain appearance of exposed aggregate concrete for example, are available which will meet the anti-carbonation requirements; however, it is important to stress that not all will.

It is also important to reiterate the need for crack-bridging capability. Some of the harder polyurethane products, e.g. acrylic polyurethanes used for anti-graffiti purposes, may not have sufficient flexibility and once ruptured will easily allow the migration of carbon dioxide.

7.8.4   Which polyurethane topcoat?

Three of the main performance properties required from a polyurethane coating have been described. It is impossible, however, to discuss in depth each potential end use and each of the potential polyurethanes which might be most suitably employed to ensure fitness for purpose.

Instead Tables 7.6 and 7.7 give an indication of which particular properties are important for certain applications and which polyurethane products are most likely to be employed for these applications. It should be noted that these tables are to be used as a rough guideline only. The table indicating polyurethane types reflects applications which are known to have been carried out using particular systems; it does not, however, necessarily preclude the use of any other system provided it is suitably formulated.

Examples

A couple of examples are now given to briefly explain the meaning of the tables.

Roof coating
   Adhesion — vitally important as the coating needs to withstand significant wind suction effects.
   Flexibility / crack-bridging — roof structures can move significantly both generally and locally. In order to maintain the integrity and in particular waterproofing properties, the coating must remain flexible, and bridge cracks without splitting.

Table 7.6 *Suitable polyurethane types.*

	Roof	Wall int	Wall ext	Car park	Floor	Bridge deck	Bund	Anti-grafitti	Pipe int	Pipe ext
Moisture cure			✓					✓	✓	
Moisture triggered	✓		✓	✓			✓		✓	✓
Twin pack	✓	✓	✓	✓	✓	✓	✓	✓	✓	✓
Water-based		✓								
High solids	✓		✓	✓		✓	✓		✓	✓
Clear		✓	✓		✓			✓		
Aromatic	✓			✓	✓	✓	✓		✓	✓
Aliphatic	✓	✓	✓		✓		✓	✓		
Acrylic		✓	✓		✓			✓	✓	✓
Polyester				✓	✓	✓				
Polyether	✓			✓	✓	✓	✓		✓	✓
Polycarbonate	✓	✓					✓			✓
Polyurea	✓			✓	✓	✓	✓			✓

Table 7.7 *Important properties.*

	Roof	Wall int	Wall ext	Car park	Floor	Bridge deck	Bund	Anti-grafitti	Pipe int	Pipe ext
Adhesion	✔	✓	✔	✔	✔	✓	✓	✓	✔	✔
Flexibility crack-bridge	✔	✓	✔	✔	✔	✔	✔		✔	✔
CO$_2$ diffusion resistance	✓	✓	✔	✔		✔	✓			
H$_2$O vapour diffusion	✓	✓	✔	✓	✔	✓		✓		
Cl$^-$ diffusion resistance			✓	✔		✔				
Abrasion resistance				✔	✔				✓	
Chemical resistance	✓			✓	✔		✔		✔	✓
Waterproof	✔	✓	✓	✔	✔	✔	✔		✔	✔
UV resistance	✔		✓	✓*			✓	✔		✓
Heat resistance	✓					✔	✓		✓	
Low temperature resistance	✓	✓	✓	✓		✓	✓	✓	✓	✓

* top deck
Key: ✔ Very Important, ✓ Important

CO_2 diffusion resistivity — some importance; however, the roof area is not usually of structural importance and therefore some carbonation of concrete is not necessarily detrimental.

H_2O vapour diffusion — in inclement environments it can take a long time for a concrete roof structure to dry out. It is important that the coating will allow significant vapour diffusion to prevent blistering/loss of adhesion due to vapour pressure.

Cl⁻ diffusion — generally not important as salt contamination is not normal, and the roof is not structural.

Abrasion resistance — generally not important unless the roof is going to be exposed to significant foot traffic.

Chemical resistance — can be important in some industrialized areas where local exhaust fumes and dust can alight on a roof.

Waterproofing — usually the fundamental requirement and therefore vitally important.

UV resistance — vitally important as the roof will be exposed to high levels of UV, particularly in hotter countries and at altitude. The coating must retain its integrity.

Heat resistance — roof temperatures, even of white coatings, can achieve 60 °C in hot countries with darker colours even higher. A degree of resistance to heat is therefore important.

Low temperature resistance — the roof may be exposed to temperatures as low as –40 °C in some countries and therefore the coating should ideally remain flexible enough to withstand movement.

The choice of polyurethane systems may be as follows:

Moisture cure — not normally used as generally high build applications are required. Moisture cure systems are not suitable as they would 'gas'.

Moisture triggered — totally suitable as they are single component and can be applied without affecting product quality under most conditions.

Twin-pack — generally suitable; however, some care with correct mixing and adverse weather conditions is required.

Water-based — generally not suitable as other water-based systems which are cheaper are available. Inclement weather can make application very difficult.

High solids — becoming increasingly important along with increased awareness of environmental and health and safety risks. High solids systems also suffer from less shrinkage which is important in high build systems.

Clear — clear systems could be used; however, there is generally little requirement to maintain the substrate appearance.

Aromatic — these may be used; however, they would generally require pigmenting to a dark grey or black colour to reduce UV attack and to mask colour change.

Aliphatic — generally the best choice, as white or light coloured coatings which will have good UV resistance and will have solar reflective qualities can be produced.

Acrylic — generally not used as high solids systems are not available; they are also expensive.

Polyester — not ideally used in direct contact with concrete as they have poor saponification resistance. Could however be used as top coats though again care must be taken in tropical environments due to their hydrolytic instability.

Polyether — a good choice even though not completely UV stable. Correct formulation can produce highly durable products which are available as high solids systems and at good value.

Polycarbonate — good roof coating choice for durability; however, viscosity and cost can preclude their use.

Polyurea — new technology which is likely to be suitable in the future due to rapid all weather application.

Case study: nuclear dome

An excellent example of the use of a polyurethane system to meet very specific requirements was the application to the top section of a concrete nuclear reactor dome. The main problem was that, when pressure tested, the dome was leaking air at a level of 2.7% per hour against a target of 1% per hour. This meant that there was the distinct possibility of radiation leakage in the event of an accident. It was found that the main reason for air loss was cracks which had developed in the top section of the nuclear dome.

One suggestion for reducing the air leakage rate was to apply a coating system to the top section of the dome to bridge the cracks. The actual criteria were as follows :

- Crack-bridging up to 0.2/0.3 mm at temperatures between –30 °C and +50 °C
- Good adhesion at pressures of up to 45 KPag
- Impact resistant
- Abrasion resistant
- Fire resistant
- UV resistant
- Waterproof
- Radiation resistant
- 20-year durability

After many tests on over 70 products, a moisture triggered single component polyurethane Decothane SP® manufactured by Liquid Plastics Limited was found to be the only product to meet the requirements. This is a proven certificated system.

The application included blasting of the concrete surface and priming with a two-component water-based epoxy. Three layers of Decothane SP® with a reinforcing mat were applied; then a layer of Decothane SP® with carborundum grit included for slip resistance, and a final wear layer of Decothane SP®.

Tests have shown that the system is performing even better than expected with the air leakage rate reduced to 0.25% per hour.

Bridge deck coating

Adhesion — not so important as the system will ultimately have the full weight of the asphalt road surface on top of it.

Flexibility / crack-bridging — extremely important as bridge deck can expand and contract considerably as well as be exposed to considerable vibration.

CO_2 diffusion resistivity — a definite consideration to prevent carbonation and ultimate corrosion of steel reinforcing bars.

H_2O vapour diffusion — as above.

Chloride ion diffusion — vitally important to prevent de-icing salts promoting corrosion.

Abrasion resistance — of no real importance.

Chemical resistance — important to be able to resist oils, petrol and de-icing chemicals.

Waterproofing — vitally important.

UV resistance — of no importance as not exposed at the surface.

Heat resistance — must be able to withstand the application of hot asphalt.

Low temperature resistance — must retain flexibility at low ambient temperatures.

The choice of polyurethanes may be as follows :

Moisture cure — not recommended as high build systems are required.

Moisture triggered — not normally used though high solids systems could be suitable.

Twin-pack — the normal requirement, usually formulated solvent free and applied by dual component spray equipment. Fast react systems are generally used.

Water-based — not suitable.

High Solids — normally solvent free.

Clear — not applicable.

Aromatic — the usual choice. Not exposed at the surface therefore UV/colour stability not important.

Aliphatic — see above.

Acrylic — not normally used as not possible to achieve solvent free systems.

Polyester $\left.\begin{array}{l}\\ \\ \end{array}\right\}$ All may be suitable provided formulated correctly.
Polyether — Polyether most likely choice as UV resistance not
Polycarbonate — required and produces lowest viscosity systems.

Polyurea — new technology but likely to find use in the future particularly in view of fast react all weather application.

Case study: New Severn Crossing, Bristol, UK

The 176,000 m² pre-cast concrete deck of the new Severn Crossing required the use of a bridge deck waterproofing system.

The choice of coating was the Baytec® system supplied through and applied by Pitchmastic. This is a two-component system applied using specialized heated plural component spray equipment. This is a proven certified system.

7.9   Other uses

Much the same can be considered with all the other potential uses for polyurethane systems. The tables can be used to match against proprietary polyurethane products to assist in making the correct choice for any particular application. No two polyurethane systems are equal and for any application it is for the end user to choose which product fits their particular purpose most accurately. There is no doubt that generally speaking there will be a suitable polyurethane product on the market which will fit the bill. The choices that might be made for a selection of end uses will now be discussed briefly.

7.9.1   Wall

Interior: While protection is important, the main function internally is likely to be aesthetic. A very important consideration internally will also be solvent fumes. The likely suitable choice would be a relatively hard water-based polyurethane dispersion or water-based two component system.

Exterior: As with an internal wall, the aesthetics become more important for exterior systems. Aliphatic systems will predominate and both single and two component systems may be suitable. Usually solvent-based systems will be used and, due to the aesthetic requirement, these are unlikely to be high solids systems. There may still be a need for crack-bridging capability and therefore a flexible product would be required. For graffiti resistance, either a stand-alone urethane acrylic or fluorinated polyurethane may be required and if necessary these may be applied over a softer, more flexible base coat. Clear polyurethanes, such as polycarbonate moisture triggered systems, are also suitable if substrate appearance should be retained.

7.9.2   Car park decking

There are several considerations here as indicated by the tables. Not only do they require similar properties to the roof coatings, but also abrasion resistance, resistance to oils and petrol, and chloride ion diffusion resistance. These are likely to be tough yet flexible twin-pack or moisture triggered high solids systems which include the use of reinforcing fabrics and may have a harder top coat with the incorporation of anti-slip grit. Aromatic systems may be suitable for internal car parks; however, levels exposed to UV light should be aliphatic systems.

7.9.3   Flooring

Many of the requirements for floors are the same as for car park decking, though generally the aesthetics become more important. It is usually required to use high solids or ideally solvent-free aromatic systems with the majority being two component due to the high build requirement. Flooring systems may again be multi-component with hard wear resistant decorative topcoats. These topcoats are very often aliphatic. Some flooring systems involve the blending of polyurethanes with fillers and granules to form screeds which are trowel applied.

7.9.4   Bund lining

The main requirement for bund lining is that the product be chemical resistant. If the bund is internal then high solids two-component aromatic systems are normally used. Externally it may be important to use an aliphatic grade. In order to contain spillage, it is obviously also important that the linings have crack-bridging capability. Often these softer urethanes do not have sufficient chemical resistance to retain strong acids for example; however, containment of milder chemicals for limited periods is perfectly feasible. It is possible to overcoat flexible urethanes with Novolac epoxies to give a high degree of chemical resistance.

A side issue here is general liquid containment and in particular within the water industry. Urethane systems are certainly suitable. However, if potable water is the concern, generally solvent-free systems will be required.

7.9.5   Pipeline coatings

Concrete pipes may be coated both internally and externally with urethane products. The requirement for the external coating will depend on whether or not the pipe is buried. For buried systems, a degree of chemical and certainly microbial/root resistance is required. These can be built into what would almost certainly be a high solids aromatic system, though aliphatics are not precluded. Moisture triggered single-packs are also suitable, especially as high build crack-bridging systems are required.

The requirement for the internal surfaces is dependent upon use although the main one would be water. Abrasion resistance can become important, particularly if the water is moving at speed or is carrying significant quantities of particulate material.

Whatever the use, the specific requirements must be accurately determined initially. Only then will it be possible to choose the correct system for the task at hand. Even then, it may be that particular systems have to be tested to ensure they meet the precise demands.

7.10   Health and safety and the environment

Much has been said and written about the hazards associated with using polyurethane systems and in particular handling isocyanates. It is probably true to say that there is more known about the effects of isocyanates than most other class of chemical. In general, the isocyanate hazard is only of importance to the applicator though others in the vicinity need to be aware of potential hazards and precautions should be taken to avoid them.

The other main hazard comes from the solvents and whilst they are not as potentially hazardous as the isocyanates, they are present generally in significantly larger quantities. The odour emitted from an application of a polyurethane system is the odour of the solvent blend.

The actual hazard is very much dependent upon situation and the application method. Internal application can obviously pose a greater threat than an external one, likewise an application by spray creates a greater potential hazard than application by brush. Generally speaking, external applications by brush or roller of urethane systems do not create a significant hazard providing the product is correctly formulated and providing the operator takes normal protective measures. Solvent-free and high solids systems will generally reduce the potential hazard and should be used when feasible. For internal applications, solvent-free two component systems or water-based systems should be the choice to minimize potential hazards.

It is not the remit of this section to enter into detail of the precise nature of the hazards or the precautionary measures to be taken. Suffice it to say that when handling polyurethane systems of any sort then guidance must be taken from the appropriate safety data sheet.

The environmental issue is becoming increasingly important. The fact is that polyurethanes pose no greater threat to the environment than any other class of polymer that might be similarly used. As with health and safety issues, the environmental impact is dependent upon the precise formulation details. Certainly the VOC level is important; however, it is not the be all and end all. Future environmental labelling standards will make it easier to choose suitable systems, whilst environmental protection legislation will have an impact on how the manufacturers prepare and formulate their products.

For the time being, it is true to say that the environmental impact of urethane systems can vary widely from product to product. Many manufacturers are very aware of environmental issues and are taking the lead by producing products in a manner and formulation which limits the impact whilst, of course, maintaining product quality.

7.11   Summary

In this chapter, the usefulness of polyurethane systems when used on concrete has been discussed. Whilst going into some chemical detail, it is hoped that this has helped to remove some of the mystery surrounding the many different types available. The many potential problems associated with concrete have been discussed and how polyurethane systems, in combination with the correct preparation and priming, can provide the answers to those problems. There are no doubt many questions left unanswered; however, asking the right questions in the first instance is usually the biggest step towards finding the solution. There are many polyurethane products on the market which can meet particular requirements. The success of an application can depend upon making the right choice.

References

Ashmore, W. (1997) Introduction to surface preparation for concrete. *Journal of Protective Coatings and Linings*, **14**(10),71–122.

Buist, J.M. (1978) *Developments in polyurethane (1).* Elsevier Applied Science Publishers, London, 280 pages.

Cowling, T.P. (1997) Maintaining concrete buildings. *Protective Coatings Europe*, Oct.

Hare, C.C. (1994) *Protective coatings – Fundamentals of chemistry and composition.* Technology Publishing Company, Pittsburg, USA, 514 pages.

Hepburn, C. (1992) *Polyurethane Elastomers.* Elsevier Applied Science, London & New York, 441 pages.

Liquid Plastics Ltd. (1997) Technical Data.

O'Connor, S. (1997) Using chemicals to clean and prepare concrete for coating. *Journal of Protective Coatings and Linings*, **14**(11), 61–65

Richardson, B.A. (1990) *Defects and Deterioration in Buildings.* Spon, 190 pages.

Stanfield, R.F. (1989) Protective coatings for concrete. *Journal of the Oil and Colour Chemist's Association,* **72**(4), 150–157.

Woods, G. (1987) *The ICI Polyurethane Book*. John Wiley & Sons, 330 pages.

8 Silanes, siloxanes and silicone resins

Haydn Thomas

8.1 Introduction

Silicones have been used for many years to improve the water-repelling properties of concrete, especially reinforced concrete. This is because water plays a key rôle in its erosion and in the corrosion of steel reinforcing. Silicone impregnants, usually based on silanes and siloxanes, line the pores of the concrete thus reducing significantly its capillary absorption capacity and hence lowering the amount of water that it can take in. At the same time they still leave the substrate 'open', having little or no effect on its water vapour permeability. This allows any water within the substrate to evaporate out. The use of water repellents, therefore, can extend the life of concrete without having any effect on the rates of carbonation.

This chapter looks at the different types of silicone impregnants and the advantages and disadvantages of each.

Alongside silicone rubber (e.g. silicone sealants) and silicone fluid (lubricants and release agents), silicone resins form the third most important type of silicone. They are already used widely in the building industry, for example as water repellents, and silicone resin emulsions are used as binders in the manufacture of masonry paints and plasters.

Almost all silicone-based water repellents, including primers, oil and water repellents and chemical damp-proof course injection fluids belong to the silicone resin type of silicone. Silanes, siloxanes and siliconates, after being applied to mineral substrates, react to form stable, weather resistant, three-dimensional silicone resin networks with strong water-repelling properties.

The chemistry of silicone masonry water repellents, as well as that of silicone binders for silicone resin emulsion paints and plasters, is essentially a chemistry of resins or, to be more precise, the chemistry of silicone T units. The next section explains this in more detail.

8.2 Basic silicone chemistry

8.2.1 Silicones

Many types of industry use silicones in various applications. The three basic types are:

- silicone fluid;
- silicone rubber; and
- silicone resin.

These form the basis of more than a thousand silicone products such as greases, release agents, antifoam agents, paint additives, paper coatings, impregnants for textiles and leather and masonry water repellents to name but a few.

- They are stable at very low to very high temperatures.
- They are excellent electrical insulators.
- They are very water repellent and are therefore used to protect organic and inorganic substrates.
- Most types are physiologically inert.

8.2.2 The structure of silicones

Silicone chemistry is based on the element silicon (chemical symbol Si). Its atomic structure is responsible for the characteristics of silicones. In addition to silicon, oxygen (chemical symbol O) and carbon (C) are essential components of silicones.

Oxygen bonded with two silicon atoms forms the so-called 'siloxane linkage'. The silicon-oxygen bond (Si-O) is remarkably stable and is inorganic in character. A series of linked siloxane units forms a polysiloxane compound.

The silicon-carbon bond is also very stable. A carbon atom bonded to a silicon atom, plus any other chemical group to which it is attached, is referred to as an organic group R. Thus, the Si-C or Si-R bond may also be referred to as an 'organosilicon linkage'.

Combinations of organosilicon and siloxane linkages are known as organosilicon compounds, silico-organic compounds and organopolysiloxanes. The three basic types of silicone – silicone fluid, silicone rubber and silicone resin – as well as their derivatives, are always composed of M, D, T or Q units (Figure 8.1). These units may be defined as the basic, non-divisible silicon units from which all silicones are formed.

Given that a silicone must include silicon atoms (Si), oxygen atoms (O) and organic groups (R), it can be seen that three different structures can be formed: M, D and T

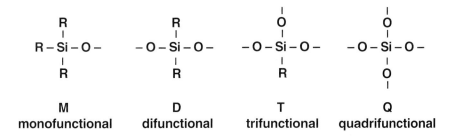

Figure 8.1 *In silicone chemistry the silicon units are distinguished according to their functionality.*

units. The organic group, which is usually hydrophobic, is inert and cannot take part in any cross-linking reactions. This means that only the oxygen atoms can bond to other units to form polysiloxanes.

The M unit has only one reactive oxygen atom and is therefore monofunctional and can only form the last link in a polymer chain. The D unit, with two oxygen atoms, is difunctional and can form chains and rings. The T unit, with three oxygen atoms

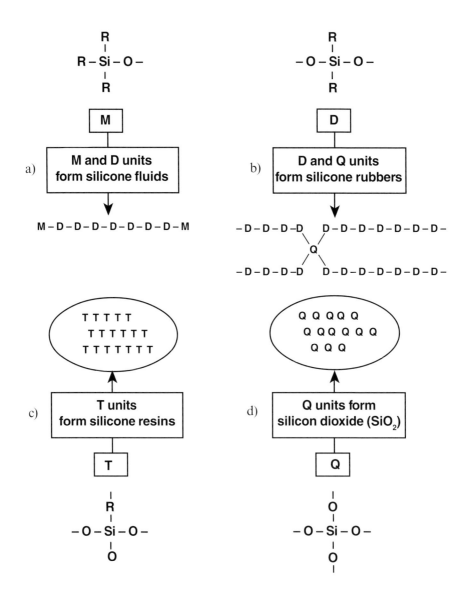

Figure 8.2 *Silicones and silicone dioxide are composed of M, D, T and Q units.*

and only one organic side group, is trifunctional and can therefore form three-dimensional cross-linked structures.

The Q unit, which does not contain any organosilicon linkages (Si – R) is not, strictly speaking, a silicone. It has four reactive oxygen atoms and is therefore quadrifunctional and, like the T unit, forms three-dimensional cross-linked structures. It is the chemical basis for quartz, sand and all inorganic and organic silicates as well as waterglass and ethyl silicates. The Q unit is often used as a cross-linking agent, especially for silicone rubber.

Figure 8.2 shows how different products can be made by combining M, D, T and Q units. Silicone fluids are formed from chains of D units at the ends of which are M units (Figure 8.2a). The viscosity of the fluid is proportional to the number of D units in the chain.

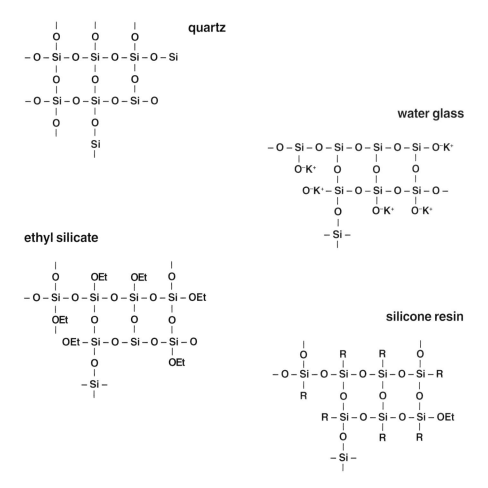

Figure 8.3 *Three-dimensional cross-linked structures composed of Q units (quartz, waterglass and ethyl silicates) and T units (silicone resin).*

Silicone rubber comprises D and Q units with up to four chains of D units being linked together by Q units (Figure 8.2b). Silicone resins are formed from three-dimensional cross-linked structures of T and Q units (Figure 8.2c), as are quartz, waterglass and ethyl silicates (Figure 8.2d).

Figure 8.3 shows the latter in more detail. Silicone resins are essentially quartz structures permanently modified by the addition of hydrophobic organic groups. Waterglass and ethyl silicates are also modifications but these are reversible. Waterglass reacts with carbon dioxide, releasing potassium carbonate to form silicon dioxide. Ethyl silicate reacts with water, releasing ethanol, also forming silicon dioxide.

8.3   Silicone resins as water repellents

Silicone resins are high molecular weight, three-dimensionally cross-linked compounds composed, like quartz, of silicon and oxygen. They differ from quartz in that, instead of a fourth oxygen group, they have an organic group R. Silicone resins can, therefore, be described as organically-modified quartz structures. Chemically, they lie between purely inorganic and purely organic compounds.

All silicone resin products contain T units, ranging in number from one to infinity, and this is reflected in the types of products derived from them, e.g. silanes, siloxanes, silicone resins and siliconates. In the building industry these are referred to as silicone masonry water repellents.

Chemical reaction of the silicone masonry water repellent on or within the mineral substrate leads to the formation of a silicone resin network, which is:
- water repellent;
- water-vapour permeable; and
- durable.

The wide variety of applications includes:
- water repellents for concrete, stone, brickwork, etc.
- oil and water repellents.
- anti-graffiti coatings.
- stone consolidants.
- chemical damp-proof courses.
- in-plant additives and impregnants for gypsum, clay, cement, concrete and mineral-fibre products.
- binders, water repellents and primers for masonry paints and plasters.

8.3.1   Silanes

In the building industry the term 'silane' denotes alkylalkoxysilane or, to be more precise, alkyltrialkoxysilane. In this molecule, which is the simplest silicon T unit, one alkyl side group and three alcohol side groups are attached to the silicon atom, the latter via the oxygen atom of the hydroxyl group. Different silanes are classified according to their attached side groups, e.g.:
- methoxysilane has a methanol side group;

- ethoxysilane has an ethanol side group;
- methylsilane has a methyl side group (this is the shortest possible organic group R); and
- butylsilane and octylsilane have longer alkyl side chains incorporating four and eight carbon atoms respectively.

Silanes tend to be transparent, low-viscosity fluids of varying volatility and incorporating different proportions of bound alcohol. Butyltriethoxysilane and octyltriethoxysilane, for example, which incorporate 63% and 50% ethanol by weight, respectively, are used for the water-repellent impregnation of concrete. The alcohol is released during the cross-linking reaction (polycondensation) on the substrate.

Alkylsilanes with longer side chains have proved to be more alkali resistant than methylsilanes. They are therefore particularly suitable for the water-repellent treatment of reinforced concrete. Their low viscosity is advantageous as it helps the silane penetrate the substrate being treated. Disadvantages are the quantity of bound alcohol, which is released on cross-linking, and their volatility. These factors lead to high losses during application. For this reason alkoxysilanes are usually not diluted before use. Another disadvantage of silanes is that their monomeric nature means that there are extremely long reaction times before the silicone resin network is formed. In unfavourable conditions (e.g. high temperature, strong winds), long reaction times mean that only negligible amounts of active substances are formed and the remainder evaporate.

Methyltriethoxysilane has the highest alcohol content of all the silanes (78%) and is essentially the monomeric form of the silicone resins used as binders in the manufacture of silicone resin emulsion paint. They are not suitable as masonry water repellents.

8.3.2   Siloxanes

The term 'siloxane' can lead to confusion as, strictly speaking, it refers to the $Si - O - Si$ linkage characteristic of all silicone products. In the building industry, however, the term 'siloxane' denotes alkylalkoxysiloxane. The expression arose because between three and six monomeric T-unit alkylalkoxysilane molecules undergo a condensation reaction involving the formation of siloxane bonds to produce oligomeric alkylalkoxysiloxane molecules, i.e. with only a few units. Depending on which silane raw material is used, the siloxane produced incorporates methanol or ethanol and, either long (octyl) or short (methyl), carbonyl groups. Siloxanes are typically transparent, mobile but non-volatile fluids. Methylsiloxane, with six T units, has an alcohol content of only 30 to 40% by weight.

A typical siloxane condensation reaction, e.g. that of methyltriethoxysilane, involves two silane molecules incorporating water (H_2O) and releasing two molecules of alcohol. The reaction proceeds via an intermediary silanol (Si-OH) stage. As a rule, the amount of water added determines the degree of condensation and thus the amount of alcohol released. The smaller the amount of water added, the lower the molecular weight of the siloxane produced and the smaller the amount of alcohol released. The condensation reaction is catalysed by organometallic, acid and alkaline materials, an example of the latter being masonry substrates.

The advantages of siloxanes over silanes are:
- they react faster;
- they are less volatile so there are fewer losses due to evaporation; and
- as losses due to evaporation are negligible, siloxanes can be diluted before application.

In practice, however, water repellents for masonry are made from silane-siloxane mixes. Dense substrates with low permeability require water repellents with a high silane content, whereas on absorbent materials, such as natural stone, high siloxane content impregnants can be used.

Oil-repelling properties can also be obtained by the addition of synthetic resins.

8.3.3 Silicone resins

If the polycondensation reaction is allowed to reach completion, highly viscous or solid materials are produced. These polymeric siloxanes are the silicone resins used as binders in the manufacture of silicone resin emulsion paints and plasters. Normally methyl silicone resins are used.

Silicone resins have a relatively low molecular weight (2000 to 5000) when compared with organic resins and comprise between 30 and 80 silicon T units. The bound alcohol (ethanol) is between 2% and 4% by weight.

When applied as an emulsion or as a solution in organic solvents, methylsilicone resins dry to form tack-free coatings with good early water-repelling properties. The remaining alcohol groups then form silanols by reaction with available groups (usually hydroxyl OH– groups) in the substrate (chemisorption) and also form a silicone resin network structure by polycondensation with other silicone molecules.

Pure silicone resins dissolved in organic solvents were used for the impregnation of exterior masonry until the mid-1980s. Their advantage was that, once the solvent had evaporated, the drying of the silicone resins was sufficient to impart water-repelling properties. Silicone resins tend, however, to remain on the surface of the substrate, thus changing its appearance. For this reason, mixtures of silanes, siloxanes and silicone resins are preferred. Now nearly all of the silicone resins produced for the building industry are for the manufacture of silicone resin emulsion paints and plasters.

8.3.4 Siliconates

Methyl silicone resins are decomposed by strong alkalis to produce aqueous solutions of alkali siliconates, which are water-soluble salts of organosilicates. Potassium methyl siliconate, with the average formula $CH_3Si(OH)_2O^-K^+$, reacts with potassium hydroxide to form a true aqueous solution. These have a low resistance to alkalinity and so are not recommended for use on concrete, especially new concrete.

Commercially available potassium methyl siliconate typically has 40% active contents, half of which is bound potassium hydroxide. This means that it is corrosive. Like waterglass, aqueous siliconate solutions react with carbon dioxide to form potassium carbonate and polymethyl silicate whose silicone resin network imparts water-repelling properties.

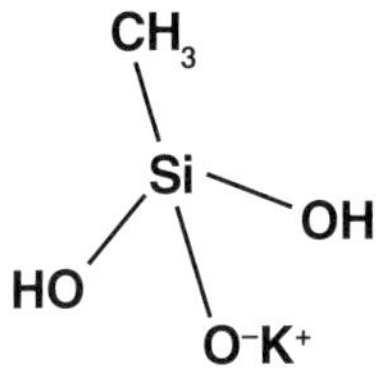

CH$_3$

Si—OH

HO

O$^-$K$^+$

Figure 8.4 *Chemical structure of potassium methyl siliconate.*

Potassium methyl siliconates are used for in-plant impregnation of building materials made from clay, aerated concrete and gypsum and in injected chemical damp-proof courses. Siliconates should not be used for the impregnation of exterior masonry since they tend to form a white film on the surface and can be washed out by rain, especially if not fully cured. They are, however, still used as primers despite the risk of efflorescence, which can be even more noticeable when porous or coloured coatings are applied.

8.3.5 The silicone resin network

Silanes, siloxanes, silicone resins and siliconates react on contact with masonry substrates to form silicone resin networks (Figure 8.5). The condensation reactions of silanes, siloxanes and silicone resins are catalysed by moisture and lead to the release of bound alcohol. Siliconates, by contrast, react with carbon dioxide and also produce potassium carbonate.

The reason for applying any silicone masonry water repellent, composed of silicon T units, is to form the silicone resin network. This is water repellent, water vapour permeable and is chemically bound to the mineral substrate (Figure 8.6). One side effect of this is that they also bond well to glass and so windows should be masked before silicone water repellents are applied. If the proportion of long-chain organic side groups is high enough, the silicone resin network may also be resistant to alkalis.

8.4 Concrete protection by water-repellent impregnation

Building materials can be protected by impregnating them to make their pore systems water repellent. Normally organosilicon compounds (silanes/siloxanes) are used. These reduce the water uptake but do not affect the permeability to water vapour or to carbon dioxide.

Limiting the water content in concrete helps to inhibit spalling, cracking and efflorescence and also to reduce corrosion of the steel reinforcing. Tests carried out over 10 years at the Olympic Village in Munich have shown that silicone water repellents have no effect on the rate of carbonation of the concrete and that they slow down or even

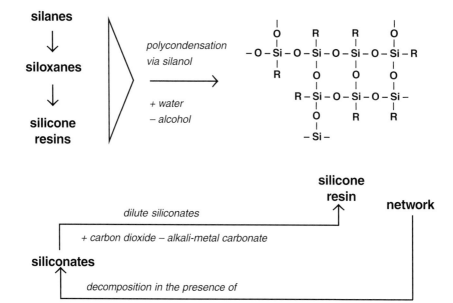

Figure 8.5 *Silanes, siloxanes, silicone resins and siliconates condense to form silicone resin networks.*

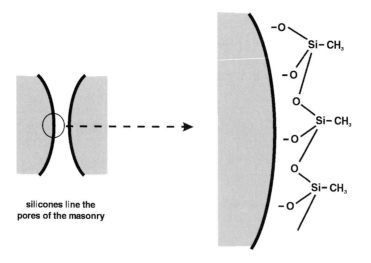

Figure 8.6 *The silicone-resin network lines the pores and capillaries of the masonry.*

stop corrosion of the steel reinforcing.

Protection of concrete can be effected by one of two methods:
- Application of a water repellent (on its own).
- Application of a water-repelling primer followed by a film forming coating.

8.4.1   Water-repellent impregnation

The impregnation of concrete with water repellents on their own is effective in protecting it against water ingress. They are colourless, are not film-forming and prevent the absorption of water and the associated materials dissolved in it via capillary action. The main requirements of a water-repellent impregnation are:
- capillary water absorption is reduced, even when the water is alkaline;
- resistance to frost and frost + road salt is improved;
- absorption of harmful materials dissolved in water is reduced;
- they do not change the appearance of the substrate.

They have no effect on the permeability of the concrete to carbon dioxide nor can they resist water under pressure.

8.4.2   Water-repellent primer/impregnant followed by a film-forming coating

If the requirement is for protection against the capillary absorption of water and against gaseous pollutants, then the water-repellent impregnation should be followed by the application of a film-forming topcoat. The water repellent in this case acts as a primer and also stops water ingress should the topcoat fail, e.g. due to UV degradation, peeling. etc. It also prevents soluble salts already in the substrates crystallizing at the topcoat/substrate interface, thus causing it to lift or causing efflorescence.

The main purpose of the topcoat is to prevent carbonation. The carbonation barrier could also be incorporated in the primer by, for example, adding suitable polymer dispersions. In this case silicone resin emulsion paints, which are vapour permeable, could be used as the topcoat, the advantages being their low dirt pick-up, their durability and attractive appearance.

8.5   Water repellents for concrete

The most important properties required for water-repellent impregnants and primers are:
- excellent depth of penetration; and
- resistance to alkalinity.

8.5.1   Depth of penetration

The factors determining the depth of penetration of a liquid into masonry are its viscosity and surface tension. The lower the viscosity and the higher its surface tension the better its penetration depth. A clear distinction needs to be made, however, between single- and two-phase liquids. Single-phase liquids are those that are applied undiluted, e.g. alkylalkoxysilanes or true solutions such as oligomeric siloxanes in organic solvents. With these the viscosity and the surface tension are the main factors that determine the depth of penetration.

Two-phase systems, e.g. aqueous emulsions, are a different case altogether. With these it is the viscosity of the oily phase, i.e. of the active component (or components), that determines the depth of penetration. In practice, this means that the lower the molecular weight of the silicone components, either undiluted or aqueous, the greater the penetration depth. Since the viscosity is essentially proportional to the molecular weight, this means that monomeric alkyltrialkoxysilanes penetrate better than oligomeric siloxanes.

When dissolved in organic solvents, the molecular weight of the active components has very little influence on the depth of penetration. Rather, this is determined by the viscosity and surface tension of the solvent. Water repellents dissolved in white spirit penetrate much better than those in alcohol.

The higher the concentration of the active contents the deeper the penetration, all other things (viscosity and surface tension) being equal. For some applications and types of concrete, a 10% solution may suffice whereas in others only an undiluted product will achieve the desired results.

8.5.2   Alkali resistance

Highly cross-linked silicone resin networks are inert both physically and chemically and the durability that offers is one of the strongest arguments in favour of the use of silicones as water repellents. They are, however, vulnerable to attack in one respect. As mentioned above, the siloxane bonds in the silicone resin network are hydrolysed by alkalinity to form siliconates.

$$R - SiO_{3/2} + H_2O/OH^- \rightleftarrows R - Si(OH)_2O^-$$

silicone   resin alkali   siliconate

If the organic group R is methyl, as in most common silicone resins, then this reaction will produce a methyl siliconate that is soluble and can be leached out by rainwater. On alkaline substrates, e.g. uncarbonated concrete, water repellents based on methyl silicone resins degrade and become ineffectual within a few months or years.

If some of the methyl groups R are replaced by longer chain organic groups, such as isobutyl, n-octyl or iso-octyl, then this degradation can be prevented. Although the silicone resin network is not completely resistant to alkali attack, the siliconates formed are not water-soluble and thus cannot be washed out.

The equilibrium in the above reaction stays on the side of the high molecular weight silicone resin and there is virtually no loss of active contents. This is an important factor in product warranties.

8.5.3   Composition of water repellents

As stated above, water repellent impregnants and primers for concrete must be composed of mainly silicones with low molecular weights and long chain organic groups. Pure alkyltrialoxysilanes, such as isobutyl or iso-octlytriethoxysilanes, are extreme cases. Because of their low viscosity, especially when not diluted, they have excellent penetration even into high quality concrete. They have one major disadvantage though, namely their volatility. When silanes are applied undiluted, under normal conditions, a large proportion will evaporate instead of penetrating the substrate. Under unfavourable conditions, e.g. strong winds, high temperatures, low relative humidity, low substrate pH, the long reaction times mean that nearly all of the active contents evaporate before they have had a chance to form a water-repellent zone. Even under favourable conditions, most of the silane evaporates from the concrete surface, which means that no water beading effect is obtained. It should be noted, however, that water beading is of only secondary importance when assessing the water-repelling properties of a substrate.

To overcome the problems mentioned above, mixes of silane, oligomeric siloxane and condensation catalyst can be used. The silane/siloxane ratio can be varied according to the type and pH of the substrate to be impregnated. A substrate with a high pH would require a mix with a high silane content. In addition, the mix can be applied as a concentrate or in a diluted form.

Aqueous emulsions can also be used; for example, silicone microemulsion concentrates, when added to water, spontaneously form silicone microemulsions. Their advantages are that they are water-based and only the concentrate need be transported to site. The disadvantage is that they have a limited pot life after dilution, normally 24 hours.

Another alternative is the so-called 'Creme' technology. These are ready-to-use thixotropic silicone water repellents that can be applied by (airless) spray, brush or roller. Their advantages include:
- water-based technology;
- negligible losses due to evaporation;
- no run-off onto pavements;
- they can be applied to the undersides of horizontal structures;
- it is easy to see the areas already treated during application;
- normally a one-coat application is sufficient to achieve excellent depths of impregnation;
- they leave no residue nor do they change the appearance of the substrate; and
- they work in the same way as all silicone water repellents, i.e. they line the pores without blocking them so do not affect the water vapour permeability of the substrate.

8.6   Summary

Silicone masonry water repellents can be made from silanes, siloxanes, silicone resins or siliconates or combinations of the first three types. After application on masonry they react to form high molecular weight, three-dimensionally cross-linked silicone resin networks whose structure is similar to that of quartz. Unlike quartz, however, instead of a fourth oxygen group they have an organic group R. Thus the silicone resin network can be described as being an organically-modified quartz structure. Chemically, silicone resins lie between purely organic and purely inorganic compounds. Their most important features are that they provide long-term water-repelling properties, they are water vapour permeable and are resistant to UV light and weathering.

It should be noted that no silicone or silane water repellent is effective at preventing the ingress of water under more than nominal pressure. This is why they are recommended for use only in above-ground (and above-water) applications. Silicones work by lining the pores of the substrate, thus allowing it to breathe. Any water within the concrete can still evaporate out, it is not trapped. If the surface of the concrete is sealed, spalling can occur as the water tries to escape. As their name implies, they are water repellents, not surface sealers.

9 Silicate paints

M.A.Gatrell

9.1 Introduction

Silicate based paints have a history that spans back many thousands of years. It is widely thought that the ancient Egyptians were the first to experiment with and produce alkali silicate products as long ago as 4000 BC. Analysis suggests that frescoes found in the 2000-year old ruins of Pompeii and Herculaneum are bound into the rock by inorganic siliceous binders, which were probably applied initially with organic binders such as milk, eggs and blood.

Work performed by scientists in Northern Europe during the late 19th century resulted in the development of the twin-pack silicate paint and led to A.W. Keim being granted a German patent in 1879. These early formulations consisted of liquid potassium silicate and pigment powder formulations that were mixed together and ripened, prior to application. These materials produced a finish similar to the Italian lime frescos, but displayed a much greater durability, being capable of withstanding the more northerly climate. Many highly decorative facades across Northern Europe, that date back to the 19th century, remain in excellent condition today and provide evidence for the durability of silicate paint systems.

It was almost a century later, in 1960, when the single-pack format was first developed and presented. These formulations incorporated an organic polymer dispersion that allowed stable formulations with a long shelf life to be produced. This facilitated the development of silicate paints that can compete with purely organic emulsion paints from a performance point of view, but offer added benefits that originate from their inorganic character.

In modern times, with growing public and legislative pressure being placed upon the paint and coatings industry to restrict the use of materials that have undesirable environmental side effects, silicate paints are considered environmentally friendly and are being promoted as a 'green solution' to solvent-based paints. Silicate paints are water-based and generally solvent-free, incorporating naturally occurring raw materials.

9.2 Components of a silicate paint

DIN 18 363 (1992) is the standard most commonly used to define silicate paints within Europe. Section 2.4.1(d) outlines 'Emulsion silicate paint made from potash waterglass, with pigments resistant to potash waterglass, with water-repellent additives and with an organic additives content of no more than 5% by mass. Emulsion silicate paints with quartz extenders are used for texturing. They shall be used on substrates containing gypsum plaster only after application of a special primer.'

Most products available state as to whether they are DIN 18 363 compliant. A typical single-pack silicate emulsion paint can be further broken down into the following components.

9.2.1   Binder system

The binder system within a single-pack silicate emulsion paint will generally comprise inorganic and organic quotients.

The larger component is the inorganic binder which is commonly referred to as waterglass and is an aqueous solution of potassium silicate. This is produced by heating together a blend of pure quartz sand and potassium carbonate to produce a glass-like melt. Once cooled it is crushed before being dissolved in hot water to give a clear, colourless and highly alkaline liquid. Only monovalent alkali ions such as sodium or potassium will dissolve, with the bivalent calcium, magnesium and aluminium silicates being insoluble in water.

Waterglass is a compound that, when applied to a porous, mineral substrate, will migrate into the surface pores before entering into a complex series of reactions commonly referred to as silicification. The net result of the silicification reactions is an insoluble coating that is incorporated into, and very strongly bonded to the mineral substrate.

The organic binder is usually a water-borne styrene-acrylate copolymer and is incorporated at much lower levels than the waterglass. Its primary function is to stabilize the single-pack formulation. In situ the organic binder will contribute to the overall performance of the coating, particularly in the early days of service, by resisting moisture ingress and longer term by enhancing the coating's durability via improved adhesion and resistance to chalking.

9.2.2   Solvent/vehicle

Always water-borne, these paints are typically formulated with a solids content of 50–60% by weight. Very low levels (less than 0.5%) of coalescing solvent may be added to assist the polymer to film-form at lower temperatures, but in the main these coatings are considered to be solvent free.

9.2.3   Fillers/pigments

Silicate paints tend to incorporate naturally occurring mineral fillers, chosen so as not to enter into in-can reactions with the silicate binder. Examples include calcite, quartz, barytes, micas and kaolin. The pigments used are preferably inorganic and include titanium dioxide, lithopone, inert earth oxides, ultramarine and cobalt blues. This retains the inorganic character of the coatings and reduces the risk of colour fading.

9.2.4 Additives

Numerous additives are commonly included in formulations by manufacturers; some are added as manufacturing or storage aids whilst others will assist or enhance specific properties of the coating.

Dispersants, wetting agents, stabilizers and defoamers are incorporated during manufacture to ensure that the final product contains no pigment/filler agglomerates and is free from excessive aeration. Furthermore, these additives will help to ensure that the viscosity and rheology of the product remain consistent on storage and will also assist the organic binder in the stabilizing of the system by preventing in-can reactions of the silicate binder.

Thickeners and rheology modifiers are often incorporated by manufacturers to control the viscosity of the product and application characteristics. Sag resistance, flow and levelling can all be controlled to suit the particular application. These additives will also help to ensure that the paint will not separate on storage. Overall, silicate paint viscosity can vary depending upon the manufacturer, though they tend to be relatively low viscosity products that lend themselves to brush, roller or airless spray applications.

One particular characteristic of silicate paint rheology is the thixotropy that these systems can often exhibit. Upon storage, paints can thicken to such an extent that the inexperienced user may be given the impression that they are faced with a very high viscosity material or even a material which has gelled. Application of shear, however, will break down this false body, returning the coating to its intended lower viscosity state. For this reason, it is always recommended that silicate paints are thoroughly stirred prior to use; this is especially important when the material is to be spray applied.

Hydrophobic additives are also used in formulations to further enhance the water-repelling properties of silicate paints without dramatically affecting water vapour permeation. In some cases they can exert a pronounced beading effect that allows the coating to visibly shed water during periods of rainfall.

One final additive commonly included in formulations is a biocide. Being predominantly inorganic, silicate paints offer little to encourage the growth of fungi or algae. However, contamination of the coating by dirt pick-up or splashing can leave deposits on the coating that will subsequently permit the growth of microorganisms. Applications that extend to ground level and are in contact with ponding water are particularly susceptible to algae growth. The manufacturer will therefore make an addition of algae/fungicide to help combat this unsightly and potentially damaging growth.

9.3 Properties and uses of silicate paints

Silicate paints are designed for use on mineral substrates upon which they will react to form a complex silicate matrix, bonded to the substrate. Being inorganic and crystalline, silicate paints contain many micropores through which moisture can leave the substrate. The often enhanced hydrophobic nature of these coatings will repel rainwater to a point, with any water absorbed being quickly released once conditions allow. This property allows the substrate to 'breathe' and permits silicate paints to be used under conditions where many other types of organic, film-forming coatings would lose adhesion and blister.

Silicate paints will protect a substrate against solar radiation and can help reduce the effects of thermal movement caused by temperature fluctuations. This is important in both temperate and hot climates where repeated heating and cooling can give rise to thermal movement and potential cracking of the substrate. In addition, silicate paints display good colour fastness; a slight colour fade can be expected immediately after application upon exposure to rainfall, but following this, significant colour change is rarely observed longer term.

Being predominantly mineral in composition, silicate paints are incombustible. Furthermore, under fire conditions, these coatings typically exhibit low smoke toxicity ratings which make them suitable for use in public utilities and gathering places, tunnels and underground rail networks. The inorganic, mineral character offers little to encourage the growth of fungi and algae and this combination of properties benefits internal applications over lining paper or anaglypta.

Silicate paints can also be used in locations that may be subject to chemical attack. They will protect mineral substrates from the effects of both acid rain and air pollution, including vehicle exhaust fumes. This makes them ideal for use around traffic, on structures such as bridges and car parks.

These coatings provide a functional product that has been adapted to give many decorative formats. Silicate paints are available in many different colours, most popular tend to be lighter pastel shades and earth colours providing either a smooth or textured finish. Varying product opacities provide finishes that range between fully opaque and translucent 'colour-washes', that allow the natural textures of the substrate to be retained. It is this architectural versatility that sees silicate paints used on many heritage buildings, churches and historic buildings.

Silicate paints lend themselves to brush, roller or airless spray application and can be applied using other, more decorative techniques such as sponging, etc. Silicate paints can also be used in the painting of murals or innovative colour schemes, being extremely opaque, colour fast and available in an almost limitless colour palette. Decorative finishes will still provide all of the necessary protective requirements and these types of applications, both internal and external, are popular in modern business premises and can have a positive psychological effect in public places.

Silicate paint systems tend to be relatively low cost and can be applied in a short time, causing minimal disruption with no fumes or odours being detectable. Once applied, the coatings provide a low maintenance, durable finish for many years. The only maintenance required is an occasional washing down to restore the coating's natural appearance. This facilitates the use of silicate paints in redecoration and renovation projects on local authority and housing association low/high rise properties as it keeps costs, application time and disruption to tenants to a minimum.

9.4   The silicification reaction

Whilst many different ingredients contribute to the overall properties of the system, it is the complex series of reactions which the waterglass binder undergoes that is the major factor defining the properties and functions of silicate paints. When applied to a mineral substrate, the waterglass (soluble potassium silicate) binder will react with components of the substrate, or atmospheric carbon dioxide, to produce an insoluble and strongly bonded silicate matrix. It is the development of this matrix (as opposed to film formation) that distinguishes silicate paints from other masonry coatings.

The vast majority of masonry coatings are formulated from organic polymer dispersions that will cure in situ to form a protective barrier that adheres to the substrate surface. These barriers often reduce the ease with which atmospheric moisture can enter the substrate, but at the same time reduce the rate at which moisture can leave. This can often be a problem when barrier coatings are applied to damp or curing concrete that wish to release large amounts of water to the atmosphere. This water may accumulate behind the coating at a greater rate than it can be released, resulting in a loss of adhesion and/or the formation of blisters.

Silicate paints are not film-forming, reacting instead to produce an inorganic matrix. This matrix is physically incorporated and chemically bonded to the substrate but contains many pores that permit moisture to enter and leave the substrate. This high water vapour permeation allows the substrate to breathe, yet the hydrophobic nature of the reacted binder and additives within the formulation are sufficient to reduce the water absorption through capillary action. When exposed to continuous rainfall, the coating will eventually reach a point of saturation, with the coating having typically absorbed circa 15% of its own weight in water. The exceptionally high rate of water vapour transmission exhibited by these coatings will subsequently allow the absorbed moisture to be released very rapidly once conditions allow.

It is absolutely critical that, to function as intended, silicate paints be applied correctly. Whilst the single-pack silicate emulsion paints may appear to be simple, ready to apply paints, their use is restricted to experienced specialist applicators who are able to identify in advance the many pitfalls that exist. The key to a successful application is to ensure that the reaction of the waterglass is facilitated by correct preparation of the substrate and careful timing of the application with regard to conditions. Furthermore, consideration must be paid to the substrate uniformity and suitability.

When applied to a cementitious substrate, the waterglass binder will react with many of the compounds with which it comes into contact. For instance:

- mechanism for the reaction with lime (calcium hydroxide);

$$K_2O \times nSiO_2 + Ca(OH)_2 \rightarrow CaO \times SiO_2 + (n-1)SiO_2 + 2KOH$$
$$+$$
$$K_2CO_3 \leftarrow CO_2$$

- mechanism for the reaction with quartz sand (especially on the grain surface).

$$K_2O \times nSiO_2 + mSiO_2 \rightarrow K_2O \times (m+n)\ SiO_2$$
$$\text{quartz} \qquad \text{higher ratio pot. silicate}$$

Furthermore, waterglass will also react with atmospheric carbon dioxide:
- mechanism for the reaction with carbon dioxide from the air.

$$2K_2O \times nSiO_2 + CO_2 \rightarrow K_2O \times (2n-1)\,SiO_2 + K_2CO_3 + SiO_2$$
incomplete silicification → raising of weight ratio higher viscosity

$$K_2O \times nSiO_2 + CO_2 \rightarrow nSiO_2 + K_2CO_3$$
complete silicification → insoluble silica gel

When a silicate paint is applied onto a substrate, the waterglass binder will migrate into the substrate. The depth and extent of this migration is governed by the porosity, temperature, moisture content and nature of the substrate. Furthermore, the coverage rate, air temperature, weather conditions and formulation of the paint will also have an effect.

The deeper the migration of the waterglass into the substrate, the more intimately the silicate matrix will be incorporated into the substrate, which should lead to better adhesion. But one must also consider the converse. Increased binder migration into the substrate will reduce the level of binder present within the surface coating and will hence effect the coating's cohesion. Should too much binder migrate into the substrate, then the topcoat may well 'powder' and will rub off with the slightest abrasion.

The key to a successful application is in achieving sufficient binder penetration to bond strongly the surface coating to the substrate, whilst retaining sufficient binder within the coating to allow the development of cohesive strength. This may at first appear to be an impossible balancing act, but most silicate paints are formulated to overcome this on all but the most extreme case substrates. It is therefore only the concern of the user to identify potentially problem substrates and act accordingly.

Very few mineral substrates resist permeation of the coating entirely. Most can be coated directly after correct preparation and, whilst the degree of binder permeation may be reduced, the coating will still bond to the substrate as intended. Where impermeable surfaces are present, such as areas previously painted or glazed engineering bricks, then careful pre-treatment requiring chemicals or abrading will be needed and more will be said about individual substrate treatment later.

Highly absorbent substrates will often necessitate the use of a primer. Most silicate paint suppliers will market a silicate based primer that is used to reduce substrate absorbency and will also equalize any absorbency variations that may occur. These primers are usually waterglass solutions that also incorporate a small amount of polymer binder. When applied to a highly absorbent surface, the solution will be absorbed and react in an identical fashion to that outlined for the coating. Once reacted, the substrate will then exhibit an overall reduction in absorbency and be more suitable for a silicate paint application.

Silicate primers are also recommended for use where any variations in the substrate age, condition or quality exist. Where localized variations in substrate porosity occur (such as when patch repairs have been carried out), the primer will be more strongly absorbed in areas leading to a more uniform substrate for overcoating. Furthermore, when applied to a friable substrate, an overall consolidating effect can be achieved.

9.5   Substrates and application

In general, silicate paints may be considered suitable for direct use on most clean, dry, sound and uniform mineral substrates that do not exhibit any extremes of high or low absorbency. This section deals with various types of substrates and with any specific pre-treatments that are required prior to the application of a silicate paint and also highlight substrates that are unsuitable for silicate paint application.

Masonry incorporating natural or synthetic bricks and blocks bound together by a cementitious mortar is generally suitable for direct application of silicate paint.

Masonry comprising natural stones such as granite, limestone, sandstone and slate are all suitable for direct silicate paint application. These materials tend to be relatively dense, with low water permeability, and can therefore be coated with no pre-treatment being required. A silicate paint will afford this type of substrate protection from the deteriorating effects of atmospheric pollutants, weathering and biological damage. Typical effects of these actions include the blackening of surface stone through pollution and biological effects, spalling through moisture and chemical ingress followed by freezing and soiling by birds in particular. A silicate paint will not dramatically effect the transmission of water vapour between the substrate and the atmosphere, allowing the substrate to breathe. This is often very important in older buildings which may lack conventional damp-proof coursing.

Masonry comprising synthetic stones in the form of brickwork or blockwork is generally suitable for direct application. Highly porous blocks may be primed with a silicate primer initially to kill suction. Granular building blocks may require surface levelling/pore filling to reduce the substrate granularity prior to applying the silicate paint topcoat. Manufacturers often produce or recommend a specific coating or mortar to produce an equalized surface texture which is more suited to the application of a silicate paint topcoat.

Numerous functional but highly decorative effects can be achieved through the use of application techniques, such as sponging and colour washing, or by incorporating aggregates to give a textured finish. The manufacturer should always be consulted prior to attempting an 'effect coating' as specific products are often available that will make the job much simpler.

Care must be taken when overcoating areas where contrasting absorbencies exist, as a pre-treatment of the substrate may be required. Dense, natural stone masonry or breeze blocks can be held together by a mortar that is relatively more, or relatively less porous. This would lead to local absorption differences between the stones and the mortar and in both instances colour shade differences may be evident in the silicate paint. If the absorbency contrasts too greatly, a lighter or darker shade outline of the blocks may be evident. This characteristic is often used to very good decorative effect.

It is worth performing a patch test prior to an application being made to determine the extent to which localized absorbency differences will effect the colour. Any variations should be apparent within hours of the patch test application.

Concretes based on ordinary Portland cement or sulphate resisting Portland cement are all suitable for overcoating with silicate paints. Care must be taken where exposed surface aggregate exists. Localized silicate absorbency differences may exist between the aggregate and the cement binder. Direct overcoating may result in a colour shade variance in the silicate paint, with a 'speckling' being apparent that corresponds to the aggregate. In this instance a patch test is again recommended prior to application. Multi-coat application will also assist in overcoming this problem.

Cement/sand renders are all suitable for direct application of a silicate paint. Highly absorbent renders will need pre-treating with a silicate primer to reduce the substrate suction. Silicate paints lend themselves ideally to providing a functional, but decorative finish over cement rendering. Renders are often used to provide thermal insulation and to alleviate penetrating dampness problems by reducing water penetration through walls.

A thick porous render can be applied to an external wall where there is an internal dampness problem. This render will draw moisture from within the wall and release it more rapidly to the atmosphere. When subjected to rainfall, the highly absorbent surface will absorb quantities of water, but the macroporous surface will allow moisture to be released at a much quicker rate once conditions allow.

Overcoating with a conventional film-forming coating will produce a virtually impermeable barrier which will affect the operation of the render and may introduce a risk of interstitial condensation. Richardson (1991) states 'A permeable structure must never be sealed at the cold external surface as there is then a danger that interstitial humidity will result in condensation immediately beneath the waterproof layer, followed by severe frost spalling in cold weather'.

A silicate paint on the other hand will impart a more hydrophobic character to the render, helping to repel rainfall, but would release any moisture building up behind the coating by allowing a less hindered rate of evaporation to the exterior. This eliminates the risk of any dampness problems, whilst the dry render will then give better thermal insulation properties.

Continuous, uniform renders can normally be overcoated directly. Freshly applied renders should be left for at least two weeks prior to overcoating. The render should have developed sufficient cohesive strength before overcoating, as silicate paints will afford a friable substrate little protection from impacts and mechanical abrasion. Any cracking within the substrate will be sympathetically reflected in the coating. Damp renders should be allowed to dry out prior to overcoating and a silicate primer may be used when extreme surface suction is encountered. Adhesion testing is recommended on polymer modified specialist mortars.

Hydraulic lime renders are also suitable for silicate paints. Again, the render should be left sufficient time for the hydration reaction to progress, prior to overcoating. Typically this can be in excess of three weeks. Also, the possibility of excessive substrate suction exists, which may need addressing with a silicate primer. Adhesion testing is recommended on specialist mortars.

Low density, aerated concrete is not a suitable substrate due to the extremely high absorption. Silicate paints would be prone to excessive binder migration which would detract seriously from the performance of the coating.

Gypsum plasters are not suitable for direct application and should be pre-treated with a silicate primer. This reduces the high porosity that these substrates typically exhibit. Freshly applied gypsum plasters should be allowed at least two weeks to cure before application of the silicate primer and paint system. This is to reduce the risk of shrinkage cracking in the topcoat as the plaster cures. In the event of shrinkage cracks occurring or a freshly applied gypsum mortar needing to be overcoated within two weeks, it is recommended that a primer and single coat be applied and overcoating be carried out after a further minimum period of four weeks.

Wood and wood fibre-based particle boards are not suitable for overcoating with silicate paints. Being organic in nature, they will not enter into the silicification reactions that are essential for the coating to develop sufficient adhesion and durability.

Inorganic particle boards, such as those based on calcium silicate and used in internal cladding, are suitable though must be pre-treated to reduce the very high porosity that these substrates typically exhibit. A silicate-based primer is again recommended; two or more coats may need to be applied to reduce the porosity to a level that permits the silicate paint to have a reasonable wet edge time, as opposed to virtually instantaneous drying.

Metals can be overcoated, but are not recommended substrates. This is particularly the case in external situations where only aluminium and its alloys are suitable. Externally, most silicate paints will afford little protection to ferrous metals, despite the corrosion inhibiting nature of alkali silicates. Penetration of moisture will be sufficient to initiate corrosion, which will in turn lead to failures and staining within the coating, thus accelerating the whole process.

Substrates upon which a silicate paint has already been applied should be suitable for direct overcoating once cleaned and prepared. This should be confirmed with the product manufacturer prior to application, though most manufacturers will be reluctant to give guarantees on coatings in situ that are not their own.

Previously coated substrates that have an organic, film-forming coating are not considered suitable for silicate paint application, although these substrates are commonly overcoated. This is particularly the case for internal applications that will not be subjected to the same degree of weathering. Removing existing paint build-ups can be an expensive process and direct application of a decorative, but low maintenance, silicate paint represents a cost effective alternative.

These organic paint build-ups can often represent a fire safety risk and overcoating with a fire retardant coating can prove expensive. Silicate paints are inherently non-combustible and can be applied over existing, flammable, organic paints leading to a dramatic reduction in the fire rating. Furthermore, under fire conditions, silicate paints tend to exhibit low smoke toxicity, unlike many halogenated fire-retardant coatings.

When applying a silicate paint to a previously painted surface, it is recommended that the surface is cleaned and any existing unsound coating should be removed. Some manufacturers produce a silicate-acrylic bridging coat or bond coat to improve adhesion; other silicate paints can be applied directly. In these instances the silicate binder will not be able to bond directly to the substrate, relying instead upon mechanical adhesion. This may leave the coating a little sensitive to water due to the higher content of unreacted silicates present.

This reduction in durability is unlikely to cause problems for internal applications, though cleaning by abrasive scrubbing with soap and water should be avoided. Manufacturers should always be consulted prior to application over previously coated substrates to ensure that the material to be applied is suitable for internal use. Adhesion testing (wet and dry) is again recommended.

9.6   Substrate considerations and problems

This section deals with the potential problems that can arise when a silicate paint is applied incorrectly, applied to an unsuitable substrate or applied under unsuitable conditions. A thorough understanding of the problems that can occur and the reasons for them is the key to a successful application.

The problems arising can be split into four key areas and these will be dealt with in turn, namely:
- crazing, cracking and flaking;
- chalking/powdering;
- colour uniformity; and
- efflorescence and staining.

9.6.1   Crazing, cracking and flaking

Crazing, cracking and flaking can all arise for a variety of reasons. The key to identifying the actual reason lies in the time after application that the fault occurs.

Development of cracks occurring across the coating's surface within hours after application is most likely to be due to a coalescence problem of the organic binder. This is commonly referred to as crazing and often resembles dried mud that has cracked in the sun. The effect may be observed in varying degrees ranging from an extensive, heavy, deep crazing to a localized, fine, microscopic surface effect. It is typically caused by low temperature application, although applying material too thickly can exacerbate the problem.

Careful adherence to the manufacturers' application instructions should prevent this problem, particularly with respect to the temperature during and immediately after application. No silicate paint should ever be applied at temperatures below 5 °C and consideration must be given to the temperature forecast for the period immediately after the application. This is particularly important when an application is being allowed to dry overnight.

Other factors must also be considered, including substrate temperature. This may be a few degrees cooler than the air temperature, particularly if the area to be coated is shaded from the sun. When crazing due to low temperature is likely to be a concern, all the individual factors must be considered and each individual item should be gauged in order to minimize its contribution to the problem.

Applying material at a higher coverage rate than recommended is a further reason why cracking can occur in a silicate paint shortly after application. This is due to the surface layer drying more rapidly than the lower material and then subsequently suffering from shrinkage cracks. Rarely would one expect to see this occurrence across a whole application, but it is commonly encountered when silicate paint is applied to a textured surface. Material will often accumulate in the recesses of the substrate and small cracks may form once this dries.

In the event of crazing occurring, two options are available to the user. Fine surface microcrazing may be remedied by lightly overcoating with an extra topcoat. Heavily crazed material should be removed as quickly as possible and re-applied. Overcoating would not resolve this situation since the coating would not sufficiently grout the cracks, which would still be apparent in the completed job. Furthermore, large scale crazing is a sure sign that material has failed to cure as intended, in which case it would no doubt fail to perform as required.

All the above effects are likely to occur within 24 hours of a silicate paint system being wrongly applied. Should any cracking or flaking of the coating subsequently occur then an adhesion problem should be suspected. When diagnosing faults occurring at a later stage, one must consider the substrate onto which the silicate paint was applied.

Permanently moist substrates may give rise to the coating flaking, particularly where an excessively damp substrate at the time of application has allowed too much binder to penetrate it. Silicate paints with their high vapour permeability are ideal for use in such situations, but careful timing of the application, coupled with the correct substrate treatment, is necessary to ensure correct performance.

Being a brittle coating, that is firmly bonded to the substrate, any cracking, crumbling or flaking at the substrate surface will be reflected by the coating. Evidence of this occurrence can be found by inspecting the underside of any removed pieces of coating for traces of the substrate. Careful inspection of any cracks appearing, with a magnifying glass, will be sufficient to determine whether these originate from the coating or substrate.

Further flaking problems can arise when silicate paints are exposed to ponding water, such as may be the case at the base of walls. Capillary water absorption can cause the substrate and coating to become saturated, which can in turn lead to blistering or adhesion loss. This can be particularly pronounced if the silicate paint has been applied over an existing organic, film-forming coating. The fundamental problems that this system presents have been discussed earlier, but a further complication can arise when water permeates the underlying coating and causes it to swell or blister. This can lead to surface cracking of the silicate paint topcoat which may still be apparent after the area has dried out.

In such cases, preventative action prior to coating, rather than remedial action afterwards, is required. Areas of crumbling substrate should be renewed prior to application and friable surfaces consolidated in the recommended manner. All traces of any previous coatings must be removed; this is especially important if signs of adhesion loss are apparent. Building defects need to be made good to ensure correct water run-off through well maintained eaves, gutters and downpipes. Correct drainage around the base of applications must be ensured to reduce the likelihood of ponding water.

9.6.2 Chalking/powdering

Chalking and powdering will typically arise within hours of application as a result of the loss of the binder system to the substrate for instance, or poor silicification. The coating will appear to have cured but, when touched, will wipe off easily to leave a powdery residue on the fingers. Numerous factors can cause this, but most tend to be factors that facilitate the migration of the waterglass binder into the substrate or promote rapid drying.

Application onto highly absorbent substrates, permanently damp substrates and fresh mortars can all lead to excessive binder migration into the substrate, leaving behind a surface coating that has a very low binder content and no cohesive or adhesive properties. Poor silicification, salt efflorescence and exposure to frost too soon in a silicate paint's service life can all lead to a similar effect.

An early warning of this potential occurrence can be provided by the paint's drying time. Silicate paint applications that appear to have dried within a matter of minutes, typically seen on highly absorbent substrates or higher temperature substrates, may have been subject to a rapid drying by water abstraction at the expense of the desired silicification reactions. This is also the case when the coating is exposed to frost too soon in its life. These applications subsequently display no resistance to mechanical abrasion or weathering and on renewed contact to water may well display a pronounced softening, since the coating contains too high a proportion of unreacted, soluble species.

Conversely, applications that exhibit an extended drying time may also have a potential problem. The presence of surface moisture implies that the substrate is still very wet, even though it may have felt touch dry prior to application. This is a likely occurrence when 'fresh' mortars are overcoated at too early a period, particularly when the mortar contains a high proportion of water or where water retaining additives, such as cellulose, are incorporated. Again this presence of moisture and extended drying time facilitate excessive binder migration.

Once again these are problems that can be avoided by careful planning of applications, by treating substrates with a silicate primer to kill porosity and by coating areas that are prone to excessive temperatures early in the morning or on overcast days, for example.

The substrate moisture content should always be measured with a suitable moisture meter prior to overcoating fresh mortars or suspected damp substrates. A substrate may feel touch dry at the surface but can be transmitting excessive quantities of moisture. Unless instructed by the manufacturer, silicate paints should never be diluted with water. Weather forecasts should be consulted and the application of silicate paints should be avoided when frost is expected within the following 24 hours.

9.6.3 Colour uniformity

Obtaining colour uniformity also requires a degree of specialist knowledge. A characteristic of silicate paints, particularly in darker shade colours, is localized colour differences that can emanate from factors such as absorbency differences in the substrate. Many of the points listed below are particularly prevalent when dark shades are used, yet do not noticeably affect applications which are in light or pastel shades. All effects can be minimized, if not entirely eliminated, and for this reason it is recommended that when selecting colours one should tend to favour the use of lighter shades but one need not be afraid of using the darker shades.

Two distinct types of shade variation tend to occur when silicate paints are used; both are often difficult to avoid, but can be minimized by correct application. The first variety often arises immediately after application and is due to the same factors that affect the silicate binder concentration at the coating's surface. The second variety generally occurs within six months of the application and causes only a temporary effect that vanishes in time.

Differences that become apparent soon after application will most likely be due to variations in the substrate's absorbency or reactivity, but can also be caused by variations in the coating's drying rate. Patch repairs with mortars, grouting in between brickwork, aggregated screeds and pebble dashing can all, when overcoated, lead to a variety of different colour shading effects.

Taking as an example a concrete containing a granite aggregate which is exposed at the surface, if this should be directly coated with a silicate paint in a dark colour without any pre-treatment, a speckling effect may be noted in the coating. This is because of the absorbency differences between the granite aggregate and the surrounding mortar. Areas of the topcoat applied over the low porosity granite aggregates are likely to be silicate-rich and therefore darker in colour; these would contrast with the overall lighter shade of the coating applied over the surrounding, higher porosity mortar.

In this instance it would be the natural solution to overcoat with a silicate primer to even out the variations, but, a word of caution. Concentrations of silicates can build up on the exposed faces of the granite aggregates and the applied silicate paint topcoat can subsequently exhibit corresponding dark, vitreous patches. A solution to this dilemma can only be provided by performing an on-site patch trial, with and without primer.

A second potentially difficult scenario worth considering is where a patch repair has been carried out to a wall using a highly absorbent plaster. A direct overcoating with a silicate paint would often leave the underlying repair 'shining' through. Reasons for this are as previously described, but in this instance the remedy would be to pretreat with a silicate rich primer. It should be sparingly applied to the area of the repair initially before lightly overcoating the whole wall. After a period of 24 hours, the silicate paint can then be applied.

In order to facilitate uniform drying conditions, the applicator must also avoid creating microclimates such as the partial shading of an application, by items such as scaffolding for instance. Anything with the potential to alter the relative drying rate of an application has the potential to effect the consistency of the colour. Application should be even and wet-in-wet, avoiding the overlapping of any dry edges by using numerous painters stationed at different levels.

Once in situ, silicate paints can still appear to present difficulties whilst the chemical curing reaction remains incomplete. In the first few weeks of service particularly, exposure to water can lead to shade variations in the form of streaks which highlight the channels down which water drains off a structure. They are thought to arise due to unreacted (and hence soluble) silicate species leaching from an application.

This situation may become particularly pronounced should a coating be exposed to rainfall too early in its service life. Poorly reacted silicate paints often exhibit pronounced water spotting with the immediate area exposed to water becoming a lighter shade and the edge of the exposure becoming darker. Fortunately this effect will rapidly wear off in the field with repeated exposure to rainfall, as the concentration of leachable species gradually reduces.

Common sense dictates the measures required to control the shade differences due to leaching. Silicate paints should never be applied when rainfall is imminent and structures to be coated should have sufficient water run-off.

To summarize, the key to obtaining a uniform colour across an application is to ensure that all efforts have been made to equalize the substrate with regard to absorbency and reactivity. This may not necessarily ensure that the colour is entirely uniform immediately after the application, but should at least ensure that following the initial short term weathering the colour will become consistent across the whole application.

Applications that exhibit colour variation immediately after drying will often become more uniform in time, due to the effects of the progressive leaching.

9.6.4   Efflorescence and staining

Efflorescence is a problem that must also be accounted for through the correct preparation and pre-treatment of substrates. Since silicate paints are non film-forming, they do not provide a barrier to efflorescence. Silicate paints react to produce an inorganic, crystalline matrix that contains many pores through which water vapour can pass. It is these pores through which soluble salts can migrate to the surface and crystallize.

Salt efflorescence is a commonly encountered problem when overcoating fresh renders and repair mortars, particularly where higher concentrations of lime and/or gypsum are present. To overcome this it is advisable to allow the substrate to cure for at least two weeks prior to the application of a silicate paint. The substrate should be pre-heated, removing any existing efflorescence with a wire brush and cleaning thoroughly, before applying a silicate fixative (primer). The primer should be allowed to react before overcoating with the silicate paint system.

Salts are not the only compounds that can migrate from a substrate and affect the aesthetics of a silicate paint topcoat. Formwork oils present in pre-cast concrete slabs can progressively leach to the surface. Again, the substrate should be pre-treated by thoroughly abrading before applying a silicate-based primer.

Corroding iron and steel can also lead to unsightly staining of a coating. This can arise from the rusting of reinforcement, such as rebars or tie wires incorporated within the substrate, but can also be caused by water run off from a corroding structure onto the silicate paint. Both are very visual signs of pending failures within or around a painted structure and should be remedied appropriately. Once this has been performed, damage to the silicate paint can be simply patch repaired.

9.7   Safety

Silicate paints represent only a limited risk to the user. Associated health risks arise from the alkalinity of the materials, which exhibit a pH of around 12. For this reason, eye and skin contact should be avoided, and accidental exposure should be washed off with water. Silicate paints are unlikely to contain any toxic compounds and tend only to incorporate very low levels of coalescing solvents, with some formulations being solvent free. Good standards of industrial and personal safety should always be observed and all the necessary precautions should be taken when the product is being spray applied.

9.8   Summary

Silicate paints represent a cost effective, high performance, decorative and environmentally friendly coating for mineral substrates, upon which they exhibit an impressive range of properties. It is hoped that this chapter may help raise their profile globally as viable alternatives to the range of organic emulsions currently in use.

References

German Committee for Construction Contract Procedures. (1992) DIN 18363. *Painting and Varnishing,* Section 2.4.1 (d).
Richardson, B.A. (1991) Defects and Deterioration in Buildings. Chapman and Hall, London.

10 Anti-carbonation coatings

H.Davies, R.Bassi and A.P.J.Yates

10.1 Introduction

Problems associated with carbonation of concrete have been thoroughly documented (BRE, 1982; Everett and Treadaway, 1980; Concrete Society, 1984; Currie, 1986; Rothwell, 1985). Carbonation may result in corrosion of depassivated reinforcement, and deterioration and loss of serviceability of structures. Surface coatings and treatments are increasingly considered as an integral part of the repair process to reduce the rate of further deterioration (CIRIA, 1987).

Surface treatments to protect concrete must have a range of properties to be effective and durable. Anti-carbonation coatings are surface treatments that have low permeability to carbon dioxide and reduce the risk of carbonation. Typical properties that a surface treatment needs to prevent carbonation are:

- a dry film thickness of at least 200 microns, in order to cover effectively a rough concrete surface with a defect-free film;
- good adherence;
- ability to accommodate anticipated movements in concrete (this is specified as the crack-bridging ability of a coating);
- good colour retention, chalking and ultraviolet (UV) resistance;
- a high liquid water resistance;
- a low water vapour resistance;
- a high resistance to carbon dioxide; and
- a service life of at least 10 years.

Systems for measuring the carbon dioxide resistance of coatings can be classified according to the type of test cell used. There are two types available; the absorption cup (or gravimetric method) and systems based on the diffusion cell. Those based on the cup method rely on the absorption of CO_2 in the cup. Absorption is measured by weighing the cup regularly to determine the increase in weight against time. Diffusion cell systems measure the quantity of CO_2 passing through the membrane by analysis of the gas stream.

A gravimetric test developed at BRE has shown that the carbonation of concrete may be reduced by a number of different coatings and surface treatments (Rothwell and Davies, 1989). Further work has shown, however, that coatings could become less effective carbon dioxide barriers over a period of 2000 hours artificial weathering (Roy *et al.*, 1996), that the reduction of barrier properties varied according to the chemical type of binder used in the coating, and that the reduction was more signifi-cant for some coatings than for others.

Klopfer and Engelfried also developed a gravimetric method of measuring resist-ance of coatings to carbon dioxide (Wang Wei *et al.*, 1990; Engelfried, 1977, 1983). They tested resistance on paper substrates, which are not suitable either for natural or for artificial weathering. The gravimetric method developed at BRE uses cementitious substrates and is destructive. It has limited sensitivity and is not suitable for measuring carbon dioxide resistance of high performance coatings. To overcome the limitations of the gravimetric test, a non-destructive test method using an isostatic partition cell has been developed.

The changes in performance of a coating produced by accelerated weathering need to be confirmed by measuring performance over a period of natural exposure. Natu-ral exposure test data are also needed to determine the relationship between accelerat-ed test results and likely in-service performance. This will allow an accelerated exposure regime for the prediction of carbon dioxide resistance of coatings to be defined.

The measurement of carbon dioxide resistance of coatings has been carried out for over 15 years in the UK, Denmark and Germany, but the methods used and the results obtained are not widely understood.

10.2   Apparatus

10.2.1   Development of partition cell apparatus

Thomas and Gent (1945) used a partition cell to study permeation and sorption of moisture vapour in varnish films. A similar method was employed to measure the permeability of plastic films for packaging applications (Davies, 1946). Pasternak, Schimscheimer and Heller (1970) first proposed the use of a partition cell coupled with a gas chromatograph to determine the permeability of films to gas mixtures, and this was further developed by Pye, Höehn and Panar (1976).

Sherwood (1975) studied the carbon dioxide resistance of coatings using a parti-tion cell. The quantity of carbon dioxide passing through the film was measured by gravimetric means, a similar approach to that later employed by Engelfried and Klop-fer (Engelfried, 1983; Thomas and Gent, 1945; Davis, 1946), whose method is derived from the DIN, BS and ASTM tests for measuring water vapour permeability of poly-mer films (DIN, 1974; BSI, 1959; ASTM, 1980). These tests employ the diffusion cell first proposed by Deeg and Frosch (1944). Brianza and Piguet (1986) have also devel-oped a test method similar to the BRE mortar block test (Rothwell and Davies, 1989; Wang Wei *et al.*, 1990).

Several others have developed apparatus based on the partition cell. Möller (1985) used a partition cell with gravimetric determination derived from Sherwood's report. Others employed instrumental techniques to measure the rate of diffusion of carbon dioxide through the test sample. Désor and Pauly (1985) used infrared analysis to determine the rate of carbon dioxide diffusion through coatings. Robinson (1986; 1987) used a gas chromatograph to measure diffusion rates of oxygen and carbon dioxide using dry gas mixtures. The equipment employed by these three is all derived from that reported by Davis for testing the carbon dioxide resistance of packaging materials (Davis, 1946). The present study was carried out using a similar system of partition cells and gas chromatographic analysis. These data indicated that mixtures of gases containing water vapour could be analysed successfully by gas chromatography.

The apparatus was designed to permit the measurement of diffusion rates in a range of test humidities which has not, to the authors' knowledge, been achieved elsewhere. The ability to alter the test gas humidity was therefore considered an essential design requirement. The results reported by Engelfried and Klopfer and by Robinson were obtained at zero humidity. The BRE partition cells were also designed to allow the use of a range of substrates for the coating materials.

10.2.2   BRE carbon dioxide permeability test

The BRE test method is based on a partition cell. The apparatus has three main parts (Figure 10.1). A gas handling system provides a stream of mixed, dried gases and a helium stream which are linked to opposite sides of a differential mercury manometer. The pressure in the two streams is equalized. The test stream is supplied through a manifold to the lower chamber of each cell, where it may be humidified. The gas is a mixture of 15% carbon dioxide in nitrogen. Helium is supplied at a pre-set flow rate to the upper chamber of each cell via a similar manifold. The manifolds also act as ballast volumes to smooth minor fluctuations in the flow rates through the cells.

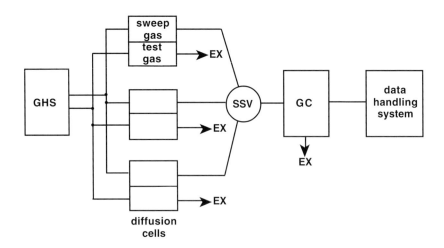

Figure 10.1   *Schematic diagram of the carbon dioxide resistance apparatus. GHS, gas handling system; SSV, stream selector valve; GC, gas chromatograph; EX, exhaust*

The coating under test is supported on a porous ceramic tile to form the test membrane. A plastic ring clamps the membrane against an 'O' ring mounted in a rebate in the wall of the upper chamber, forming a seal and defining the area of coating under test. The pressure balance ensures that the two chambers of each cell contain different partial pressures of gases at the same overall pressure. The partition cell is shown schematically in Figure 10.2.

Gas transport through the membrane occurs by diffusion. Gas diffusing through the membrane from the lower (test gas) chamber enters the sweep-stream in the upper chamber. At equilibrium the rates of diffusion of the component gases in the test mixture and of helium through the membrane reach a steady state and the test gas content of the helium sweep-stream reaches a constant value.

A selection valve connects the cells to the sampling valve of the gas. The sweep gas of each cell is sampled in turn, followed by the helium and test streams. The cycle is repeated ten times. Typically the steady state condition is reached in about eight hours. The data processor controlling the apparatus is programmed to analyse the gases after eight hours conditioning.

A plot of the GC detector response against time give a series of Gaussian peaks, each of which correspond to one component of the test gas mixture under ideal conditions. A digital integrator gives values of peak area, height and retention time. The peak area is used to determine the concentration of carbon dioxide in the samples from the partition cells.

Given the volume of sample injected, the flow rate of the sweep helium through the partition cell and the concentration of CO_2 in the sample, the quantity of carbon dioxide passing through the specimen per minute may be calculated, thus:

$$Q = (FCM)/V \ 10^{-6} \text{ g min}^{-1} \qquad [10.1]$$

where: F = flow rate of helium sweep stream (cm^3 min^{-1})
$\quad\quad$ C = concentration of CO_2 in the sample (parts per million)
$\quad\quad$ M = relative molecular mass of CO_2 (g $mole^{-1}$)
$\quad\quad$ V = molar gas volume at 200 °C (cm^3 $mole^{-1}$)
$\quad\quad$ Q = quantity of CO_2 in g min^{-1} passing through the coating at steady state.

From this value it is possible to calculate the flux, J_{CO_2}, in g m^{-2} day^{-1}:

$$J_{CO_2} = \frac{Q.1440}{A} \text{g m}^{-2}\text{day}^{-1} \qquad [10.2]$$

where A = area of coating in m^2.

10.2.3　Measurement and calculation of carbon dioxide resistance

Carbon dioxide resistance may be calculated and quoted in several ways. The terms and units most commonly used are: flux (g m^{-2} day^{-1}); diffusion coefficient (m^2 s^{-1});

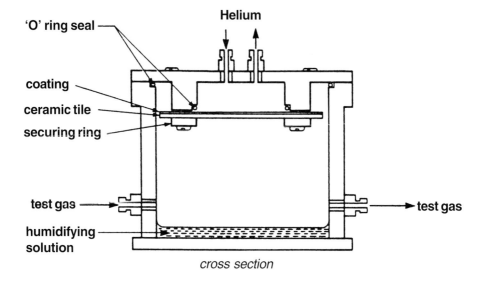

cross section

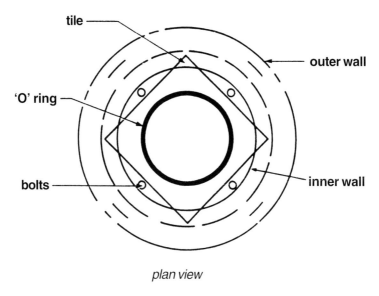

plan view

Figure 10.2   *Partition cell.*

diffusion resistance coefficient (dimensionless) and equivalent air layer thickness (m).

The derivation and calculation of these values is as follows. The flux is a function of the concentration gradient across the coating and of the thickness of the coating. Applying Fick's Second Law of Diffusion, it is possible to determine the coefficient of diffusion for a given thickness of coating, $D_{Coating}$, from the flux and concentration difference of CO_2 across the coating, thus:

$$D_{Coating} = \frac{J_{CO_2} \cdot s}{[c]}$$ [10.3]

where: J_{CO_2} = flux (g m^{-2} day^{-1})
   s = thickness (m)
   $[c]$ = concentration difference (g m^{-3}).

This value has units (m^2 d^{-1}), and is therefore not a dimensionless coefficient. It is converted to a dimensionless diffusion resistance coefficient, μ, which compares the diffusion of CO_2 through the coating with the diffusion of CO_2 through still air under the same conditions and is independent of applied coating thickness. It is calculated as follows:

$$\mu = \frac{D_{CO_2}}{D_{Coating}}$$ [10.4]

where D_{CO_2} = diffusion coefficient of CO_2 through air (m^2 s^{-1}).
Typical values for the diffusion resistance coefficient are in the range 106 to 108 for surface coatings with a high resistance to CO_2. This coefficient is used to calculate the effectiveness of the coating in terms of the equivalent air layer thickness, R_{CO_2}. The equivalent air layer thickness equates the barrier property of a coating to the thickness of still air with the same diffusion resistance. It is obtained by multiplying the diffusion resistance coefficient, μ, by the coating thickness, s, as follows:

$$R_{CO_2} = \mu s$$ [10.5]

Typical values for R_{CO_2} are between 1 m and 500 m, but higher values are not unknown.

10.2.4   Effects of relative humidity on carbon dioxide resistance

Unpublished research at BRE has shown that there are some variations in the values obtained from measurements carried out with the two humidities of test gas, but the general trends observed are similar at both humidities.

The humidity at which the test is conducted clearly does not have as much effect on the measured carbon dioxide resistance as the type of chemical binder used in the coating or the duration of exposure of the coating. In practice, coatings are applied in conditions where they will almost invariably be exposed to moist air. It would therefore seen prudent, where possible, to carry out the measurement of carbon dioxide resistance using a humidified test gas.

This will have significant implications for the choice of test method. The gravimetric method can only be carried out with humidified test gas if the humidity of the whole test apparatus is maintained at a uniform level. This may prove difficult with the gravimetric method based on the Payne Cup tests (BSI, 1959; ASTM, 1980; DIN, 1974). These usually employ an absorbent solid on one side of the coating, and these usually absorb water as well as carbon dioxide.

BRE has undertaken extensive research into anti-carbonation coatings and a summary of the findings is given below.

1. The most resistant coatings tested were those which undergo chemical reaction and cross-linking during film formation. Polyurethane and chlorinated rubber coatings showed consistently high resistance. Eggshell emulsions showed good carbon dioxide resistance although they also chalked quite heavily. Other emulsion coatings generally exhibited low carbon dioxide resistance and are not generally suitable for application to reinforced concrete where durable resistance to carbon dioxide is required.
2. The carbon dioxide resistance of coatings diminishes on exposure to natural or artificial weathering. The rate of reduction in resistance is greater than the rate of general deterioration and loss of conventional durability.
3. Coatings should be tested for carbon dioxide resistance under prescribed conditions of relative humidity; this should preferably be a value which is similar to that which the coatings will be exposed in practice.
4. The current requirement for coatings to satisfy an initial test value is inadequate to assess the potential longer term protection afforded by a coating.

10.3 European Standards

A number of European Standards relevant to coatings for masonry and concrete are under development (*see* Chapter 13). The two most significant with respect to anti-carbonation coatings are the European Standard EN 1062-6: Standard test for carbon dioxide permeability and Part 2 of the draft prEN 1504 that gives specifications for products and systems for the repair and protection of concrete structures. The latter is one of six standards for products and systems and defines a coating as 'a treatment to produce a continuous protective layer on the surface of the concrete'. The typical thickness is 0.1–5 mm and the binders may be organic polymers, organic polymers with cement as a filer, or cementitious. The approach of EN 1504 (the overall standard for concrete repair) is described elsewhere (e.g. Davies, 2001)

References

American Society for Testing and Materials (1980) *E96-80. Test methods for water vapour transmission of materials*. ASTM, Philadelphia.
Brianza, M.A. and Piguet, A. (1986) Praxisbezogenes Schnell verfahran zur Beurteilung der Einwerkung von C02 auf zementgebundene Baustoffe. *Proceeding of 2nd International Colloquium on Materials Science and Restoration*. Esslingen, 651.

Table 10.1 *Contents of EN 1504: Products and systems for the protection and repair of concrete structures.*

EN number	Part title
EN 1504-1	General scope and definitions
prEN 1504-2	Surface protection systems
prEN 1504-3	Structural and non-structural repair
prEN 1504-4	Structural bonding
prEN 1504-5	Concrete injection
prEN 1504-6	Grouting to anchor reinforcement or to fill external voids
prEN 1504-7	Reinforcement corrosion prevention
prEN 1504-8	Quality control and evaluation of conformity
ENV 1504-9	General principles for the use of products and systems
prEN 1504-10	Application of products and systems and quality control of the works

British Standards Institution (1959) Method of determining the permeability to water vapour of flexible sheet materials used for packaging. *BS 3177:1959*, BSI, London.

Building Research Establishment (1982) Durability of steel in concrete: Parts 1, 2 and 3. *BRE Digests 263, 264 and 265*, Garston, BRE.

CIRIA (1987) Protection of reinforced concrete by surface treatments. *Technical Note 130*, CIRIA, London.

Concrete Society (1984) Repair of concrete damaged by reinforcement corrosion. *Concrete Society Technical Report No. 26*, 23–25.

Currie, R.J. (1986) Carbonation depths in structural-quality concrete: an assessment of evidence from investigations of structures and from other sources. *Building Research Establishment Report*. Garston, BRE.

Davies, H. (2001) European Standard for repair and protection of concrete. *Structural Faults 2001*.

Davies, H. and Rothwell, G.W. (1989) The effectiveness of surface coatings in reducing carbonation of reinforced concrete. *BRE Information Paper 7/89*, Garston, BRE.

Davis, W.W. (1946) Gas permeability… an isostatic test method. *Modern Packaging*, May 1946, 144.

Deeg, G. and Frosch, C.J. (1944) Diffusion of water through plastics. *Modern Plastics*, Nov. 1944,155.

Desor, U. (1985) Protection restoration of concrete with emulsion paints; Experiments on carbon dioxide and sulphur dioxide permeability. *Proceedings of a PRA Symposium on Coatings for Concrete*, PRA, London, Paper 3.

Desor, U. and Pauly, S. (1985) Betonschutz und Betonsanierung mit Dispersionsfarben. *Farbe und Lacke*, **91**(6), 500–504.

DIN (1974) *DIN 53 122. Determination of water vapour transmission; gravimetric method*. DIN, Berlin.

Durbeck, H.W. and Niehaus, R. (1978) Simultaneous gas chromatography of, O_2 N_2, CO, CO_2, N_2O, SO_2, CH_4, C_2H_6, C_2H_4 at ppm levels. *Chromatographia*, **11**, 14.

Engelfried, R. (1977) Carbonisation von Beton, irhe Bedeutung und ihre Beeinflussung durch Beschichtungen. *Defazet*, **31** (9), 353–359.

Engelfried, R. (1983) Diffusion resistance coefficients for carbon dioxide and water and their practical applications. *Farbe und Lacke,* **89** (7), 513.

Everett, L.H. and Treadaway, K.W.J. (1980) Deterioration due to corrosion in reinforced concrete. *BRE Information Paper 12/80*, Garston, BRE.

Moller, L. (1985) Research on protection of steel reinforced concrete in Scandinavia. *Proceedings of a PRA Symposium on Coatings for Concrete*, PRA, London, Paper 2.

Pasternak, R.A., Schimscheimer, J.F. and Heller, J. (1970) A dynamic approach to diffusion and permeation measurements. *J Polymer Sci.*, A-2 8, 467–479.

Pye, D.G., Hoehn, H.H. and Panar, M. (1976) Measurement of gas permeability of polymers: II. Apparatus for determination of permeabilities of mixed gases and vapours. *J. Applied Polymer Sci.*, **20**, 287–301.

Robinson, H. (1986) Evaluation of coatings as carbonation barriers. *Proceedings of 2nd International Colloquium on Materials Science and Restoration*, Esslingen, 641–645.

Robinson, H. (1987) Evaluation of coatings as carbonation barriers. *Construction Repair* (Feb), 12–18.

Rothwell, G.W. (1985) Coatings for the protection of steel reinforced concrete. *Proceedings of a PRA Symposium on Coatings for Concrete,* PRA, London.

Roy, S.K., Northwood, D.O. and Poh, K.B. (1996a) Effect of plastering on the carbonation of a 19 year old reinforced building. *Construction and Building Materials,* **10** (4), 262–272.

Sherwood, A.F. and Haines, M.J. (1975) The carbon dioxide permeability of masonry paints. *PRA Technical Report TR/1175*, PRA, London.

Thomas, A.M. and Gent, W.L. (1945) Permeation and sorption of water vapour in varnish films. *Proc. Physics Soc.*, **57**, 324–349.

Wang Wei, Rothwell, G.W. and Davies, H. (1990) Investigation of the gas and vapour resistance of surface coatings on concrete and effects of weathering on their carbonation protective performance. *Corrosion of Reinforcement in Concrete Proceedings of the 3rd International Symposium on Corrosion of Reinforcement in Concrete Construction, Wishaw, May 1990*, Elsevier, London, 397–408.

The BRE Carbon Dioxide Permeability Test was developed as part of a government funded research programme for the Construction Industry Directorate of the Department of Trade and Industry.

11 Cathodic protection of steel reinforcement

James Phipps

11.1 Background

Corrosion of steel is a naturally occurring process whereby the refined material is progressively returned to its low energy state of oxides of iron, more commonly termed rust. The process is both chemical and electrical in nature (Fontana, 1986). The factors which control the rate of this transformation can be complex, and are generally outside the scope of this chapter. A simple corrosion cell can be thought of as consisting of four components; (i) anodes, (ii) cathodes, (iii) a moist environment, and (iv) an electrical conductor between the anodes and cathodes.

The anode represents the site of corrosion and, using the example of steel, it is here where iron is oxidized through the loss of electrons (e⁻), i.e. a corrosion current is generated. The cathode, which can be a different metal or more commonly an area of the same metal adjacent to the anode, receives the electrons and, in the presence of water (H_2O) and oxygen (O_2), generates hydroxyl ions (OH^-). These reactions are summarized below:

$$\text{Anodic: } Fe = Fe^{2+} + 2e^-$$

$$\text{Cathodic: } O_2 + 2H_2O + 4e^- = 4OH^-$$

The combination of Fe^{2+} and OH^- produces the characteristic hydrated ferric oxide or rust, commonly associated with the atmospheric corrosion of steel.

Cathodic protection is a technique by which the rate of corrosion of a metal can be reduced through the application of a small, direct electric current applied in the opposite sense to the reactions described above. Correctly applied, this renders all the treated metal cathodic, and therefore not liable to metal loss through oxidation. The current can be supplied by two sources;(i) by the deliberate corrosion of a more base material, a so-called sacrificial anode, or (ii) by the application of a current from a power supply unit (PSU) through a similar or more noble anode, an impressed anode.

11.2 Introduction

Steel in reinforced concrete is largely protected from the outside environment by a dense layer of aggregates and alkaline cement paste. The concrete not only acts as a barrier to potentially aggressive materials, but the inherent alkalinity imparts a fine protective layer (a passive oxide film) to the steel. Through this mechanism, steel in concrete is subject to significantly better protection than atmospherically exposed steel.

Various degradation mechanisms can occur by which this protective barrier can be breached, principally carbonation and chloride ions, leading to the onset of steel reinforcement corrosion. Such situations are often characterized by the cracking and spalling of cover concrete, which left unchecked can ultimately lead to visual and structural distress.

The application of cathodic protection is an effective means of controlling this destructive mechanism in reinforced concrete. By introducing an artificial anode to the concrete, either sacrificial or impressed, the corrosion current can be effectively reduced to a tolerable level (SCPRC, 1995).

There are several basic categories of cathodic protection anode that can be employed with reinforced concrete:

- discrete anodes – rods of material, drilled in to the concrete surface (Cope *et al.*, 1996);
- anode meshes – meshes built in to the concrete surface, or contained within a sprayed overlay (Haywood, 1995);
- conductive overlays – sprayed overlays containing conductive fibres;
- remote anodes – anodes located away from the structure; and
- conductive coatings – coatings applied directly to the concrete surface.

Other categories exist, but their usage is minimal.

11.3 Coating-based anode systems

Coatings for the cathodic protection of reinforced concrete can be divided into two distinct categories: conductive paints and sprayed metal layers. Both these systems are applied directly to the prepared concrete substrate and provide protection through an impressed current. A number of the sprayed metal coatings can also protect through sacrificial action.

11.3.1 Conductive paint systems

Conductive paints are essentially formulated in the same manner as normal paints and coatings for application to concrete substrates (as discussed elsewhere), with the exception that they are laden with conductive fillers, generally carbon. The carbon filler material is usually in a spheroidal or fibrous form.

The conductive paint permits the application of the protective current to the reinforcement which is supplied by a PSU. Electrical continuity between the coating and PSU is established by means of current distributors, commonly referred to as primary anodes. Such primary anodes form the interface between the coating and the electrical cabling, and are typically constructed from wires, ribbons or braids employing such materials as niobium, platinum, titanium, nickel or carbon fibre.

In order to function correctly, the following requirements must by achieved by the conductive paint system as a minimum:
- good adhesion to the concrete substrate;
- low electrical film resistance;
- even distribution of conductive filler;
- resistance to weathering, whilst maintaining properties;
- resistance to alkalis, acid and chlorination within anticipated limits; and
- resistance to bacterial and fungal growth.

In addition to the above, the paint system must be capable of being successfully applied with relative ease. Products currently available are formulated for application using brush, roller or airless spray techniques. Such products are presently available as both water and solvent-based systems; however, the former tends to hold the greater market share from an environmental viewpoint.

In formulating such paint systems, the products require to maintain a sufficiently low viscosity to enable ease of mixing and application. However, following application on to the surface, the viscosity must be such that the paint remains stable and does not flow inadvertently (especially on vertical surfaces and soffits). In order to achieve this, specific modifiers have been developed and incorporated.

For its success as a cathodic protection product, the conductive coating must demonstrate a low volume electrical resistivity (typically less than $10\,\Omega$ cm) in order that it may distribute current adequately and will lower energy loss. The sheet or film resistance is often used as an alternative means of expressing this variable, with values typically less than $40\,\Omega/$ square (Chess, 1998). The sheet resistance is derived from the following:

$$\text{sheet resistance}(\Omega/\text{square}) = \frac{\text{volume resistivity }(\Omega\text{cm}) \times 10000}{\text{wet film thickness (mm)} \times \text{solids content (\%)}}$$

Products presently available can typically yield current density values of up to 15–20 mA/m², for lifetimes of approximately ten to fifteen years. Inevitably, continually operating systems at current densities in excess of the manufacturer's guidelines may be expected to reduce significantly the effective operating life. Conversely, lower maintenance current densities may well prolong the lifetime of the coating, although beyond ten years other factors such as weathering may contribute to the deterioration of the paint system. The moderate capacity for current density can restrict the employment of such systems to applications with low to medium reinforcement densities.

The most essential element in achieving successful and durable cathodic protection using conductive paints lies in the preparation that is required prior to the application process. In many cases, these are applicable to any cathodic protection system applied to reinforced concrete. The stages that need consideration are as follows:
- a well considered and detailed design compiled by appropriately experienced and qualified persons;
- confirmation of electrical continuity within the reinforcement;
- repair of any defective concrete or reinforcement with suitable products;

- installation of monitoring electrodes, and provision of connections to the reinforcement;
- surface preparation of the concrete to a standard which will accept the particular paint system selected;
- distribution of the primary anode network in accordance with the design requirements;
- application of the system to the manufacturer's guidelines; and
- allowance and confirmation of adequate curing time prior to providing additional coatings or energising the system.

As a guideline, surface preparation of the concrete typically involves either abrasive blasting or high pressure water cleaning to remove cement laitance and remnants of previous coatings or surface treatments. Oils, grease and organic growths not removed by these processes should be treated with approved de-greasers and biocides. These factors, along with the inherent material characteristics, must be able to create an environment whereby the coating can achieve an acceptable adhesion strength with the substrate. Adhesion strengths of 0.5 N/mm^2 are often reported as a minimum acceptable criteria; however, these guidelines are often more stringent, e.g. average adhesion strength of 1.5 N/mm^2, with no individual values less than 1.0 N/mm^2. Adhesion promoters are often specified prior to the application of the conductive coating.

Typically, the coatings are applied at wet film thicknesses of up to 500 μm, with a corresponding dry film thickness of around 200–300 μm, although there are systems with higher average recommended film thicknesses. Carbon loaded paint systems tend by nature to be black in colour, thus in areas where aesthetics are important it is commonplace to provide a decorative top coating. In regions where the conductive paint may be subject to weathering, it may also be necessary to provide such an additional coating to help extend the service life of the conductive paint system.

11.3.2 Sprayed metal layer systems

This category of coating for cathodic protection is based upon the provision of the protective current from a thin layer of metal, deposited directly on to the concrete surface. Materials that have been employed for this purpose include alloys of zinc, aluminium, titanium and nickel.

The configuration and basic requirements of the metal layer cathodic protection systems are broadly similar to that of the conductive paint coatings previously described. The largest contrast between the two types of system is the method of application. While conductive paints essentially rely on standard materials and techniques for coating concrete, the sprayed metal systems employ technology originally developed for the protection of steel components and structures. Several different techniques are available (Bennett *et al.*, 1995):

Flame spraying – the metal or metal alloy is fed in a wire format to a hand held gun in which an oxygen/acetylene gas flame locally melts the wire. The molten material is transferred to the concrete surface by a jet of compressed air.

Arc spraying – using a high voltage d.c. supply, two oppositely charged wires are fed to a gun which induces localized melting of the metal or metal alloy. A jet of compressed air passes through the arc and delivers the molten material to the concrete surface.

Plasma spraying – a gas mixture is passed through an electric arc produced between inert electrodes, which generates a plasma. The metal or metal alloy is introduced into the plasma stream and transferred to the concrete interface by a high velocity gas stream.

The surface requirements for the application of sprayed metal coatings are fundamental to the success of the anode, as previously discussed for conductive paints. Aside from ensuring that no short circuits are likely to result from surface breaking reinforcement or junk steel (e.g. tie wires, shuttering nails, etc.), the concrete must be free from defects (cracks, delaminations, etc.), and the surface thoroughly cleaned to removed foreign debris and laitance. The most suitable method for such preparation is abrasive blasting as this not only serves to clean but, used correctly, will also provide an appropriate profile for optimum adhesion.

Regions where remaining surface breaking steel is present and areas where cathodic protection is not required can be masked using a suitable non-conductive material (e.g. two-pack epoxy), which is compatible with the overlay. This technique can also be applicable to other cathodic protection systems.

Of the metallic systems identified above, zinc and aluminium are widely used in the field of sacrificial anode cathodic protection due to their relative activity when compared to iron in the electrochemical series. In particular, zinc, aluminium and their alloys have long established records for the protection of submerged pipelines and other offshore structures.

With the advent of cathodic protection for reinforced concrete, and the means to apply successfully metallic layers to concrete surfaces, alloys of zinc and aluminium have been employed as sacrificial anodes for the protection of reinforced concrete. Sacrificial anode technology for concrete has been predominantly developed and employed in the USA. Early applications employed discrete layers of zinc applied directly to the surface of concrete bridge decks. This approach soon developed into the sprayed systems which offered much greater intimacy with the concrete substrate and thus yielded higher outputs and levels of cathodic protection. It was apparent, however, that the zinc anodes were greatly influenced by relative humidity, temperature and pH, which tended to prevent their application in situations such as reinforced concrete in tidal splash zones. Developments over the last 20 years have produced sacrificial anode materials based on alloys of aluminium, zinc and indium which display much greater tolerance to these effects.

The greatest drawback of sacrificial anode coatings for the protection of reinforced concrete is the same as experienced in conventional sacrificial anode use, namely restricted service life. Typical service lives to first maintenance quoted at present range from 10–15 years, based on coating thicknesses of around 200 to 300 μm.

Sprayed zinc anodes, with their reportedly superior adhesion characteristics, are also employed as impressed anodes on concrete substrates. Sprayed zinc anodes receive current in much the same way as conductive paint systems, through the use of primary anodes. The advantage of applying impressed current through the zinc is the potentially increased life expectancy, although quoted figures do not necessarily exceed those quoted for the same materials when used as sacrificial anodes, e.g. service life to first maintenance of 10 to 20 years at coating thickness of 200 to 500 μm.

While sprayed anodes of zinc and aluminium have demonstrated their value for the cathodic protection of reinforced concrete, their limitations must be taken into account when considering their application. In addition to having lower service lives when compared to other anodes types, the environmental issues surrounding these materials, particularly zinc, must also be taken into consideration. It is possible that such environmental concerns have been the principal reason for the limited employment of these sprayed materials in the UK and mainland Europe.

A further development of the sprayed anode materials is the use of more inherently noble metals such as nickel and, in particular, titanium. Due to its thin and tightly adherent passive film, titanium is an extremely corrosion resistant material. The presence of this protective layer, however, interferes with the performance of this material as an impressed anode for the cathodic protection of reinforced concrete. In order to overcome this barrier, electro-catalytic coatings have been developed for titanium which allow the treated titanium to serve as a suitable corrosion resistant anode. The composite now functions such that the titanium provides a suitable means for distributing the protective current, whilst the catalytic coating (based on mixed metal oxides) serves as the surface for the anodic reactions. The catalyst is not consumed by the anodic reactions, although it may deteriorate through damage or other chemical reactions.

The reported anodic reaction for such systems is believed to be based on:

$$4OH^- = O_2 + 2H_2O + 4e^-$$

The most common means of applying the catalytic coating is to treat directly the sprayed titanium layer, allowing the catalysing material to penetrate to the titanium/concrete interface. Using this technique, it should in theory be possible to re-apply the catalyst once the original surface has been consumed. Service lives to first maintenance in excess of 20 years are commonly reported for similar titanium/catalyst systems.

A direct comparison can be made between the catalysed titanium sprayed coating, and the electro-catalytically coated expanded titanium mesh, which has been widely employed in conjunction with cementitious overlays for the cathodic protection of reinforced concrete.

11.4   Associated products

In addition to the anodic materials themselves, two further topics require consideration, namely decorative coatings and primary anodes. These are applicable to both the conductive paints and sprayed metal anodes.

11.4.1   Aesthetic/protective topcoats

As described earlier, the conductive paint systems produced for the cathodic protection of reinforced concrete are inherently black in nature and, as such, decorative topcoats are often specified for the overcoating of the anode to improve the appearance of the structure while imparting a degree of protection to the conductive layer. In specifying materials for such a task, several factors and requirements must be taken into consideration.

In order to function adequately, the reactions associated with corrosion must be capable of proceeding. In more specific terms, oxygen and water must be able to reach the system, and gases such as chlorine must be able to escape. To achieve this, any coating material applied on top of the anode surface must be vapour permeable. The nature of cathodic protection is to generate conditions of acidity (or reduced alkalinity) at the anode and therefore coatings must also be tolerant to these conditions.

A typical product for overcoating anodic paints/metal would essentially be based upon a material with low modification and good adhesion characteristics. It should be possible to apply the material directly to the anodic coating without the need for any significant surface preparation.

11.4.2   Primary anodes

As described previously, primary anodes serve to form the interface between the d.c. positive cables from the PSU and the secondary anode (the conductive/sprayed coating). The terminology employed can be somewhat misleading as primary anodes typically serve no anodic function, unlike the secondary anodes which supply all the necessary current. The type of primary anodes employed and their distribution is very much dependant upon the individual design characteristics as well as the type of secondary anode used.

Several basic categories of primary anode are presently employed, which tend to be based upon one or more of the following materials:

1. platinized titanium;
2. niobium;
3. mixed metal oxide (MMO) coated titanium;
4. brass or stainless steel plates; and
5. carbon fibre tape.

It is usual for the primary anodes to be connected up to the d.c. cabling and laid on the prepared concrete prior to the application of the coating or sprayed metal layer.

11.5   Application criteria

The choice of anode type must be considered at an early stage in the design process for any successful cathodic protection system.

The two main anode systems considered in this section, conductive coatings and sprayed metallic layers, are perhaps most suited to situations where:

- the reinforcement density is low to medium;
- the distribution of the reinforcing steel is fairly consistent;
- maintenance free lifetimes of between 15 years and 20 years are required;

- heavy weathering or regular saturation of the concrete surfaces is not commonplace; and
- the protected surfaces are in the vertical or overhead position.

The conductive coating's main benefits are apparent from their use where:
- there are tight tolerances on increasing the effective thickness, or depth of the concrete surface;
- there is a restriction on increasing the effective dead load of the concrete surface;
- it is awkward to apply alternative anode systems, e.g. variable profile surfaces; or
- where architectural features require to be maintained.

As previously discussed, there appears to be a reluctance within the UK and mainland Europe to employ sprayed metallic coatings on a significant scale. This is most likely to stem from environmental considerations associated with the application of sprayed zinc coatings. The improving technology and increasing track record of alternative materials such as titanium and aluminium/zinc alloys may help to increase the application of this technology.

References

Bennett, J.E., Schue, T.J. and McGill, G. (1995) A Thermally Sprayed Titanium Anode for Cathodic Protection of Reinforced Concrete Structures. *Technical Paper 504, National Association of Corrosion Engineers (NACE), Corrosion 95*, 504/1–504/13.

Chess, P. (1998) *Cathodic Protection of Steel in Concrete*. E. & F.N. Spon.

Cope, M.P., Lambert, P. and Weale, C.J. (1996) Borlum Bridge – The Assessment and Protection of Reinforced Concrete. *Construction Repairs*, **5**, pp 39–43.

Fontana, M.G. (1986) *Corrosion Engineering*. McGraw-Hill, Singapore.

Haywood, D. (1995) Approach Shot. *New Civil Engineer*, 23 Mar. , 26–27.

Society for Cathodic Protection of Reinforced Concrete (SCPRC) (1995) *Cathodic Protection of Reinforced Concrete*. Report No. 001.95.

Acknowledgements

The authors wish to thank Permarock, Corrpro and Harris Specialty Chemicals for providing technical and performance data on many of their systems.

12 Coatings for desalination and realkalisation of concrete

M.Decter

12.1 Introduction

Desalination and realkalisation are electrochemical techniques to halt and prevent corrosion in reinforced concrete. Desalination, also known as chloride extraction, is used on chloride contaminated concrete while the realkalisation technique is used on carbonated concrete.

The first realkalisation project was carried out at Tromsö in Norway in 1987 and both realkalisation and desalination are now licensed in 22 countries, worldwide. Some 350 projects, comprising nearly 250,000 square metres of concrete, have now been completed.

12.2 Desalination

Desalination is carried out by applying an electric field between the reinforcement in the concrete and an externally mounted electrode mesh (Figure 12.1). The reinforcement acts as the cathode and the electrode mesh as the anode. The mesh is embedded in an electrolyte reservoir on the concrete surface and the treatment proceeds for four to eight weeks depending on the nature of the concrete. Chloride ions are transported out of the concrete. At the same time, electrolysis at the reinforcement surface produces hydroxyl ions.

The chloride levels in the concrete are significantly reduced and the generation of hydroxyl ions produces a high pH area around the steel. All corrosion, even in pits on the surface of the steel, is halted and the reinforcement is passivated.

Desalination is largely a non-destructive technique. Only loose and spalled concrete is repaired prior to treatment. It is not necessary to remove large areas of chloride contaminated, but otherwise sound, concrete. The electrolyte is contained in a spray applied fibre, coffer tanks or, sometimes, felt cloth. After treatment, the surface is protected by a coating to prevent new chloride ingress into the concrete.

Acknowledgements: The author would like to thank the following companies for their support during the research phases of this work: Fosroc (UK) Limited; NCT Oslo, Norway; Martech Services Limited and Makers Industrial Limited.

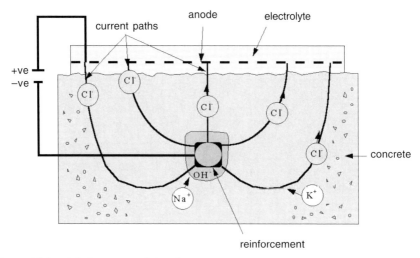

Figure 12.1 *Mechanisms of desalination.*

12.3 Realkalisation

This technique also involves the application of an electric field between an external electrode mesh (the anode) and the reinforcement (the cathode). During realkalisation, an alkaline electrolyte, usually sodium carbonate solution, is transported into the concrete (Figure 12.2).

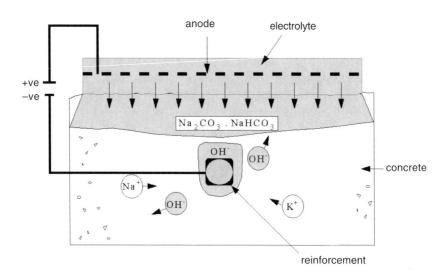

Figure 12.2 *Mechanisms of realkalisation.*

At the same time, electrolysis at the reinforcement surface produces a high pH environment. The treatment continues until the alkalinity of the cover zone has been re-established. This can be determined by chemical analysis for sodium levels and testing with phenolphthalein solution. The treatment time is usually three to seven days, after which the reinforcement becomes passive.

Realkalisation is also largely non-destructive, requiring only the repair of loose and spalled concrete. The alkaline electrolyte is usually contained in a spray applied fibre, although solution in tanks has also been used. After treatment, the surface of the concrete is cleaned and frequently a surface coating is applied.

The introduction of sodium carbonate solution, as well as the production of hydroxyl ions at the reinforcement, maintains sufficiently high pH in the cover zone to provide long term protection to the reinforcement.

12.4   Practical application

Realkalisation and desalination can be performed under all weather conditions as long as the electrolyte does not freeze. As would be predicted from simple chemistry, the efficiency of the desalination treatment is enhanced by increased temperatures. The methods are suitable for most types of reinforced concrete, but are not necessarily universally applicable. Pre-stressed and post-tensioned structures and any concrete with unusual characteristics need thorough investigation to assess suitability. Detailed descriptions on practical use are given in the model specifications. The most important steps only are briefly mentioned in the following sections.

12.4.1   Preparation prior to electrochemical treatment

Only loose, spalled and delaminated concrete needs to be removed before treatment. Any exposed and corroding rebars should be cleaned and the area repaired using an approved cement based mortar.

Concrete surface coatings should be removed since coatings may increase the treatment time or limit the effect of the treatment. If for any reason the removal of the surface finish must be avoided, a trial is required to establish the treatment time necessary.

12.4.2   Rebar connections

Rebar continuity is of utmost importance prior to any electrochemical treatment. The number of rebar connections needed depends upon rebar continuity, but a given minimum number of connections always applies.

12.4.3   Installation of the anode system

The anode system consists of an anode mesh embedded in an electrolytic reservoir on the concrete surface. The purpose of the anode mesh is to distribute the current, while the electrolyte conducts the electricity and, in the case of realkalisation, also provides alkalis to the carbonated concrete. The purpose of the reservoir is to keep the electrolyte in contact with the concrete surface and the anode mesh. The most commonly used reservoirs are sprayed on cellulose fibre, felt cloth and tanks, as described below.

Cellulose fibre, saturated with the electrolyte, is sprayed directly onto the concrete surface to a thickness that encapsulates the mesh. Its adhesion properties make the cellulose fibre suitable for most concrete surfaces. During treatment, regular wetting is required.

Tanks may consist of plastic sheets with sealing edge strips of compressible expanded plastic and with a built-in anode mesh. Tanks are fastened directly to the concrete surface and are particularly suitable for the treatment of smaller, separated areas, provided that the concrete surface is relatively smooth and even. During treatment, the tanks are topped up with fresh electrolyte as required.

12.4.4   Performance monitoring: control and documentation

The process is monitored by means of current and voltage readings, and, if necessary, adjusted to maintain the desired current density, typically 1 mA/m² (92.9 mA/ft²) of concrete surface. Two transformer-rectifiers have been developed for realkalisation and desalination work. One is a large, electronically controlled unit, the other is a smaller computer controlled unit for easier current control and process monitoring.

The effect of treatment is determined by analysis of concrete samples taken at defined test locations before, during and after treatment. For realkalisation, the pH indicator phenolphthalein is used for qualitative measures, while sodium and sometimes potassium analyses are used if quantitative measures are required. The level of desalination is determined by chloride analysis of the concrete. The treatment continues until the defined acceptance criteria is achieved, as proven by the test results.

12.4.5   Dismantling

When the test results confirm satisfactory treatment, the entire installation is dismantled. The surface is washed with clean water and remaining cavities and core drill holes are repaired.

12.4.6   Post-treatment monitoring and maintenance

On structures in severe environments, it is recommended that reference electrodes be installed to monitor the stability of the treated concrete. Where the application of a subsequent decorative and/or protective coating is required, the concrete surface must be allowed to dry and a compatible material must be chosen.

12.5   Compatibility of coatings applied over realkalised and desalinated concrete

In addition to the usual requirements for concrete coatings, the realkalisation and desalination treatments produce some special factors that must be considered. These are listed below:

1. Both treatments involve soaking the concrete with electrolyte solution so that post-treatment the concrete is saturated and this can take weeks or even months to reach more normal levels.
2. If the fibre electrolyte reservoir is used, it must be cleaned off the surface of the concrete prior to overcoating to allow the coating to bond properly to the surface.
3. In the case of realkalisation, the electrolyte, which impregnates the concrete, remains very alkaline. Coatings which may be applied to relatively fresh concrete are often assumed to be alkali resistant, but in fact the very top surface of fresh concrete carbonates rapidly.
4. Sodium carbonate can produce efflorescence. This can interfere with the development of a good bond to the concrete and can cause blistering in areas were a good bond has not been achieved.

Some failures of coating systems applied over concrete that has undergone realkalisation or desalination have been seen. Within days or months of inappropriate coatings being applied after the Norcure process, problems can occur resulting in film breakdown. This becomes evident through blistering, cracking and peeling of fairing coats and topcoat systems, and the presence of efflorescence. Where failures of coatings systems have been seen, it is not necessarily related to generic coating type.

12.5.1   Factors affecting coatings systems

The on-site evidence of failures indicated that a number of factors were involved in the mechanism of coating failure. In general realkalisation, and to a lesser extent desalination, tend to move the balance between coating adhesion and debonding pressures to the latter (Table 12.1). Therefore, coatings fail over realkalised or desalinated concrete due to a combination of factors which both further weaken the adhesion and increase the pressure, moving the balance towards failure.

12.6   Test methods

As there are several factors which affect coating performance over realkalised or desalinated concrete, it is important to simulate these in test methods for coatings systems. As failure on site often occurs after many months, laboratory screening tests are vital.

The development of test methods stemmed from on-site evidence that more coatings failures occurred due to efflorescence and blistering on jobs that had been carried out fairly soon after the realkalisation process or during the winter months, accompanied with fluctuations in ambient conditions. It was surmised that humidity levels had to be high within the substrate for a long period of time resulting in a steady loss of water vapour and subsequently the deposit of crystalline salts.

Laboratory tests should be carried out on test block systems that have been taken to saturation point. Several laboratory test methods have been established that accelerate but simulate the types of failure encountered on site. These then help to determine conclusively the mechanism of coatings failure and its solution.

Table 12.1 *Mechanisms influencing coating performance.*

Factors reducing adhesion (to keep coating on)	Factors increasing pressures (to push coating off)
1. The process results in a wet, saturated substrate reducing penetration.*RA, DS*	1. Loss of water vapour through semi permeable coatings leaves sodium carbonate behind coating due to "molecular sieve" effect. *RA*
2. If the surface is dried, crystals will fill the pores reducing coating penetration.*RA*	2. Sodium carbonate recrystallises, causing substantial debonding pressure. *RA*
3. If dry, rapid water loss may occur from the dispersion coatings, resulting in inadequate film formation.*RA, DS*	3. If the substrate remains wet, then increased concentration results in osmotic pressure under the coating.*RA*
4. Poor film formation of the dispersion coatings in the presence of an electrolyte gives rise to defects.*RA*	4. Possible chemical reactions with the coating. Alkali attack.*RA*

(*RA* refers to factors relating to realkalisation, *DS* to factors relating to desalination)

12.6.1   Hollow block test

The hollow block test, as the name suggests, uses concrete cubes (150 mm) which have been cored through (100 mm). The external sides are coated, leaving the applied systems to dry for seven days (Figure 12.3). A watertight seal is created at the bottom edge of the block and the core filled with sodium carbonate solution. Failure is indicated by blistering of the coatings and the presence of efflorescence (Figure 12.4).

12.6.2   Back pressure test

For this test, two groups of 100 mm diameter concrete cores are used, one set is soaked in water, the second in sodium carbonate solution. The cores are then dried to constant weight and the coating systems applied. After the films are left to cure for 7 days the cores are then bonded into a pipe cap and connected to a pressurized water system. The test cores are subjected to stepwise increases of back pressure up to 4 bar pressure, until the coating shows signs of failure due to blistering and debonding (Figure 12.5).

12.6.3   Upside down ceramic tile test

This test method involves coating the surface of unglazed ceramic tiles with the coating system under test and leaving them to dry for seven days. A silicone sealant is applied to the back edge of the tile to create a reservoir into which sodium carbonate is poured.

Figure 12.3 *Cored concrete cubes (150 mm) used for the hollow block tests.*

Figure 12.4 *Examples of hollow block which has been filled with sodium carbonate solution. Where evaporation occurred from the top edge of the coating, salt crystals debonded the coating.*

Figure 12.5 *Blistering and debonding in the back pressure test.*

The systems are left in these conditions for two/three days after which the solution is poured off and the tiles left to dry for 24 hours. The whole procedure continues until the systems have been subjected to 28 days continual soaking (Figure 12.6).

12.6.4   Soaked concrete slabs

Concrete slabs are immersed in a molar sodium carbonate solution for several weeks until saturation is achieved. Some are removed and left to air dry prior to being wire brushed and the coating systems applied over the surface. Other slabs are left soaking and then wiped over with a cloth and the coating systems applied to the surface. The panels are then immersed to three-quarters of their depth in sodium carbonate solution to maintain their saturated state. The panels are observed at seven-day intervals up to a total of 28 days, and adhesion tests are carried out on the systems.

12.7   Coating systems

A number of coating systems have been evaluated to date using the tests described above. After treatment, and before application of any coating system, concrete must be cleaned to remove any remaining cellulose fibre, contamination and, in the case of realkalisation, sodium carbonate deposits. (Grit blasting may be recommended.) Those systems that worked well fulfilled certain requirements outlined below.

Figure 12.6 *Ceramic tile test showing growth of crystals on the surface (left) and crystals breaking through the film surface (right).*

12.7.1 Requirements

1. The coating system must bond well to saturated concrete (greater than 1 N/mm^2 and preferably greater than 2 N/mm^2).
2. Coating systems for realkalised concrete must not degrade in long term contact with high alkalinity. Bond strength and other properties must be maintained.
3. Effluorescence resistance is also a requirement for coatings for realkalised concrete.
4. If a cement based material is to be used over realkalised concrete, it must be compatible with sodium carbonate. The setting process of some cementitious materials is affected by the presence of sodium carbonate.

Although generic type does not guarantee performance, the most promising materials have been water-based epoxy coatings and polymer-cement composites.

Coating systems may need to fulfil other criteria. Coatings over desalinated concrete may need to provide protection to the concrete from further chloride ingress, where this has been the cause of the original contamination. Anti-carbonation properties are not necessary after realkalisation of concrete, but may be advisable in some circumstances for desalinated concrete.

Depending on the structure which has been repaired, other factors, for example good abrasion resistance and anti-skid properties for a car park deck, or resistance to UV light for a coating on the outside of a building, may also be important requirements.

Note in proof

Since this chapter was written, there have been developments with the temporarily applied electrochemical processes.

Realkalisation may be neither complete nor durable unless it is carried out with a solution containing 1M alkali metal carbonate applied to concrete carbonated to the depth of reinforcement. This places a strain on coatings, particularly commonly-used acrylic-based materials. A preferred electrolyte is potassium carbonate since this gives rise to relatively little efflorescence – a potentially disruptive force to coatings. The preferred coatings comprise cementitious levelling mortars at a thickness of around 5 mm or water-based epoxy compositions. These may be further overcoated if required. Compatability should be established before use.

The preferred electrolyte for chloride extraction is a saturated solution of calcium hydroxide, furnished by using an elctrolyte with excess solid alkali present. The benefit of chloride extraction goes beyond the value of removal of this aggressive ion. The treatment significantly raises the chloride threshold for the initiation of corrosion.

R.F. Viles, Technology Manager, Fosroc Group Development

13 Selection of coatings systems and international tests

R.Bassi and S.A.Hurley

13.1 Introduction

The mineral materials of good quality concrete are inherently durable. Colour, texture and surfacing requirements for architectural purposes can be accommodated. The flexibility for design and construction has led to universal acceptance for building and civil engineering. Nevertheless, when concrete is subjected to the rigours of weather and other aggressive environments, loss of appearance, deterioration of the surface and even disintegration can occur.

For many years, coatings have been applied for aesthetic reasons. Depending on design and environmental requirements, weatherproofing treatments have also been widely used and more durable paints have evolved. The need to protect structural concrete by coatings with more specific properties has been slower to develop.

The increasing use of steel-reinforced concrete in modern building has led, however, to widespread deterioration problems associated with reinforcement corrosion. These are related to the specification and quality of concrete, the depth of protective cover, efficiency in placing and curing, or to factors in design or environmental exposure.

Coatings are increasingly being used to protect reinforced concrete structures against the penetration of carbon dioxide, water and other aggressive agents, such as chlorides, to ensure a satisfactory service life. Suitable barrier coatings provide a logical option. The number of cases requiring such protection is growing.

There is more than 20 years' experience with some types of coatings in this field, enough to establish their performance. In the last decade, many new systems have been introduced and the need to continue evaluation remains. The appropriate choice, specification and application of coatings is very important. Selection of a coating for an appropriate application can be difficult and, often, the only data a specifier has are laboratory test results.

This chapter gives a brief overview of the selection of coatings and discusses related international standards and their implications, in particular the development of new European Standards.

13.2 Process of selection

Ideally, application and service requirements would lead to the relatively simple selection of an appropriate coating system. However, in practice, the situation is often complex for the following reasons:

1. Cost requirements, the application conditions and service demands can vary significantly from one project to another.
2. The surface treatment often has to fulfil several requirements at the same time: for example, an anti-carbonation coating that must provide and maintain an acceptable appearance and allow moisture vapour transmission.
3. Products of the same generic type can exhibit marked variations in certain properties due to formulation differences.
4. Different products may satisfy a specific requirement, but to different levels of effect.
5. There are no detailed schemes available which relate environment categories to the likely service life for treatments commonly used on concrete. The BRE is undertaking research to address this issue.
6. There are very few agreed and quantified performance criteria. However, this situation will change in Europe with the introduction of European Standards for coatings on concrete.
7. The relationship between available test data and in-service performance is often unclear. This is illustrated in the standard (EN ISO 11057) for artificial ageing of coatings which states that there is generally no direct relationship between natural and artificial weathering.
8. Prevailing application and/or surface conditions may be unsuitable for some products.
9. Health and safety requirements can have a significant influence on selection in certain circumstances; for example, where hazardous solvents are unacceptable.

An overview of the selection process is given in Fig. 13.1. This emphasises that properties before and during cure must be suitable for the prevailing application and surface conditions. These properties must be considered in addition to those connected more directly with the main requirement.

Figure 13.1 takes no account of the type of specification associated with a given project. The form and content of the specification is significant, as it determines how the responsibility for selection is apportioned, for example, between a designer/engineer and a contractor. Clarity here is essential – the specification must ensure that there is an unambiguous responsibility for all the relevant factors.

Where maintenance rather than new work is being carried out, the selection process is likely to differ significantly as the nature, present condition and earlier performance of the existing treatment are paramount. In some cases, account may have to be taken of changes in service conditions or requirements. New and in-service concretes may also require different approaches in the selection of a surface treatment.

13.3   International tests

The properties and requirements listed below should always be acknowledged in a coating specification:

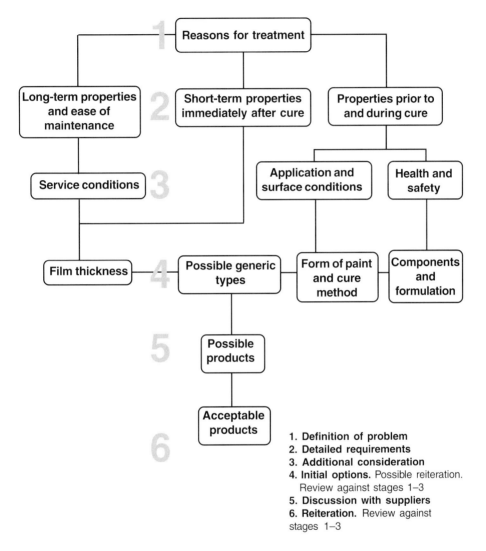

Figure 13.1 *The selection of a surface treatment (courtesy Taywood Engineering Ltd).*

- alkali resistance;
- good adherence to the substrate;
- low liquid water permeability;
- water vapour permeability;
- durability, i.e. service life to first maintenance; and
- the minimum dry film thickness required to cover defects or unevenness in the concrete (or to be applied to a levelling/fairing coat).

It is essential that a coating has good adhesion to the concrete. A widely accepted requirement is that the coating should have a pull-off value equal to or greater than 1 MPa. Preferably, the failure should be in the concrete (or in the coating) and not at the coating-concrete interface. Low liquid water permeability and a high water vapour permeability are required to prevent the penetration and build-up of moisture beneath the coating as this may lead to early loss of adhesion (although for some applications a low vapour permeability is essential).

In addition to the above requirements, the binder used in the coating must resist the alkalinity of the substrate, water, weathering conditions, or, where applicable, contact with aggressive chemicals. The substrate will undergo thermal movement due to atmospheric changes, and possibly ageing and structural movements. Some flexibility, retained on ageing, is desirable in all coatings but additional provision may be required for accommodating cracks in the concrete substrate. Durability of five to ten years has been generally acceptable for decorative coatings on accessible surfaces. Developments have produced coatings that, applied properly on sound concrete surfaces, can last beyond ten years in normal conditions. This level of durability is generally essential for protective coatings on structural concrete.

There are concrete surfaces that, because of type or condition, may require specific pretreatment. The range of cements, aggregates and other constituents in general use is wide and great care is necessary in assessing the characteristics of the concrete as a substrate for coating. Porosity, for example, is a variable factor. Texture, roughness, casting defects, blowholes and micro-cracks also have to be considered. The use of a penetrating surface sealer or a levelling coat may be required.

The properties listed below are requirements that may be needed depending on particular circumstances:
- carbon dioxide permeability;
- resistance to chloride ingress;
- crack-bridging properties;
- abrasion and skid resistance;
- chemical resistance;
- algal and fungal resistance;
- contact with potable water; and
- fire performance.

Table 13.1 summarizes standards for testing used primarily in Europe and the USA. The most significant recent developments in classification and testing standards for coatings on concrete has occurred in Europe.

13.4   Implication of European Standards

One important aspect of European Standards is that they are divided into harmonized and non-harmonized parts. Compliance with the harmonized parts will be mandatory for manufacturers. The non-harmonized parts cover requirements that are voluntary. Another important consequence is that public bodies are required to specify, wherever

Table 13.1 *Standards for testing of coatings for concrete.*

Property	TEST STANDARD European (EN)	USA (ASTM)	ISO or BS
A. Classification System			
Coatings for masonry/concrete	EN 1062-1*	-	-
Coatings for concrete	prEN 1504-2	-	-
B. Barrier properties			
Water vapour transmission	EN ISO 7783-1/2*	E96-00	-
Liquid water permeability	EN 1062-3*	-	-
CO₂ permeability	EN 1062-6	-	-
Resistance to liquids	EN ISO 2812-1*/2	-	-
Resistance to chemical attack	pr EN 13529	-	-
Chloride ingress	Under discussion	-	-
C. Durability			
Artificial or accelerated weathering	EN ISO 11507	G154-00	-
Thermal compatability	prEN 13687-1/5 prEN 13581	D2243-95	-
Resistance to industrial pollutants (SO₂)	EN ISO 3231*	-	-
Resistance to alkaline surfaces	pr EN 13578	-	-
Evaluation of degradation	-	-	ISO 4628-1/6
D. Fire properties			
Various tests	Under discussion	-	BS 476
E. Toxicity			
Effect on potable water	-	-	BS 6920
Fungal attack	-	-	BS 3900 Part G6
F. Other properties			
Tensile strength	-	D 412-98a	ISO 527
Bend test	EN ISO 6860*	D 522-93a	-
Adhesion (pull-off)	EN 1542*	D4541-95e1	-
Abrasion resistance	EN ISO 5470-1*	D 4060-95	ISO 7784-1/3
Scratch resistance	EN ISO 1518	-	-
Static & spark resistance	-	-	BS 5958
Impact resistance	EN ISO 6272*	-	-
Wet scrub resistance	EN ISO 11998*	-	-
Crack-bridging ability	prEN 1062-7	C836-00	-

* Also published as national standards.

possible, to European Standards for all construction products and this includes coatings for concrete i.e. European standards are mandatory for public or privatized utilities, if applicable.

Most of the standards and classification systems for coatings on concrete will be in force by 2002. European Standards will play an important part in the future selection and testing of coatings. Of particular interest to the industry are EN 1062-1 (Coating materials and systems for exterior masonry and concrete), EN 1504-2 (Surface protection systems for concrete), ENV 1504-9 (General principles for the use of products and systems) and EN 1504-10 (Site application of products and systems and quality control of the works).

Surface treatments for concrete with a typical maximum dry film thickness of 5 mm are covered by EN 1504-2. This standard gives guidance on the selection of coatings for concrete and the required mandatory tests for properties of coatings for particular applications. For example, if a coating is to be used for ingress control, the manufacturer will have to test the coating for adhesion (pull-off test), liquid water and water vapour permeabilities. The specifier then has to consider whether protection is required from carbon dioxide or chloride ion ingress as additional performance requirements. EN 1062-1 and associated standards deal with tests for the decorative aspects of coatings. ENV 1504-9 gives guidance on the principles of protection and repair of concrete, and covers the use of coatings as part of a repair strategy. Finally, EN 1504-10 gives guidance on the site application of repair materials and coatings and quality control systems.

British Standards have been voluntary in the past, but many future European Standards, because of their mandatory nature, will have a greater impact on the classification, selection and specification of coatings.

13.5   European Standards for surface treatment of concrete

An important development is that five concrete mixes have been specified as reference substrates (EN 1766). This will eliminate the use of numerous concrete substrates and will simplify the comparison of results, e.g. for adhesion, from different laboratories in Europe.

More generally, the test methods can be divided into identification and performance tests. The identification tests are to be used, where appropriate, as part of a quality control system during manufacturing. Table 13.1 summarizes some of the performance test methods under consideration and the state of their development. The development of test methods for properties usually quoted in manufacturers' data sheets is discussed below. The most widely used performance tests are also described below.

13.6   Measuring the adhesion of a coating (pull-off test)

The European Standard for measuring the adhesion of coatings (EN 1542) is based on the same principle as earlier BS and DIN methods. They all use an aluminium or steel dolly which is glued to the coating, and the force needed to pull the dolly and coating from the concrete is then recorded.

For certain in-situ coatings it may not be practicable to test the adhesion using the pull-off method. An alternative adhesion test is the cross-cut method. A European Standard for the cross-cut test for coatings on concrete is currently being considered.

13.7   Water vapour permeability

EN ISO 7783 is based on the same principles as earlier DIN, BS and ISO tests, which employ a Payne cup. A free film of the coating, or the coating on a porous (and characterised) substrate, is placed on the Payne cup and the edges sealed. The cup contains either a water absorbing material or a solution with a specific (generally high) relative humidity. By controlling the external humidity/temperature and measuring the weight gain or loss of the cup with time, the water vapour permeability of a coating can be determined.

The water vapour permeability can be expressed as a flux (g m^{-2} d^{-1}) or an S$_D$ value. The S$_D$ value, which equates the water vapour transmission to an equivalent air layer thickness (generally, in metres), is a parameter widely used in Germany and quoted by many UK manufacturers. The classes listed below are given for water vapour permeability in the European Standard (prEN 1504-2) for coatings applied to concrete.

Class	Equivalent air layer thickness, S$_D$ (m)
I	< 5
II	5–50
III	> 50

13.8   Liquid water permeability test

The water permeability of a coating is derived by measuring the weight gain of a test specimen (EN 1062-3). The coating is applied to a mortar specimen or calcium silicate brick and the other faces are sealed with an epoxy. A value of < 0.1 kg m^{-2} h$^{-1/2}$ has been proposed for coatings applied to concrete (prEN 1504-2).

13.9   Crack-bridging test

A crack-bridging test (prEN 1062-7) is undertaken in order to determine a coating's ability to accommodate movement of the concrete substrate about a crack. There are two types of crack-bridging test: static and dynamic. The static test is a one cycle test, giving an indication of the maximum crack width that can be accommodated by the coating. A French AFNOR static crack-bridging test will be adopted as the European Standard test. The classes that have been proposed (prEN 1504-2) are listed below.

Class	Recommended test temperature (°C)	Width of bridged crack (µm)
A1	21	> 100
A2	–10	> 250
A3	–10	> 500
A4	–10	> 1250
A5	–10	> 2500

The specimens used in the test are mortar prisms in accordance with EN 196-1, with the coating applied to one face. A notch, to control the position where the crack occurs when the test piece is extended, is cut across the width of the opposite face and to within 5 mm of the coating. The test piece is extended at 0.05 or 0.5 mm per minute in a tensometer, depending on which class is applicable to the coating being tested. When a pinhole is detected in the coating, the test is terminated and the extension of the coating, i.e. the crack width, is noted. Different test temperatures to those given above can be agreed.

The dynamic test gives information on the crack-bridging capability of a coating applied over an active crack. The test is carried out at a low temperature, usually –10 °C. There are over nine national standards in Europe, each with a different testing regime and pass/fail criteria. The dynamic test is being developed in three different technical committees dealing with coatings on concrete and masonry, liquid applied water proofing systems and flexible waterproofing systems. The committees have not been able to produce a common test method. A draft has been prepared for coatings on concrete and masonry (prEN 1062-7). Classes for the dynamic crack-bridging test and desired crack movement profiles for coatings on concrete are discussed in Chapter 19.

13.10   Artificial ageing

Artificial ageing of a coating can be used to indicate changes in properties that may occur during natural weathering. The regime usually employed is fluorescent UV light and water ageing as described in EN ISO 11507. The ageing cycle consists of four hours wetting at 50 °C (no UV) followed by four hours drying under UV at 60 °C (black panel temperatures). This cycle is repeated as required. Usually the minimum recommended total period is 2000 hours. Artificial ageing does not give a precise indication of how durable a coating will be in practice and care is required in the interpretation of results. Although there is no simple correlation between artificial ageing and durability of coatings in-situ, the results of this testing can be invaluable for comparative purposes and for providing confidence in the likely performance of a system.

13.11   Carbon dioxide permeability

There are no national standards for measuring the gas permeability of a coating. There is an industry accepted test in the UK based on a partition cell and a gas chromatography detection system. This test will form the basis of the European Standard test for carbon dioxide permeability (prEN 1062-6). The results of the test are given as an equivalent air layer thickness (S_D value; often referred to as an R value). It is generally accepted that an S_D value greater than or equal to 50 m will provide excellent anti-carbonation performance.

13.12   Algae and fungi resistance

The standard test used in the UK is BS 3900 Part G6. A coating is exposed to a culture of fungi and algae for 12 weeks. After the test period, the area of culture growing on the paint surface is used to classify the coating into one of six classes. It is recommended that coatings should be in Class 1 or possibly Class 2. Coatings in Class 1 exhibit no algal and fungal growth, while Class 2 coatings have 1% of their area covered with algae and fungi. An ad hoc group is discussing a proposal to develop BS 3900 Part G6 and/or a much simpler screening test as a European Standard.

13.13   Chloride permeability

The measurement of resistance to chloride ion ingress of a coating is a complex area as transmission can take place by varied mechanisms, depending upon the service/test conditions. Ingress can be driven, for example, by capillary absorption, sorption, diffusion, a hydraulic gradient or by some combination of these mechanisms; wetting and drying further complicate the transmission process. Test procedures that reproduce each of these processes are available (and are used) for the assessment of surface treatments as barriers to chloride ingress.

These variations lead to complexity in evaluating this property. However, a greater difficulty arises from the timescales that can be required for chloride ions to penetrate the surface barrier. Even when these periods are relatively short in comparison with service requirements, they can be unacceptably protracted for experimental work.

Various means are available for accelerating chloride ingress, for example, by increasing hydraulic pressure, temperature or the concentration of chloride ions or by applying an electric potential across a test specimen. Although such procedures may provide a simple ranking of systems, it is difficult to quantify the acceleration factor. Additionally, it is essential that the acceleration method does not modify the coating system or distort the complex chloride transmission mechanisms.

At present it is not possible to recommend one specific test or to interpret laboratory results in terms of natural exposure.

13.14   Wet scrub resistance and cleanability of coatings

The European Standard for wet scrub resistance and cleanability is EN ISO 11998. The coated specimen is weighed prior to testing and subjected to 200 wet scrub cycles in a scrub testing machine. It is then weighed again to determine its loss in mass, and hence the change in dry film thickness. The results are expressed as loss in dry film thickness.

13.15 Conclusion

European Standards will have a profound impact on the European coating industry. For the first time, there will be standard requirements for surface treatments applied to concrete. Coatings used by public bodies will be specified by CEN standards. Industry needs to be alert to the new European Standards and the requirements that will be in place within the member countries.

References to standards

Readers will appreciate that standards and codes of practice are in a constant state of development. Although every attempt has been made to quote the current version, readers are advised to check their national databases to ensure that the up-to-date document is consulted. In addition, there are several helpful websites in his respect: www.astm.org, www.bsi-global.com, www.iso.ch/iso.en, www.cenorm.be/catweb or www.cenorm.be/sectors/construction.

ASTM C836-00 Standard specification for high solids content, cold liquid applied elastomeric waterproofing membrane for use with separate wearing course.
ASTM D412-98a Standard test methods for vulcanized rubber and thermoplastic rubbers and thermoplastic elastomers-tension.
ASTM D552-93a (2000) Standard test method for mandrel bend test of attached organic coatings.
ASTM D2243-95 Standard test method for freeze-thaw resistance of water-borne coatings.
ASTM D4060-95 Standard test method for abrasion resistance of organic coatings by the Taber abraser.
ASTM D4541-95e1 Standard test method for pull-off strength of coatings using portable adhesion testers.
ASTM E96-00 Standard test methods for water vapour transmission of materials.
ASTM G154-00ae1 Standard practice for operating fluorescent light apparatus for exposure of non-metallic materials.
BS 476: 1970 onwards Fire tests on building materials and structures
BS 3900 Part G6:1989 Methods of test for paints – Assessment of resistance to fungal growth.
BS 5958: 1991 Code of practice for control of undesirable static electricity.
BS 6920 1/4: 2000/2001 Suitability of non-metallic products for use in contact with water intended for human consumption with regard to their effect on the quality of the water.
EN1062-1: 1996 Paints and varnishes – Coating materials and coating systems for exterior masonry and concrete.
EN 1062-3: 1998 Paints and varnishes – Coating materials and coating systems for exterior masonry and concrete – Part3: Determination and classification of liquid water transmission rate (permeability).
EN 1062-6 : 2002 Paints and varnishes – Coating materials and coating systems for exterior masonry and concrete – Part 6: Determination of carbon dioxide permeability.
ENV 1504-9: 1997 Products and systems for the protection and repair of concrete structures – Definitions, requirements, quality control and evaluation of conformity –Part 9: General principles for the use of products and systems (draft for development).

EN 1542: 1999 Products and systems for the protection and repair of concrete structures – Test methods – Measurement of bond strength by pull-off.

EN 1766: 2000 Products and systems for the protection and repair of concrete structures. Test methods. Reference concretes for testing.

EN ISO 1518: 2000 Paints and varnishes – scratch test.

EN ISO 2812-1/2:1994 Paints and varnishes – Determination of resistance to liquids – Part 1: General methods; Part 2: Water immersion method.

EN ISO 3231: 1997 Paints and varnishes – Determination of resistance to humid atmospheres containing sulphur dioxide.

EN ISO 5470-1 Rubber- or plastics-coated fabrics – Determination of abrasion resistance. Part 1: Taber abrader.

EN ISO 6272:1994 Paints and varnishes – Falling weight test.

EN ISO 6860:1995 Paints and varnishes – Bend test (conical mandrel).

EN ISO 7783-1:1999 Paints and varnishes – Determination of water-vapour transmission rate – Part 1: Dish method for free films.

EN ISO 7783-2:1999 Paints and varnishes – Determination and classification of water vapour transmission rate (permeability).

EN ISO 11507: 2001 Paints and varnishes – Exposure of coatings to artificial weathering – exposure to fluorescent UV and water.

EN ISO 11998: 2001: Paints and varnishes. Determination of wet-scrub resistance and cleanability of coatings.

prEN 1062-7 Paints and varnishes – Coating materials and coating systems for exterior masonry and concrete – Part 7: Determination of crack-bridging ability.

prEN 1504-2 Products and systems for the protection and repair of concrete structures – Definitions, requirements, quality control and evaluation of conformity – Part 2: Surface protection systems for concrete.

prEN 1504-10 Products and systems for the protection and repair of concrete structures – Definitions, requirements, quality control and evaluation of conformity – Part 10: Site application of products and systems and quality control of the works.

prEN 13529 Products and systems for the protection and repair of concrete structures. Test method. Resistance to severe chemical attack.

prEN 13578 Products and systems for the repair of concrete structures. Test method. Compatibility on wet concrete.

prEN 13581 Products and systems for the repair of concrete structures. Test methods. Determination of loss of mass after freeze-thaw salt stress-testing of impregnated hydrophobic concrete.

prEN 13687: 1–5 Products and systems for the protection and repair of concrete structures. Test methods. Determination of thermal compatibility.

ISO 527: 1–5: 1993–2000 Plastics – Determination of tensile properties.

ISO 4628-1–6: 1982 – 1990 Paints and varnishes – Evaluation of degradation of paint coatings.

ISO 7784-1/3:1997/2000 Paints and varnishes – Determination of resistance to abrasion.

14 Surface preparation and application of coatings

John Midwood

14.1 Surface preparation

Surface treatments are designed to provide lasting protection in any number of environments. This, almost inevitably, will mean that the choice and application of surface treatment may vary considerably from one locale to another.

Concrete is not any different in terms of preparation than, say, timber or steel. The surface must be clean, free from grease, flaking paint, efflorescence, fungal growth, corrosion products, mould release agents, curing membranes and, most importantly, be in a good state of repair.

Most signs of degradation will be apparent from the general surface appearance, such as reinforcement corrosion, spalling or mechanical damage. The level of breakdown must be assessed before attempting to decide on the final surface preparation. Many types of concrete repair systems are commercially available and any repairs should be carried out in accordance with established practices for such procedures. Guidance may be sought in the Concrete Society Technical Report No. 26 (Concrete Society, 1984).

As previously stated, once a satisfactory repair is achieved, the concrete surface must be thoroughly cleaned to remove any materials which may create a poor bond and cause delamination later in the structure's life. It is impossible to generalize on the cleaning of concrete as every example will have its own inherent problems BS 6270 Part 2 (BSI, 1985), ASTM D4258 (ASTM, 1992a) and ASTM D4259 (ASTM, 1992b) give advice on surface cleaning and abrading concrete surfaces.

Some suggested methods for cleaning are:
1. For small areas, mechanical wire brushing.
2. High-pressure water jetting (provided adequate, suitable drainage is present). Detergents may be used with this system, if so desired.
3. A fungicidal wash.
4. Wet, dry or vacuum abrasive blasting.
5. Mechanical impact techniques, such as needle gunning or bush hammering.
6. Mechanical abrasion.

Mechanical abrasion methods of cleaning are effective for removing deeply ingressed contamination but may remove unacceptable quantities of surface concrete. Needle gunning and bush hammering are extremely effective but are often too aggres-

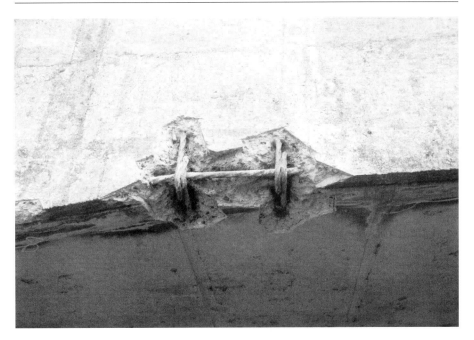

Figure 14.1 *Concrete cut out prior to repair.*

sive and lead to micro-cracking and form deep textures in previously smooth concrete, thus rendering the final surface unacceptable for coating without carrying out expensive skimming. The use of washing techniques may also be flawed, as the correct choice of detergent is not always obvious and an incorrect material may just spread surface contaminants. Using solvent-based or sodium hydroxide-based products are often more effective, but may lead to health and safety problems for operatives and surrounding periphery such as aluminium and glass. Removal of these products efficiently is also vital, as remaining traces may interfere with the application of surface treatments at a later stage.

Grit-blasting techniques are becoming increasingly popular as effective means of removing surface grime and lightly penetrated contaminants. Dry blasting is less favoured nowadays due to its impact on the environment and possible health and safety issues. Wet or vacuum dry-blasting reduce the risk to an acceptable level, although disposal of grit-rich water may pose problems.

Whichever method appears to be the most suited to any project, it is always advisable to carry out trials on sample areas, with reference to material suppliers, contractors and/or applicators before proceeding.

Blow-holes are not always apparent as they may well be covered by a thin film of concrete prior to cleaning and the most effective cleaning system will often remove this film so that the once apparently smooth concrete surface is now badly pitted. One of the most popular finishing systems is the application of one or two coats of thin film, smooth, semi-gloss anti-carbonation paints and these surface defects make it impossi-

Figure 14.2 *Close examination of any concrete structure will reveal many surface defects such as blow-holes, small voids and shutter marks, many of which will have been enlarged during the cleaning process.*

ble to get a pinhole-free finish. Success will only be achieved if these defects are re-profiled or filled using a 'scrape-coat' or by applying a 1–2 mm thick fairing coat. New concrete will invariably suffer from shutter marks, fins, grout runs and protrusions which either must be ground away or filled prior to the application of any fairing coat to allow a smooth finish to be achieved for the finishing coats. Where a coating system is being considered during the planning stages of a new structure, it is advisable to use closed permeability formwork which will reduce blow-holes and the need for shutter oils and therefore reduce the surface preparation costs. In addition to the above mentioned problems, poorly filled bolt holes, repair patches and general protrusions will all be greatly magnified if overcoated with thin film clear or pigmented systems. They may also result in water tracking, leading to staining of the applied coating in a very short time.

Using high-build elastomeric coatings that may be applied by roller or spray can mask small surface defects. These may effectively reduce the cost of the surface treatment by eliminating the necessity of a fairing coat but advice must be sought from material suppliers as to the suitability of their product for such an application before any final decisions are made.

Most surface coatings that will be used for the protection of concrete are unlikely to withstand water pressure from inside the concrete. Many of these problems will have been identified during preliminary investigations into repair requirements and

Figure 14.3 *Concrete surface showing defects which should be covered with a fairing coat prior to coating with a thin-film product.*

dealt with using repair systems, as previously detailed. There will, however, be situations where no damage to the concrete is apparent, yet water ingress is still occurring. These situations must be dealt with separately and may involve investigation of surrounding rainwater goods, drainage systems and leaking decking in the case of car parks. Yet again, these problems must be rectified, using waterproofing materials if appropriate, prior to any coating taking place.

14.2   Choice of coatings

As with cleaning systems and concrete repair products, the choice of final protective and decorative coatings is wide ranging.

The final choice of coating may be influenced by many factors, such as the state of the concrete substrate, maintenance cycles, environmental issues, colour, desired finished appearance and, of course, the client's budget.

Coatings may be split into two main generic categories; inorganic and organic coatings. Inorganic coatings again may be sub-divided into low cost decorative cement based masonry paints and polymer-modified cementitious coatings which are more expensive, give a greater thickness (2–3 mm) and are more protective. Organic coatings may be split into four categories; thermoplastics and synthetic rubbers, alkyds and drying oils, bituminous materials and thermosetting polymers.

Thermoplastics and synthetic rubbers tend to be the most widely used systems due to their ease of application and the fact that they are invariably one-pack, ready to use products. They may be solvent-borne or waterborne and are frequently based upon (meth) acrylic polymers which form a film by a physical drying process rather than by chemical reaction. Anti-carbonation coatings are available as water-based acrylic as well as solvent-based acrylic. Solvent-based systems tend to be used when atmospheric conditions would prohibit the use of water-based products.

Provided that the structure being coated is not submerged for prolonged periods of time, the following benefits may be expected:
- good adhesion;
- good resistance to weathering and water ingress;
- effective barrier to carbon dioxide and other common atmospheric gases;
- good resistance to chloride and sulphate ion ingress;
- low resistance to the passage of water vapour;
- crack-bridging; and
- minimal long-term dirt pick-up.

Chlorinated rubber paints are the exception to the above generalizations as they will perform quite happily when immersed in water; in fact, they will probably last longer when immersed as they are readily affected by UV radiation.

Alkyds and drying oils dry by solvent evaporation or oxidation using metallic dryers but find little use for long-term protection, as they tend to become brittle over a relatively short period of time. For use on concrete surfaces, it is necessary to modify the basic formulation for good resistance to the alkaline conditions. Such products are generally available in a wide range of colours and a variety of fine and coarse textures.

Bitumen-based products are possibly the oldest materials to be used for waterproofing and damp-proofing concrete. They are available in two main categories:
- cold applied materials, which are available as waterborne emulsions or in more traditional solvent-borne systems; and
- hot applied systems of bitumen or coal-tar pitch.

These products have good resistance to acids and alkalis. The hot applied and solvented versions are particularly useful for underground works or in extremely damp conditions. Water-based products are not recommended for use where prolonged exposure to water may re-emulsify the film; however, they can be recommended for over-ground structures where they will be less prone to 'alligatoring' than hot-applied products. Like alkyds, bitumens will become brittle with age and are not particularly resistant to oils and solvents; therefore maintenance cycles will be required.

Thermosetting epoxy and polyurethane coatings are particularly versatile as penetrating sealers, solvented and waterborne topcoats. These coatings are recommended for use where conditions are severe and high degrees of chemical resistance are required. Thermosetting systems are more difficult to use than any of the earlier groups as, in general, they are two-pack products and a high degree of skill is required during mixing and application. Some single-pack moisture curing polyurethanes exist but the application conditions must be carefully controlled, as the ingress of water during curing will lead to excessive carbon dioxide evolution, which will affect the cured film.

Figure 14.4 *Many car parks and high blocks, where chemical protection is not an issue, are coated with thin film acrylic systems to give many years protection. This is the newly constructed Cherry Pink car park in Telford coated with Glixtone anti-carbonating coating AC1.*

14.3 Application methods

No matter what choice of coating has been made, there are three main methods of application to post-fabricated concrete structures; brush, roller or spray. Environmental considerations, surface area to be coated, accessibility and final choice of finish will be the main criteria to be considered when making a decision on the method of application.

The environment is of increasing concern and many owners or local councils are beginning to move away from solvent-based products in favour of waterborne or high solids systems in enclosed areas or town centres. Due to solvent emissions from the atomized paint, this is of increasing importance if a sprayed finish is desired. These emissions will be reduced if a roller is used but the method will be very labour intensive if large areas require coating and the use of a brush in such circumstances is not recommended. Textured coatings may be sprayed or rolled to a desired pattern as required and the emissions from such systems are generally much lower than standard paint products. When spraying smooth coatings, either an airless or air assisted unit may be used. Most contractors favour the use of airless systems which are quicker to use, reduce wastage and almost eliminate over-spray if set correctly. Spray equipment is now available to apply two-pack materials without the necessity of pre-mixing the components, as all mixing takes place in the nozzle prior to atomization. Whichever spray system is used, the final environmental consideration is the immediate locale and great effort must be made to mask off all surrounding areas.

Brushing and rolling may be used on small surface areas, for 'cutting-in' or where access is limited and spraying is impossible. Where a two-pack epoxy of polyurethane has been specified and the use of specialized spray equipment is impracticable, the utilization of a roller is recommended, but only sufficient product should be mixed at one time as can be applied within the 'pot life'.

The systems and products outlined in this chapter should give the prospective specifier the opportunity to discuss the requirements with cleaning, repair materials and coating suppliers.

References

American Society for Testing and Materials (1992a) *D4258. Standard practice for surface cleaning of concrete for coating*. ASTM, Philadelphia.

American Society for Testing and Materials (1992b) *D4259. Standard practice for abrading concrete*. ASTM, Philadelphia.

Concrete Society (1984) Repair of concrete damaged by reinforcement corrosion. *Technical Report 26*, Concrete Society, Slough.

British Standards Institution (1985) Code of practice for cleaning and surface repair of buildings. *Part 2; Concrete and precast concrete masonry, BS6270*, BSI, London.

15 Emission of volatile organic compounds

J.Boxall and D.Crump

15.1 Introduction

The construction industry is a major user of surface coating products and these are employed to increase the durability of construction materials and provide decorative finishes. There are increasing concerns about the health and safety and environmental consequences resulting from the emission of volatile organic compounds (VOCs) from coating products. Health and safety concerns centre on issues relating to flammability, storage and transportation of solvent-based coatings, and protection of individuals in occupations where coatings are produced and used, or in the immediate vicinity of such operations. However, with training and adoption of best practice procedures in use, many of the occupational health and safety problems associated with solvent-based coatings can be accommodated.

A further aspect of health and safety is the exposure of people to solvents in non-occupational environments. This can occur through the use of coating materials for do-it-yourself (DIY) applications in homes. It may also occur through exposure to occupants as a result of work by tradesmen, such as painting of nearby rooms, and due to exposure resulting from off-gassing of coating materials after they have been applied and the room re-occupied. The potential of this route of exposure to VOCs was shown by the Building Research Establishment Indoor Environment Study (Berry *et al.*, 1996) which measured concentrations of VOCs in 174 UK homes over a 12 month period. This found a statistically significant relationship between the total VOC concentration indoors and the occurrence of painting activity.

For the DIY painter, there is the possibility of exposure to VOCs equivalent to that which might occur for a professional tradesman for the duration of the task. Hence adequate ventilation should be ensured during such work, and safety instructions supplied by the manufacturer should be followed. The significance for health of lower concentrations of VOCs that occur in the building following works is not well understood. A review of likely health effects of exposure to VOCs in UK homes published by the Institute for Environment and Health (IEH, 1996) concluded that the precise consequences of exposures to VOCs are difficult to evaluate because of the complexity and variable nature of the mixture, but the main effects relate to comfort and well-being and there is no evidence of a health risk at current levels.

Environmental concerns centre on the contribution that solvents from surface coatings make to the total emission of VOCs to the atmosphere. VOCs react with other pollutants, notably those from car exhaust fumes, to create ozone which, at ground level, causes photochemical smog which is implicated in crop and tree damage. Photochemical smog is also believed to have an adverse effect on individuals suffering from respiratory illnesses such as asthma.

It has been estimated that in Europe solvents contribute about 40% of VOC emissions resulting from human activities, which in turn are over 70% of the total VOC emissions to the atmosphere. Solvent emissions arise from a number of sources, primarily from commercial cleaning of metals and fabrics, and from the manufacture and application of surface coatings. Recent and proposed national and international legislation designed to reduce the level of solvent emissions present a major challenge to industry and will ultimately lead to the wide introduction of low-VOC technologies in most areas, including coatings (Passant, 1995).

This review deals with available information about the market sizes for different types of product and estimates are provided of total amounts of solvents released as the result of use of each product type. Some indications of amounts of VOCs associated with the decorative-related sector (i.e. DIY) are also includedfor completeness. The fourth section describes national schemes in Finland and Denmark that classify building products, including surface coating materials, according to the amounts of VOC they emit. The final section considers likely future changes in the amounts of VOCs emitted from coating products used by the construction industry.

15.2 Coatings in construction

About 60% of the 550 million litres of paint produced each year in the UK is termed decorative (as opposed to industrial), and this goes largely into construction applications (Central Statistical Office, 1995; Passant, 1993). The construction industry is therefore a major user of surface coatings and, as such, indirectly contributes significantly to current VOC emissions.

15.2.1 Composition of surface coatings

Surface coatings can be considered to be composed of fine particulate pigmentary materials dispersed in a polymeric binder (resin) which is normally dissolved or dispersed in a liquid carrier phase. These constituents form the bulk of the composition, although minor additives are invariably present to control and modify the properties of the resultant coating.

Pigmentary materials

A pigment can be defined as a solid material in the form of small discrete particles which are mainly insoluble in the resin or solvent constituents of the coating. A wide range of organic and inorganic pigments are added to impart colour or modify the protective properties of the coating. Particulate, non-colouring materials, known as extenders, are also used in certain coatings. The pigment components in coatings do not directly contribute to VOC emissions.

Binders

Binders are polymeric complexes which provide integrity to the applied coating and bind the film to the surface to which it is applied. A wide variety of binders are used in the manufacture of surface coatings and, with some exceptions, these are all organic in composition.

Most common binders are supplied in a diluted form, the diluent being either an organic solvent or water, depending on resin type. As such, binders can be considered to contribute to VOC emissions. Binders also undergo complex chemical changes during the conversion stage from a liquid to the fully-cured film; small amounts of volatile compounds are created during this drying process and as such are also considered to contribute to VOC emissions from coatings. These components, however, make only a minor contribution in volume terms to the total emissions that come from the other, solvent components, and are not specifically covered in this part of the review.

The most commonly-used binders in surface coatings, together with an indication of their end-use application, are shown in Table 15.1.

Table 15.1 *Binders used in surface coatings.*

Name	Composition	Application
NATURAL		
Oil, e.g. linseed, soya or tung	complex fatty acids	Basis of traditional paints
Resins e.g. rosin or copal	mixtures of complex acids	Combined with oils to produce varnishes
SYNTHETIC		
Acrylic	e.g. polymethyl methacrylate	Water-borne decorative coatings
Alkyd	polyester-oil complex	Main binder in solvent-borne decorative coatings
Amino	e.g. urea-formaldehyde	Industrial coatings
Cellulose ester	e.g. nitrocellulose	Industrial coatings
Epoxy	diglycidyl ethers of epichlorhydrin	Industrial and some specialized site coatings
Phenolic	e.g. phenol-formaldehyde	Industrial coatings
Polyurethane	complex isocyanates	Industrial and some specialized site coatings
Rubber	e.g. chlorinated rubber	Specialized decorative coatings
Silicate	mineral binder, complex silica-carbonate	Specialized decorative coatings
Vinyl	e.g. polyvinyl acetate	Water-borne decorative coatings

Table 15.2 *Solvents used in surface coatings.*

Class of solvent	Examples
Aliphatic hydrocarbons	Cyclohexane, mixtures of aliphatic hydrocarbons of specific boiling point range
Aromatic hydrocarbons	Toluene, xylene, styrene, mixtures of aromatic hydrocarbons of specific boiling point range
Chlorinated hydrocarbons	Dichloromethane, 1,1,1-trichloroethylene, trichloroethylene
Alcohols and glycols	Methanol, ethanol, iospropanol, butanol, ethylene, diethylene and triethylene glycols, propylene glycols, ether derivatives of glycols
Ketones	Acetone, methyl ethyl ketone, methyl isobutyl ketone, cyclohexanone
Esters	Ethyl acetate, butyl acetate, esters of glycol ethers

Solvents

Solvents are low viscosity, volatile organic liquids, which dissolve or carry the resins, and provide appropriate conditions for coating manufacture, storage, application and drying. In some types of coating, solvents may be the major component of the final product. Coatings in which water serves as the solvent or, more correctly, the carrier phase, have been available for many years, and already form an important route for introducing low-VOC technologies. The solvents most widely used in surface coatings are shown in Table 15.2.

15.3 VOC emissions from construction coatings

This part of the chapter presents the data required to estimate the volume of VOC emissions (as solvents) from construction coatings. It comprises an analysis of the coatings market and, from this information, estimates of solvent emissions from each of the main coatings sectors.

15.3.1 Market sectors

Analysis and reworking of statistics from published sources indicates that the market profile of the coatings industry in the UK is as shown in Table 15.3 (Anon, 1994; Hunt Marketing Research, 1992; Hyatt, 1995; Marketing Strategies for Industry, 1993; Passant, 1993). For the purposes of this chapter it is assumed that the coatings used di-

Table 15.3   *Market profile of UK coatings industry.*

Sector	Market share (%)
Industrial	
light industrial ⎫	
automotive ⎬	37
marine ⎭	
heavy industrial	3
Decorative	
trade	
solvent-borne	10
water-borne	20
retail	30

rectly by the construction industry comprise those products within the decorative/ trade sectors. Arguably the decorative/retail sector could also be ascribed to construction since these coatings would largely be used for the decoration of buildings by their occupants. However, since such activities are outside of the control of the construction industry, only general indications of market size are presented here.

The data shown in Table 15.3 indicate that 30% of coatings are used by the construction industry. This data further indicates that within these trade coatings the ratio of waterborne coatings to solvent-borne coatings is 2:1. However, the materials embraced within this decorative/trade sector only include coatings used on masonry and timber substrates and largely exclude the specialist coatings for metalwork. For this report, the sector described as industrial/ heavy industrial in Table 15.3 can be considered to include those coatings that are site-applied to construction metalwork. This additional market increases the size of the construction coatings sector to approximately 33%, i.e. one third of all coatings used in the UK are used directly by the construction industry.

15.3.2   Market size

The latest statistics for the production of paints, varnishes and allied products in the UK indicate a total market size of 551 million litres (Central Statistical Office, 1995). Thirty-three per cent of this is approximately 182 million litres, which can be further broken down into the main coating classes as shown in Table 15.4.

Current technology within the heavy duty category of construction coatings is also heavily biased towards solvent-borne technologies. This therefore suggests that the present ratio between waterborne and solvent-borne coatings used in construction is about 60:40, which is comparable with data from other sources.

Table 15.4 *Volume of 'trade' coatings used by the construction industry.*

Class of coating	Volume (million litres)
Water-borne: all types	111
Solvent-borne: general-purpose	45
Solvent-borne: "woodcare"	10
Solvent-borne: heavy duty	16
Total	182

15.3.3   Procedure for estimation of solvent emissions

Precise production/consumption data for the coatings used in construction are not available. Accordingly, solvent emissions from each of the important generic groups identified in Table 15.3 have been calculated, and estimates made of the contribution of the major solvent components from the coating types in these groups.

This approach has required estimation of:
- an average density for the coatings in each sub-group in Table 15.4; and
- an average solvent content for all of the coatings within each sub-group.

These estimates, based on the practical experience of one of the authors (JB), are shown in Table 15.5. Total solvent emissions derived from this data, expressed in tonnes per annum from each generic group, are shown in Table 15.6.

It should be noted that collateral use of solvent by the industry, for cleaning, etc. has not been included in these estimates of emissions. Furthermore, the assumption has been made that all coatings produced in one year are used, and also no estimate has been made of the use of imported coatings. It is assumed here, however, that the latter two balance out, and that the incidental solvents used in site painting operations are within the margin of error of the data.

Table 15.5 *Assumptions used to determine solvent emissions.*

Class of coating	Average density (kg/litre)	Average solvent content (%m/m)
Water-borne: all types	1.2	3
Solvent-borne: general purpose	1.2	35
Solvent-borne: "woodcare"	1.0	65
Solvent-borne: heavy duty	1.4	35

Table 15.6 *Total emissions from trade coatings.*

Class of coating	Volume used (million litres)	Mass of coating used (tonnes)	Solvent emissions from coatings in group (tonnes)
Water-borne:			
all types	111	133,000	4,000
Solvent-borne:			
general purpose	45	54,000	19,000
"woodcare"	10	10,000	6,500
heavy duty	16	23,000	8,000
Total	182	220,000	37,500

15.3.4   Solvent emissions from coatings

Data calculated in Table 15.6 indicate that solvent emissions from the categories of surface coatings defined here as being directly used by the construction industry totals approximately 37,500 tonnes per annum.

The information on market sector and size does not enable detailed analysis of the composition of the solvent emissions from construction coatings to be derived, though broad estimates can be derived.

The major emissions of solvents are from the coatings described as solvent-borne: general purpose. Within this group are paints used for general building works, including masonry. The major solvent type used in such paints is the largely aliphatic hydrocarbon white spirit, with some additional aromatic hydrocarbon in speciality products; "woodcare" products are also primarily based on white spirit. It may therefore be reasonable to assume that the total ca. 25,000 tonnes of solvent emissions from these two categories of coating is comprised largely of aliphatic hydrocarbon. It should however, be noted that the most commonly used white spirit solvent contains some 18% aromatic hydrocarbon, suggesting that emissions from these categories may be of the order:

aliphatic hydrocarbon	20,000 tonnes per annum; and
aromatic hydrocarbons	5,000 tonnes per annum.

Differentiating the speciality group of coatings comprising the solvent-borne: heavy duty class, largely used on metalwork, is not possible from the data available though a wide range of solvent types can potentially appear in such coatings. It is therefore not possible to define precisely the composition of the ca 8,000 tonnes of solvent emissions from this category of coatings, only to indicate that it is likely to be composed of examples from the hydrocarbon, ester and ketone groups of solvent listed in Table 15.2.

The final category identified in this survey – the water-borne class – is by far the largest in volume terms. However, containing only small amounts of organic solvents, this group is responsible for the emissions of the lowest quantity of VOCs. The 4,000

Table 15.7 *Classification of emissions by boiling point.*

Type	Boiling point
VVOC (very volatile organic compounds)	< 0 to 50–100°C
VOC (volatile organic compounds)	50–100 to 240–260°C
SVOC (semi-volatile organic compounds)	240–260 to 380–400°C
POM (particle-bound organic compounds)	>380°C

tonnes of solvent emissions from this group would be largely composed of glycols and glycol ether derivatives.

15.4 VOCs emitted by paints to the indoor environment

All materials used in building structures, interiors and fixtures are a potential source of organic emissions. Interior paints emit the highest level of VOCs of any product in the indoor environment of a building. The WHO classes organic compounds (Anon, 1994) found in indoor air into four groups (Table 15.7).

VVOCs and VOCs include all solvents and formaldehyde. SVOCs include plasticizers of low molecular weight as well as other additives, such as antioxidants. POMs are not volatile, but they can leach out of the material containing them and become bound to dust particles.

Humidity in the internal environment also determines the emission of volatiles emitted by paints. The emissions from paints, shown in Table 15.8 were observed in trials undertaken in Norway in the 1990s (Anon, 1992).

Paints are sources of aromatic hydrocarbons, alcohols and aliphatic hydrocarbons (Sterling, 1985). Solvents used in the mixing, removal, and application of paints are sources of VOCs, such as methylene chloride in paint stripper (Wallace, 1991). VOC concentrations of between several hundred to several thousand milligrams per m³ are common after application of solvent-based interior paints (Shriever and Marutzky, 1990; Tichenor *et al.*, 1990; Sparks *et al.*, 1990). Levels of aromatic and aliphatic

Table 15.8 *Emissions from coating systems.*

Paint system	Potential emission source or emission	Actual emissions or emission
water-borne emulsion paints and lacquers	plasticizers, solvents, monomers	long-chain alcohols, e.g. texanol, glycols, glycoethers
solvent-borne paints and lacquers	solvents, monomers	solvents
two-component lacquers	solvents, monomers	solvents, formaldehyde

compounds may be elevated by a factor of 100 during and after painting (Sheldon, 1988).

Gustaffson (1991) observed that paints continue to emit VOCs after drying. Several researchers have observed that waterborne paints, after six months, emit film-forming agents such as glycol ethers, polychlorobiphenyl and dibutylphthalate (Wolkoff *et al.*, 1990; Virgin, 1984; Todd, 1987). Virgin (1984) noted an unusual effect from emissions of dibutylphthalate (DBP), a commonly used plasticizer and ingredient in many indoor paints. Its emissions can cause plant leaves to become white with chlorophyll deficiency; this effect was observed in homes painted with DBP-containing paints for more than three years after painting the walls.

Environmental factors significantly influence the emissions from paints (Wolkoff *et al.*, 1993). The emission process is controlled by evaporation depending on the thickness of the boundary layer.

Oil-based paints containing mineral spirits or white spirits can emit significant concentrations of the following VOCs (Brown *et al.*, 1990):

toluene;
naphthalene;
o-xylene;
m,p-xylene;
1-methyl-ethylbenzene (cumene);
2-ethyl,1-methylbenzene;
n-propylbenzene;
3-ethyl, 1-methylbenzene;
1,2,3-trimethylbenzene;
4-ethyl, 1-methylbenzene;
1,.2,4-trimethylbenzene;
1,3,5-trimethylbenzene (mesitylene);
sec-butylbenzene;
1,2,3,3-tetrahydronaphthalene;
o-diethylbezene;
C_4-benzene;
1,4-diethylbenzene;
1,2,3,4-tetramethylbenzene;
1,2,3,5-tetramethylbenzene;
1,2,4,5-tetramethylbenzene; and
n-pentylbenzene.

15.5   Voluntary labelling scheme

In Denmark, emission tests are used as a basis for a voluntary labelling scheme for building material including paints based on their likely impact on indoor air quality (Wolkoff and Nielsen, 1995). A fairly simple model is used to link the emission rate with the likely concentration of chemicals the product would give in the air in a standard room. Acceptable concentrations in the room have been derived based on irritant and odour thresholds for chemicals in air. The model is used to derive target emission rates for building products and the basis for the labelling scheme is the time for VOC concentrations to decline below these thresholds. A further scheme proposed in Finland classes materials into one of three categories (M1–M3) based on the rate of emission of TVOCs, formaldehyde, ammonia and carcinogens as well as an odour test undertaken using environmental chambers (Passinen, 1995). Paint is tested four weeks after application. Guidance is provided about the type and amount of materials in categories M1–M3 that may be used to result in a certain class of indoor air quality in a room. Hence national schemes are under development that can be used by a practitioner such as an architect to select materials, including paints, that will not result in adverse indoor air quality in a new building. The European Commission established an expert working group under the auspices of the Collaborative Action on Indoor Air Quality on Man to recommend procedures for assessing the effect of a building material on indoor air quality using environmental chamber tests of emission (ECA, 1997). It is likely that such tests will be a specified method for demonstrating compliance with an Essential Requirement of the Construction Products Directive (ER – Health, Hygiene and Environment) concerned with toxic gases emitted by construction materials and their effects on indoor air quality.

15.6   Future trends

The data presented in the previous sections show the construction industry to be a major user of surface coatings, using directly approximately 180 million litres of product and generating some 37,500 tonnes of VOC emissions per annum from the solvents contained therein.

Most commentators accept that in the near future environmental and legislative pressures will drive down solvent contents, and thus VOC emissions, from this source (Anon, 1992; Newbould, 1992). The Environmental Protection Act (EPA) already constrains emissions from industries with in-house coating facilities that use more than 5 tonnes of organic solvent a year. Along with the EPA, the Montreal Protocol on Substances that Deplete the Ozone Layer required the reduction of all VOCs by 30% by 1999, and the Proposed EC Directive on VOCs will also impose restrictions on the solvent content of all types of surface coatings. The Construction Products Directive may also add to pressures to reduce permitted levels of emission in order to reduce health and safety risks.

As permitted levels of emissions are reduced by such legislation, measures will necessarily be introduced to ensure compliance. Coatings manufacturers and user industries with in-house application facilities controlled under the EPA already rely on abatement equipment, but the capital investment is often considerable. Because of such factors, the preferred option of reducing VOC emissions will undoubtably be a technology change to produce coatings with low or zero solvent content.

The coatings industry has a number of technological options to meet this requirement for coatings of lower VOC content. Prime amongst these are:

- water-borne coatings;
- solvent-borne coatings with high solids (i.e. low solvent) content;
- solvent-free (i.e. 100% solids) coatings; and
- powder coatings.

Of these, powder coatings are suited only for industrial applications but the other technologies will have an impact on the types of coating used in construction.

The analysis presented here has indicated that water-borne coatings in particular are already widely used and comprise some 60% of the coatings applied directly by the construction industry. The benefit of these water-borne coatings is confirmed by their relatively minor, 11%, contribution to the total emissions from all construction coatings.

It may, however, be unrealistic to expect the residual 40% of the construction coatings sector to change over completely to water-borne technologies. Whilst research and development in recent years has seen many technology advances in water-borne coatings, for some applications their properties and performance are not acceptable to specifiers, users and clients. In particular, in situations where high levels of wear or chemical resistance are required, water-borne coatings would not equal current solvent-borne technologies, nor can they equal the appearance qualities achieved from a traditional alkyd gloss paint.

Despite these shortcomings from the current generation of water-borne coatings, coatings formulated on the alternative low-VOC technologies – solvent-free and high solids systems – are known to at least equal the performance of the solvent-borne coatings now used, and their introduction should pose few problems for the construction industry.

It is clear therefore that the future trend will be for reduced VOC emissions from coatings used by the construction industry, as alternative technologies are introduced into areas currently dominated by solvent-borne coatings.

A number of hypothetical scenarios can be created, however, to show potential levels of reduction:

- If all coatings in the solvent-borne classes shown in Table 15.6 could be converted to water-borne technologies, then total emissions might reduce from 37,500 tonnes per annum to ca 6,500 tonnes.
- If all coatings in the solvent-borne general purpose and "woodcare" categories converted to high-solids solvent-borne technologies, then emissions from these groups would approximately halve to give total emissions of ca 25,000 tonnes per annum.
- If this were combined with a conversion of the heavy duty construction coatings to entirely solvent-free technologies, then total emissions from the group could reduce to ca 17,000 tonnes per annum.

The time scale over which such changes might occur cannot be determined with accuracy, nor is it clear what might initiate the change. Legislation is one factor, but shorter term changes may arise from the growing promotional opportunities for manufacturers to exploit the potential trend in demand for water-borne coatings due to environmental and health and safety pressures. Basic commercial pressures will undoubtably then cause other manufacturers to follow, forcing potentially rapid reductions in total VOC emissions across all coatings sectors, not just those used in construction.

15.7 Conclusions

1. The construction industry directly uses approximately 180 million litres, or one third, of the 550 million litres of surface coatings produced in the UK per annum.
2. Construction coatings contribute about 37,500 tonnes to the total UK industrial VOC emissions of ca 800,000 tonnes per annum. It is estimated that an additional and broadly similar amount of VOC emission results from the use of coating materials in the retail (DIY) sector.
3. The composition of the emissions are primarily aliphatic hydrocarbons, though examples from all of the major classes of solvent are included. The emissions are often a complex mixture of compounds which require investigation on a product by product basis in order to study human exposure to VOCs resulting from use of coating materials.
4. It has been estimated that if the construction industry converted to coatings based on alternative technologies, then reductions in solvent emissions in the region of 30–80% could be realised.
5. It is suggested that significant reductions in emissions from the coatings used by the construction industry could occur within five to ten years. This is likely as a result of the industry response to environmental and health and safety concerns associated with the release of VOCs from coating products.

References

Anon. (1992) Our greatest challenge ever. *Finishing,* August, 24–25.

Anon. (1994) Paint market prepares for growth. *Builders Merchants Journal*, May, 36–42.

Berry, R.W., Brown, V.M., Coward, S.K., Crump, D.R., Gavin, M., Grimes, C.P., Higham, D.F., Hull, A.V., Hunter, C.A., Jeffrey, I.G., Lea, R.G., Llewellyn, J.W. and Raw, G.J. (1996) Indoor air quality in homes: The Building Research Establishment Indoor Environment Study. *BRE Report BR 299*, Building Research Establishment, Watford.

Brown, W.M., Crump, D.R. and Gardiner, D. (1990) Determination of aromatic hydrocarbon emissions from paint and related products by an impinger method. *Environment International*, **16**, 283–89.

Central Statistical Office (1995) *Annual Abstract of Statistics, No 131, Section 8.23 Industrial materials: synthetic dyestuffs, colours, paint, varnish and allied products*, HMSO, London.

ECA (1997) *Evaluation of VOC emissions from building products – solid flooring materials.* European Collaborative Action report, EUR 173334 EN, European Commission, Luxembourg.

Gustaffson, H. (1991) Building materials identified as major emission sources. *Proceedings of the ASHRAE conference IAQ 91: Healthy Buildings*, 259–61.

Hunt Marketing Research (1990) *The UK paint market: Trends in volume and value, 1979 to 1992.* Hunt Marketing Research, Wantage.

Hyatt, K. (1995) Staying solvent. *Masterbuilder*, Oct., 32–34.

IEH (1996) IEH Assessment on indoor air quality in the home. *IEH Assessment A2*, Institute for Environment and Health, Medical Research Council, University of Leicester.

Marketing Strategies for Industry (UK) Ltd. (1993) *MSI data report: Decorative paints UK.* MSI, Chester.

Newbould, A.J. (1992) Pollution control legislation and caotings manufacturing processes. *Polymers Paint and Colour Journal*, 4308, 316–318.

Passant, N.R. (1993) *Emissions of volatile organic compounds from stationary sources in the United Kingdom: A review of emission factors by species and process* September 1993 update, Warren Spring Laboratory.

Passant, N. (1995) Source inventories and control strategies for VOCs. In: Volatile Organic Compounds in the Atmosphere, Royal Society of Chemistry, Issues in *Environmental Science and Technology*, **4**, 51–64.

Passinen, A. (1995) Tikkurila, O.Y., Vantas, Finland, Personal communication. Gehrig, R, Hill, M, Zellweger, C and Hafer, P (1993). VOC emissions from wall paints – a test chamber study. *Proceedings of Indoor Air 93*, Helsinki, July 1993, **2**, 431–436.

Schriever, R. and Marutzky, R. (1990) VOC emissions of coated parquet floors. *Indoor Air 90: Proceedings of the 5th International Conference on Indoor Air Quality and Climate*, **3**, 551–55.

Sheldon, L.S. (1988) *Indoor Air Quality in Public Buildings, Vol 2. EPA/600/6-88/09b.* US Environmental Protection Agency, Research Triangle Park, North Carolina, USA.

Sparks, L.E., Tichenor, B.A., White, J.B. and Jackson, M.D. (1990) Comparison of data from an IAQ test house with prediction of an IAQ computer model. *Indoor Air*, **1**, 577–92.

Sterling, D.A. (1985) Volatile organic compounds in indoor air: An overview of sources, concentrations, and health effects. *Indoor Air and Human Health.* Edited by R.B. Gammage and S.V. Kaye, Lewis Publishers, Inc., Chelsea, Michigan, USA, 387–402.

Tichenor, B., Guo, Z., Mason, M.A. and Dunn, J.E. (1990). Evaluation of indoor air pollutant sinks for vapor phase organic compounds. *Proceedings of Indoor Air 90: Fifth International Conference on Indoor Air Quality and Climate*, **3**, 623–8.

Todd, A.S. (1987) A unique source of PCB contamination in public and other non-industrial buildings. *Practical Control of Indoor Air Problems*, 104–109.

Virgin, H.I. (1984) Effects of di-*n*-butyl-phthalate on the chlorophyll formation of green plants. *Indoor Air.* Vol 3, Sensory and Hyper reactivity Reactions to Sick Buildings. Edited by B. Berglund, T. Lindvall and J. Sundell. D18, 355–60. Swedish Council for Building Research, Stockholm, Sweden.

Wallace, L.A. (1991) Volatile organic compounds. *Indoor Air Pollution: A Health Perspective.* Edited by J.M. Samet and J.D. Spengler, Johns Hopkins University Press Baltimore, Maryland, USA.

Wolkoff, P., Clausen, P.A., Nielsen, P.A.and Molhave, L. (1990) The Danish twin apartment study: Part I: Formaldehyde and long-term VOC measurements. *Proceedings of Indoor Air 90: Fifth International Conference on Indoor Air Quality and Climate*, **2**, 657–62.

Wolkoff, P., Clausen, P.A., Nielsen, P.A. and Gunnarsen, L. (1993) Documentation of field and laboratory emission cell FLEC: Identification of emission processes from carpet, linoleum, paint, and sealant by modeling. *Indoor Air*, **3**, 291–7.

Wolkoff, P. and Nielsen, P. (1995) A new approach to label the emission of VOCs from building products. *Proceedings of Healthy Buildings 95*, **2**, 887–92, Milan, September.

16   Soiling and colour changes of coatings

M. Murray

16.1   Introduction

Predicting the long-term future appearance of a modern building in an urban environment is difficult. Currently coatings are often specified to protect concrete without an understanding of why concrete soils and changes colour. This chapter explains some of the reasons why concrete changes colour, and some recent ideas for controlling changes in colour which may prove useful to architects and engineers who wish to use concrete as a surface finish in modem designs.

The appearance of a surface is more complex than just an even mixture of colours. Appearance also involves textures and shades. Viewed from a distance a slate roof may appear to be dark grey, whilst close up there are different coloured slates, weathering effects and lichens visible. To predict future changes in appearance is also complex. For example, surfaces on cloudy days will reflect grey tones whilst in sunny conditions may reflect brighter tones. Natural weathering, atmospheric conditions and pollution will decay and recess the surface to reveal subsurfaces of a different appearance. Surfaces may also build up layers of dust; lichens and smoke will alter appearance. Acceptability of such soiled surfaces is difficult to judge. For example, some of the Georgian buildings in London's Bloomsbury have a characteristic even and extensive black soiling over the brickwork which appears to suit the area, whereas plaster rendered buildings in Kensington are better suited to whitewashed tones.

Architectural details and the overall building design may affect future appearance changes. Detailing and design can alter the air, dust and water flows and settlement of soiling particles over the building surface. This can be used to good or bad affect: the fluting in columns may become more pronounced but areas below features and widows may pick up excess soiling. This can add dramatic and unwanted emphasis to flush details or distort geometric designs. Adhering to tradition in building design will limit uncontrolled affects. For example, gargoyles on gothic churches often functioned as a mechanism to project roof water away from the building, whilst the Bauhaus school aimed to produce designs which incorporated industrial efficiency with the functionality of more traditional experience. As a result, functional features such as sills, copings and eaves are retained to control water.

Modern architecture has often minimized or removed traditional features. However, any subsequent loss of control of water movement over the building surface may produce unwanted appearance changes. Nowadays concrete cladding can be made to have a customized and controlled appearance. These materials may be referred to as 'artificial stone' or 'reconstituted stone'.

16.2   The structure of a concrete surface

The surfaces of concrete which set against a mould can develop a 'skin' 1–2 cm thick. Settlement and vibration causes smaller particles to collect over the larger aggregate stone and pebbles. At the very surface of the concrete skin there is a superficial cement layer sometimes called laitance. Laitance has very different chemical and physical properties from the rest of the skin or the inner materials. The skin as a whole may also undergo decay processes, which make its future appearance more complicated to judge than stone or brick. These changes will be influenced by local exposure conditions on the.building, the climate and the concrete mix; for example, a mix with a high cement content and low water/cement (W/C) ratio may produce a more homogeneous and durable material.

16.3   Cleaning concrete surfaces

Cleaning the surface of concrete requires an understanding of what the soiling is and what the cleaning method will do to the surface. Additionally, the nature of the concrete construction, the money available for cleaning and the level of surface damage expected will be significant in forming a judgement of the need to clean. Removal of soiling from concrete may require the simultaneous removal of live lichen and algae, dead organic residues, pollution soiling adhered to the cement and pollution soiling adhered to aggregate particles. Exposed fine aggregate particles may produce an appearance of soiling just by revealing their darker aggregate colour.

16.4   Concrete coatings and aesthetics

Some coatings are applied to concrete with the aim of reducing the absorption of acidic gases and so reducing the advancement of low pH environments in the masonry. By slowing the acidification or carbonification, this will slow the rate of decay of the steel reinforcement. It may be possible to extend the lifetime of the construction as a whole by applying coatings. Anti-carbonation coatings, however, do not necessarily take into account aesthetics. Concrete can appear extremely dirty and soiled after years of exposure. Observation of older concrete buildings in an urban environment has identified a number of types of decay and appearance change (concrete in other climates and environments may soil differently). The buildings were 20–30 year old tower blocks with moulded wood cut finish.

• Sheltered areas of concrete undergo low levels of surface loss. Subsequent soiling from dust, smoke and small particulates can build up to a blackened surface, often streaked by very low levels of water run off. Any original contours of the concrete surface will still remain (Figure 16.1).

- Where concrete is exposed to flowing water, higher rates of decay and loss occur. If this loss is low, dirt and organic growths can adhere. They locate in the spaces between sand and aggregate particles on the newly exposed cement surface. The overall dark soiling produced may appear similar to pollution soiling. Closer examination, however, shows lichens present (Figure 16.2). Lichens require water and sun to live so they tend to populate exosed locations

- Where there is a fast pace of concrete surface decay (either from harsh exposure conditions, site supervision or bad mix design) the lichens, pollution and dirt are lost as well. The decay exposes large aggregate particles giving a pebble dashed appearance (Figure 16.3). Concrete will lose all its original surface contours.

- Rain and wet conditions can produce unsightly dark, wet streaks over the buildings.

- Build up of minerals such as chlorides, carbonates, sulphates and hydroxides can stain by relocating soiling on adjacent surface layers. Iron compounds present in the concrete surface may produce red rust marks.

16.5   Research into concrete coatings

It may be possible that some commercially available concrete coatings can alter the soiling and surface decay characteristics of concrete. By forming a film over the sur-

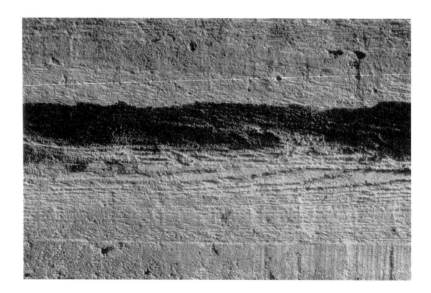

Figure 16.1   *Concrete surface showing original contours.*

Figure 16.2 *Lichens producing a the same effect as dark soiling.*

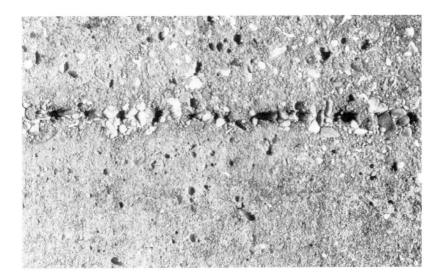

Figure 16.3 *Exposure of large aggregate particles due to surface decay.*

face, a coating may consolidate the laitance, along with the concrete skin and surface material, slowing the rate of surface loss. Hydrophobic coatings or coatings which fill surface pores will affect the movement of water over the concrete surface. The result may be changes to surface soiling, the level of surface dissolution by rain, and frost related surface loss. The colonization of plant life and lichens may also change, either increasing or decreasing due to the different chemical and physical environments. The surface may be easier to clean as the adhesion of soiling to the concrete surface will change as the soiling is now in contact with the coating.

To observe some of the effects of a concrete coating, a new building development in a UK city dockland location is being used as part of a research programme on concrete surface colour change. The concrete cladding, or reconstituted stone, used on the building has been treated with a general protective silane surface coating. The purpose of the silane is to reduce the concrete porosity, decrease carbonation and reduce waterborne soiling. The cladding itself uses carefully specified aggregates and finishes for a more durable and aesthetic finish and, as a result, the final material may not have a skin or laitance. The cladding surface was also pre-weathered by acid etching to remove the laitance. It was the manufacturer's intention to produce a top quality cladding to stand the test of time and exposure. The dockside exposure conditions are harsher than a normal urban environment: sea spray, strong winds combined with rain, and dust-producing local industry. Research started in 1997 is looking at the appearance changes of the building due to different weather conditions and over time.

16.6   Results

Figure 16.6 shows the change in colour of silane treated and untreated reconstituted stone cladding when the surface becomes wet due to rain. On the untreated surface, the water causes a temporary darkening, a 'wetting' effect. However, the surface coating reduces this effect substantially. The effect over a whole building would be that surfaces will look even and uniform in colour when it rains. Without the coating, darker streaks and discolouration would have occurred. The uniformity of appearance will thus be maintained over the whole building. Colour measurements after several months' exposure have also shown that little soiling of either the treated or untreated concrete has occurred. Longer term measurements are underway.

l6.7   Conclusions

16.7.1   Soiling and appearance change

Traditional concrete can develop dark soiling caused by pollution in rain sheltered areas and lichen growth in rain exposed areas. The design of both building and concrete mix can result in different decay, soiling and lichen growth patterns on a building. The resulting loss of surface due to decay can remove moulded patterns such as wood panelling after only 20 years.

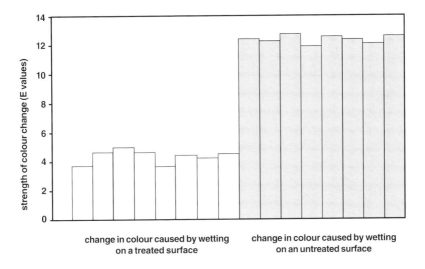

Figure 16.4 *Comparative change in colour due to wetting.*

16.7.2 Cleaning concrete

Cleaning concrete requires assessment of algae, lichens, aggregate particles and soiling types, and possible previous treatments. Different methods of cleaning will be required for these different soiling scenarios.

16.7.3 New developments in concrete and concrete coatings

Assuming the design life of the building and the proposed treatments are appropriate the decay of materials through natural weathering and pollution effects can be designed out:

- Modem concrete cladding can now be designed with the intention of reducing soiling and durability problems.
- The appearance of old concrete buildings should not be considered a judgement on new concrete buildings due to substantial developments in modern concrete products.
- Coatings are available which help reduce or prevent the soiling problems of concrete.
- The dark wet streaking on concrete buildings in wet weather can be minimised by selecting appropriate proprietory concrete coatings.

Bibliography

Soiling and Cleaning of Building Facades. LGW *Verhot Report of Technical Committee 62* SCF RILEM 1998.

17 General principles of biocide application in paint coatings

P. Chan and S.K.Chew

17.1 Introduction

There are two basic functions of paint: protection and decoration of substrates. Fouling of paints in the wet stage or on dried film may destroy these functions. Paint fouling is mainly caused by microbes – bacteria, fungi, yeast and algae. The habitats of these microbial organisms differ greatly around the globe and thus microbial contamination pressure on paints and coatings produced and used in different regions of the world also vary. For example, while bacteria can grow in a very wide range of environmental conditions, some higher forms of microbes grow only within a narrow range. Fungi do not grow well at extreme temperatures and algae grow only where there is sunlight. In some colder, drier, or less sunny regions, some species of microorganisms will not grow well or are totally absent. On the contrary, almost all species of microbes can flourish in the tropics where temperature, humidity, sunlight and other environmental factors are ideal for growth, creating the heaviest contamination pressure on paints and coatings in this part of the world. Some species of microorganisms only flourish in the tropics. The algal species, *Trentepohia odorata* which has been associated with widespread defacement of walls in Singapore, is a typical example (Wee, 1991).

The heavy microbial contamination pressure in the tropics, coupled with many unique industrial practices, governmental regulations, and social values in these regions, make them ideal for the illustration of the general principles for using biocides to combat microbial fouling of paints and coatings. This chapter examines these general principles from the perspective of the tropical region of South East Asia.

South East Asia has been experiencing miraculous economic growth during the last decade. The paint industry in the region, responding to the blooming economy, has also been enjoying record growth to the present size of about US$3 billion a year. The growth of the regional paint industry is driving a number of related supplying industries, of which the biocide industry is a key supplier to paint manufacturers. It has been estimated that the total potential market value of biocides for the paint industry in South East Asia amounts to about US$40 million a year – a market becoming increasingly more competitive and with customers becoming more sophisticated. Unlike in the past, paint manufacturers nowadays have a choice of many biocides and those suppliers who understand the key performance, cost and environment health elements required by paint manufacturers will have an edge in this competitive regional paint biocides market.

17.2   Use of biocides in paints and latex in South East Asia

Microbial organisms are everywhere and can colonize rapidly on most organic surfaces when growing conditions are right. Some of the ideal growth conditions are listed in Table 17.1. Matching these with the typical tropical climate and weather conditions in Singapore, a country located almost right on the equator, one would easily find that these conditions are almost perfect for the growth of many species of microorganism on organic substrates such as paint. Due to the all-year-round warm, moist, and sunny climate, coupled with the abundance of organic and inorganic pollutants available as nutrients, algal growth on exterior paint film has been detected as a major cause of wall defacement in Singapore (Wee, 1991). Similarly, the warm and humid climate,

Table 17.1   *Comparison of ideal growth conditions for microbial organisms and climatic and other conditions in Singapore, North American and European cities.*

	Ideal microbial growth conditions		
	Bacteria /Yeast	**Fungi/Mould**	**Algae**
Temperature	30 °C 25 °C		30 °C
Water	liquid water	moisture	liquid water (water droplets)
pH	wide range	acidic	alkaline
Nutrients	organic carbons	organic carbon	electrolytes, CO_2
Others	—	—	sunlight

	Climatic and other conditions in Singapore, N. American and European cities		
	Singapore	**New York**	**London**
Temperature	tropical	seasonal	seasonal
Jan	30 / 23	3 / –4	6 / 2
July	35 / 24	28 / 19	22 / 14
Oct	35 / 23	21 / 9	14 / 8
Nov	31 / 23	11 / 3	10 / 5
Rainfall (mm/yr)	2415	1086	593
Rel. humidity (%)	70–95	53–60	56–81
Solar energy (cal/cm²/day)	405	286	242

typical of that in many countries in the region, is also a haven for many species of fungi to colonize building walls.

Most paint manufacturers in the region are now fully aware of the importance of using biocides to protect their wet paints from spoilage by bacteria and fungi (in-can preservation) and to protect dried paint film from fungal and algal infestations. Nowadays, biocides are widely used in most of the paints produced in the region, but there are still too many cases of performance failure of biocides, which have resulted in wet paint spoilage, and paint film deterioration.

17.3   Criteria used by paint manufacturers in selecting the right biocides for their paints in the region

Paint manufacturers in South East Asia traditionally operate based on performance and cost, and recently also on environmental and health concerns. From these three perspectives, the trends of biocides applications in this industry in the region have been examined.

17.3.1   Performance perspectives

A host of biocides and their combination formulations are now commercially available to paint manufacturers in South East Asia. Of these, only a handful are being produced locally; the majority are developed, tested and produced in North America or Europe. The performance of these imported biocides may or may not hold up under the unique South East Asia climatic and environmental conditions, regional paint manufacturing and application practices, or locally specific microbiological pressure. A comparison of some of these conditions between North America, Europe and South East Asia is given in Table 17.1 and 17.2. There are wide variations and differences. From the perspective of performance, the paint manufacturers must ask biocide suppliers to provide performance data from tests conducted in the region. The data which could be helpful to a local paint manufacturer may include, but is not necessarily limited to: stability data of biocide products under storage conditions of the region; stability data of biocides in paints produced in the region; efficacy data of the biocides against local species of microbes in the air, raw materials, water and factory environments; compatibility data between biocides and components in paints produced in the region; leaching rate of biocides from paint film under local conditions; and last, but not least, chemical stability of biocides in paints applied on construction materials commonly used in the region.

For an in-can biocide to perform according to its specifications, it must be chemically and physically stable under storage, and its active ingredients must be chemically stable and biologically available in paints during the wet stage. Some typical mechanisms which can degrade biocides are listed in Table 17.3. The temperature in South East Asia, all-year-round could reach 50 °C in warehouses and 60 °C in uncovered areas; some biocides may not be stable under such storage conditions. Paints in this region may contain raw materials different from those used in North American and

Table 17.2 *Some factors relevant to the variation in performance of biocides in South East Asia, North America and Europe.*

Factors	S. E. Asia	North America	Europe
Building substrate	concrete/plaster pH = alkaline	wood/brick pH = acidic / neutral	wood/stone/brick pH = acidic / neutral
Climate	hot, humid, rainy, sunny	seasonal, drier, less rainy and sunlight	seasonal, drier, less rainy and sunlight
Arch. paints characteristics water plant hygiene product self-time application practices	more contaminants poor (some areas) months–3 years dilution before application common practice	less contaminants cleaner 1 year apply undiluted	less contaminants cleaner 1 year apply undiluted
Microbial loading pressure	high; some unique local species	lower; some unique local species	lower; some unique local species
Air pollutants Acid rain	high in some areas some areas	lower in general some areas	lower in general some areas

Europe. Some of them may be incompatible with certain biocides. In South East Asia, bacterial counts in water and raw materials, pH of the paint, binder to pigment ratio, and manufacturing temperature may be very different. Furthermore, diluting paint before application is a common practice in this region. Any one or combination of these factors may cause instability of biocides and may lower their effective concentrations in paints, and thus may result in spoilage and performance failure.

For a film biocide to perform according to its specifications, it must be stable on surface substrate, stable under exposure conditions such as UV, air pollutants, rainwater and in some cases acidic rain, and have a balanced leaching rate. Unlike in the West where wood is the predominant building material surface for architectural coatings, concrete and plaster are the norm in South East Asia (Table 17.2), and some biocides may not be chemically stable on these high pH substrate surfaces. Because South East Asia is sunny all year round, the intensity of UV solar energy is much higher than in northern countries. The intense UV exposure could degrade some biocides. Certain chemical degradation reactions require water and heat. Unlike in northern countries, where many lack one or both of these conditions, South East Asia is rainy and hot all year round – a favourable condition for degradation reactions to occur. Air pollutants

Table 17.3 *Some possible mechanisms for the degradation of biocides in paint.*

Possible instability or degradation factors for biocides in paint
pH: acidic or alkaline   high temperature (> 45 °C)   light, UV, radicals   reducing agents: H_2S, sulphite, sulphides, sulphydryls, mercaptans   oxidizing agents: halogens, peroxides, iron oxides   ammonium, amines, amides   pyridines   surfactants: cationic, anionic, non-ionic, amphoteric   chelating agents: hard water, EDTA   metals: aluminium   other biocide interactions   biological agents or compounds: proteins, casein, anerobic bacteria

such as hydrogen sulphur, sulphur dioxide, carbon sulphide, and nitrogen oxides may react with some biocides (Table 17.3). These air pollutants are commonly found in South East Asia. As in some of the metropolitan areas in the West, acidic rain is also a problem in the developing South East Asia region and some biocides could be degraded by acidic rain. Rainfall in South East Asia is generally higher than in North America and Europe; some biocides may therefore have a higher leaching rate in the rainy climate of South East Asia which may thus shorten their efficacious duration. Any one or combination of these factors may decrease the effective biocide concentration on paint film, which not only could result in performance failures but, in some cases, could also lead to paint film discoloration (such as yellowing) caused by degradation products.

Local species of microbes that can infect paints in South East Asia may be different from those found in North America and Europe. Although a comprehensive study has not been conducted on the distribution of local microbial species in South East Asia, at least one study has shown that one species of algae, the *Trentepohlia odorata*, a species rarely found in other regions, is the predominant species colonizing exterior wall paint film in Singapore (Wee, 1991; Chua *et al.*, 1972). Performance failures will occur if a biocide is ineffective against the local microbial species, even it has been shown to be able to control microbial species in colder regions such as Europe and North America.

17.3.2   Cost perspectives

The paint market in South East Asia is just as brutally competitive as that in the West, if not more so. In such a wide open competitive market, every penny counts.

Biocide suppliers often believe that they can demand a high premium on their products with good customer services. This thinking to some extent had some merit in the past. However, in today's increasingly competitive biocide market in South East Asia, good customer service from biocide suppliers is expected and paint manufacturers in the region no longer consider this a premium item. To maintain competitiveness in such a market, biocide suppliers must find ways to drive down the treatment cost of biocides for paint manufacturers. This can be accomplished by developing more efficacious and safer biocides to reduce treatment dosages, by cutting their manufacturing and distribution costs to enable them to supply biocides at rock bottom prices to paint manufacturers, and by providing good technical assistance to help paint manufacturers establish optimal dosages, to identify factors causing instability and find remedial actions to reduce wastage. This list of examples is not exhaustive; those who can come up with innovative approaches to save the cost of using biocides for their customers will certainly put themselves ahead of their competitors.

Paint manufacturers too can help bring down the cost of using biocides. For example, modifying a paint formulation or replacing some ingredients which are not compatible with an efficacious biocide will increase the stability of some biocides, and this can certainly lower the cost. Adjusting pH is another way to increase the stability of some biocides. On the other hand, decreasing microbial loading pressure by tightening plant hygiene also can decrease the amount of biocides needed. Changing some manufacturing processes, such as adding some biocides during a lower temperature process, may greatly increase the stability of some biocides and lower cost. Strict raw material quality control and proper storage of biocides can maximize the efficient usage of biocides.

The biocide suppliers should take note that the cost of using a biocide is not just limited to material cost: other costs could include compensatory material and labour costs in case of a performance failure, especially when the paint is under certain predetermined performance standards such as the six year guarantee in Singapore for some public building (e.g. the Housing Development Board buildings), waste disposal costs, and the intangible cost to the paint manufacturer's product brand after a performance failure.

17.3.3   Environment and health perspectives

Economic development and growth have, for the last decade, been considered much higher social priorities than environmental and health protection. Since the late 1980s, environmental awareness in the region has been rising. One country after another has been enacting new laws and enforcing old ones to tighten environmental protection, occupational safety and toxic substance control. Singapore, for example, has long adopted strict laws to deal with the environmental protection and occupational health and safety aspects of the sale, use, transportation, import and export of poisonous substances (Table 17.4). To supplement the existing laws dealing with some toxic substances, Malaysia has recently enacted a comprehensive Occupational Safety and Health Classification, Packaging and Labelling of Hazardous Chemicals (Table 17.4).

These new laws are bound to have an impact on the paint manufacturers' concern over the use of biocides. Mercurial biocides, for example, which were used in the past and still are being used in some countries today, have been banned in Singapore for

Table 17.4 *Toxic substances control laws and regulations in Singapore and Malaysia.*

Singapore	Malaysia
The Poison Act (Chapter 234)	Sales of Drug Act (1952)
The Poison (Hazardous Substances) Rules of 1986	Pesticides Act (1974)
The Clean Air Act	Environmental Quality (Schedule Wastes Regulations) (1989)
The Water Pollution Control and Drainage Act	Occupational Safety and Health (Classification, Packaging and Labelling of Hazardous Chemicals) Regulation (1997)
Environmental Public Health (Toxic Industrial Waste) Regulations, 1988	
The Singapore Standard 286 (Caution Labelling of Hazardous Substances)	
The Factory Act – Section 60 Toxic Substances	

more than 20 years. Phenolic biocides are now obsolete in the paint industry in Singapore. The use of organic tin in marine antifoulant paint is being discouraged. Although these are extreme cases of imminent public health and environmental risk concerns, they nonetheless have highlighted governmental and public awareness of the risks associated with the use of biocides.

To a professional toxicologist, there is no such thing as a toxic substance, but there are only safe ways of using chemical substances. In other words, all chemicals under some conditions can cause harm but it is the right dose that differentiates between a poison and a remedy. Biocides, by their functional definition, are supposed to have certain biological activities. An ideal biocide, however, should perform its intended function at doses well below those that can pose an unreasonable risk to public health or to the environment. Most biocides at their usage levels, to some extent, can satisfy this criterion, as indicated by their low acute toxicity and high degradability or low mobility after release into the environment. What concerns paint manufacturers most is whether a biocide can cause harm to workers in manufacturing and professional applicators at occupational exposure levels, which are often characterized by short to medium term exposure at levels higher than that to which the public is normally exposed.

Therefore, one of the criteria a paint manufacturer would use to select a biocide is whether the biocides can be employed safely in the workplace without causing any harmful effects to their workers. Of course, one could always argue that any chemical can be used safely if adequate engineering designs, such as an enclosed dosing system, can be put in place, or if sufficient personal protective equipment is used. However, these are not valid arguments with respect to economics and the availability of engineering technologies in this region. Those biocides suppliers who know how to make their biocides easier and safer to use with minimal engineering control devices or protective equipment would have a tremendous advantage in this region. For example, reformulating a biocide into a form less dusty, less volatile, less misty, less acidic or alkaline, more physically and chemically stable, easier for pouring and handling, etc., can reduce occupational exposure and thus increase the margin of safety for its users. Adequate hazard communication from biocide suppliers to their paint manufacturer customers is also of utmost importance. With the appropriate information, their customers can make an informed decision on whether sufficient and economical control measures exist or can be put in place for the use of the biocides. This will avoid surprises and mistrust. Of course, any help from a biocide supplier to assess and to manage properly any potential hazards associated with the use of biocides would be an advantage and greatly increase their chance of success with the paint customers.

17.4   Conclusion

This chapter has attempted to examine systematically the general principles of biocide application from three perspectives – performance, cost and environmental and public health. Substantial variations exist between South East Asia and North America or Europe from where most of the biocides are developed, tested and produced. To those biocide manufacturers who have keen interest in the South East Asia paint market, the magnitude of the variations would provide full justification for devoting some of their resources to develop biocides uniquely for this region with respect to performance, cost and the environment and public health.

References

Chua, N.H., Kwok, S.W., Tan, K.K., Teo, S.P. and Wong, H.A. (1972) Growths on concrete and other similar surfaces in Singapore *J. Singapore Instit. Archit*, **51**, (13), 5.
Wee, Y.C. (1991) Algal fouling of building surfaces in Singapore – the search for a solution. *European Polymers, Paint, Colour Journal*, **181**, (4289), 468.

18 Assessing the biological resistance of exterior paint films

C.A.Hunter, M.Greenhalgh and J.Gillatt

18.1 Summary

Decorative masonry coatings are subject to disfigurement by the growths of fungi and algae under specific conditions. Hence there is a need for rapid, reliable and reproducible laboratory methods which predict the resistance of the coatings in service. Over the last 20 years, the International Biodeterioration Research Group (IBRG), a group of experts from industry and academia, have developed a number of tests to evaluate the bioresistance of materials such as paints.

This chapter reports on the laboratory test methodologies developed by the IBRG to assess the performance of exterior masonry coatings. It also describes an evaluation of eight commercial formulations, comparing the laboratory methods with long-term outdoor exposure. The vermiculite-bed test and humidity cabinet/panel test proved effective in identifying products with limited effectiveness in preventing algal or fungal colonization. These tests therefore offer effective and reliable rapid screening methods for traditional exterior coatings under controlled laboratory conditions.

18.2 Introduction

Masonry coatings are commonly used both to enhance the appearance of external building surfaces and to provide protection against moisture penetration. Prolonged periods of surface wetting and contamination with wind-borne detritus can encourage colonization of such surfaces by a range of biological growths, in particular by fungi and algae. Such growths are visually disfiguring and can contribute to the premature failure of the coating itself. Algae are often the most important cause of disfigurement under external in-service conditions. Those belonging to the classes Chlorophyceae (the 'green algae') and Cyanophyceae ('blue-green algae') are the ones most commonly found on masonry surfaces. Other classes of importance include the Chrysophyceae, Xanthophyceae, Bacillarophyceae and Rhodophyceae (Grant, 1982). A wide range of moulds is also capable of invading intact paint films when sufficient moisture is present. On exterior surfaces those which dominate are the dark pigmented species, such as *Cladosporium*, *Alternaria* and *Aureobasidium*, which cause the serious problem of blue/black disfigurement of pale exterior coatings.

Figure 18.1 *Vermiculite-bed algal resistance test.*

Figure 18.2 *Exterior exposure assessment.*

The extent to which algae can cause significant degradation of constructional materials or of paint films applied to them is sometimes questioned but it is certainly likely that sheets of algal growth trap water, retard drying and therefore increase water-induced damage of the underlying material. Also, the subsequent entrapment of fungal spores, dust and debris from the atmosphere by the algal patina introduces the potential for colonization by fungi, lichens and subsequently by higher plants, all of which have a greater ability to induce decay.

Algal growths are often green when fresh, although a number of other colours may occur, depending upon the predominant species present. These growths may become dark, frequently black, under dry conditions, giving the affected surface an unacceptably dirty appearance. Consequently, a large number of biocides have been developed intended to be effective against algae and fungi, both in biocidal washes and when incorporated into paint films (Allsopp and Allsopp, 1983; Hale and Springle, 1986; Bravery, 1992; BRE, 1992).

18.3   Methods for assessing the microbial resistance of exterior masonry paints

Despite the range of organisms involved and the consequences of premature failure, there is no general agreement on standardized methods to test masonry paints for their resistance to microbial colonization.

Evaluation of the efficacy of exterior paints is basically a three stage process: the first stage involves assessment of the active ingredient alone or as a formulation in agar or liquid culture, whereas the second stage normally attempts to incorporate a relevant model substrate (such as mortar blocks) so the test is carried out under simulated environmental conditions. Field trials, which may be considered as the tertiary phase, offer the most realistic method of assessment but are time consuming because they may take up to five years, are sometimes unreliable because external conditions can vary and may be impractical for rapid screening of large numbers of products. A number of rapid screening methods have been developed, for example, the 'streaked plate' method developed by Drisko and Crilly (1974), which assesses the extent of development of algae on a simple inorganic medium to which the compound under test has been added. Tests providing for the substrate interactions have, for example, involved coating glass tubes with a mortar paste to which the product under test is applied (Springle, 1975) followed by incubation in a cabinet in which the temperature, humidity and lighting levels are controlled at or near an optimum for the algal or mould species used.

18.4   Role of the International Biodeterioration Research Group in developing paint film tests

The International Biodeterioration Research Group (IBRG) was originally founded in 1968 under the auspices of the Organisation of Economic Co-operation and Development (OECD), Paris. Its membership is made up predominantly of microbiologists from industry, private and government laboratories and academic institutions. The main objectives of IBRG are in the field of test method development and work to investigate basic principles of biodeterioration. These objectives are met in a number of ways: firstly, by discussion at meetings; secondly, by carrying out and reporting on individual laboratory investigations; and, most importantly, by organizing, performing and reporting on collaborative experimental work or round robin testing.

18.4.1   Dry-film fungal testing

The Paints Working Group is one of the oldest of the four Working Groups of IBRG; the others deal with Plastics Protection, Biodegradable Plastics and Leather. From the mid-1970s for a period of more than ten years, the Paints Working Group concentrated on studying aspects of the growth of fungi on surface coatings. The desire was to produce a test which would allow the in-use fungicidal performance of paints to be evaluated in the laboratory. Following extensive laboratory trials, during which comparisons were made between filter paper/agar plate tests and solid substrate/humidity chamber methods, a large field trial/laboratory comparison took place. Panels were exposed at a number of outdoor sites and the growth compared with similar panels exposed in a laboratory test chamber. Close correlation was found between the two methods of test. The results of this work were published and reported to the committee of the British Standards Institute. As a result, the IBRG humidity chamber test was adopted as BS3900 Part G6.

   The outline of the test is as follows: replicate panels, of a calcium silicate building board (or another inert substrate) coated with the test product are conditioned in an environment of high humidity before being inoculated with a mixture of seven mould species and three yeasts (Table 18.1). The panels are incubated in a test cabinet where the humidity is cycled and condensation routinely appears on the test surfaces (Figure 18.3). At specific intervals, up to 12 weeks, the panels are inspected for fungal growth and compared with susceptible control paints (Table 18.2). The method is described in greater detail by Bravery et al. (1983).

18.4.2   Dry-film algal testing

A similar process has been followed for the laboratory evaluation of paints intended to be resistant to algal growth. Various laboratory techniques were investigated and a vermiculite-bed method, where test panels are laid on a moist substrate (vermiculite), inoculated with algae and incubated with standard illumination, was developed.

   In the vermiculite-bed test, coated panels of an inert substrate (calcium silicate) are placed on a bed of moistened vermiculite within a closed incubation chamber. The exposed surface of the panels are inoculated with a mixture of five algae species considered to be representative of those commonly found on masonry (Table 18.1). The test specimens in their containers are incubated on a light bench with a daily photoperiod of 16 hours. Panels are monitored for 12 weeks and the extent of algal colonization rated using a subjective scale (Table 18.2). This method is explained in greater

Table 18.1 *Composition of mixed inoculum for (a) fungal and (b) algal laboratory tests.*

Fungal Test Species and strain number		Algal Test Species and strain number	
Aspergillus versicolor	IMI 45554	*Gloeocapsa alpicola*	CCAP 1430/1
Aureobasidium pullulans	IMI 45533	*Nostoc commune*	CCAP 1453/29
Cladosporium cladosporioides	IMI 178517	*Pleurococcus* sp.	CCAP 464/1
Penicillium purpurogenum	IMI 178519	*Stichococcus bacillaris*	CCAP 379/1a
Phoma violacea	IMI 49948ii	*Trentepholia aurea*	CCAP 483/1
Rodotorula rubra	NCYC 1659		
	NCYC 1660		
Sporobolomyces roseus	NCYC 717		
Stachybotrys chartarum	IMI 82021		
Ulocladium atrum	IMI 79906		

IMI : International Mycological Institute   NCYC: National Collection of Yeast Cultures
CCAP: Culture Collection of Algae and Protozoa

Table 18.2 *Subjective rating scale for assessment of algal or fungal growths on test panels.*

Rating	Description
0	No growth on surface
1	Trace of growth present
2	1–10% of test surface colonized
3	10–30% of test surface colonized
4	30–70% of test surface colonized
5	> 70% of test surface colonized

detail by Gillatt (1991). Field trials, in which panels are being exposed at a number of external locations and the results compared with similar panels tested according to the IBRG laboratory method, are currently taking place.

These two laboratory methods, together with exterior exposure to natural colonization, are commonly used in research and test laboratories to evaluate the fungal and algal resistance of masonry paints.

18.5   Evaluation of commercial formulations using the IBRG test methods

A study carried out at BRE utilized these laboratory tests to assess the resistance of a

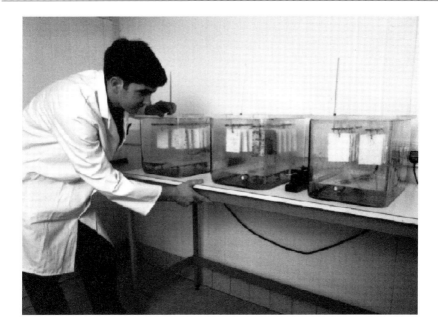

Figure 18.3 *Laboratory test for mould resistance.*

range of commercial paints to colonization by algae and fungi and to identify any factor(s) which might influence biological growth in situ. Commercial formulations were selected rather than model paints to which a range of biocides were added, since it is well known that interactions between the specific biocide and other components of the paint (such as the binder) can play a significant role in determining the efficacy of the biocide. Also this test is designed to be used as a screen for novel active compounds as well as for developmental and near-market products.

Eight commercial products were chosen for this trial (Table 18.3). They were selected on the basis of their common usage, type of finish and on their predicted performance under in-service conditions. The predicted performance was based on criteria such as resistance to chalking and cracking, but excluded susceptibility to algal growth. Paints were applied to panels at a rate equivalent to the mid-point of the manufacturers' recommended application rate or at half the maximum application rate recommended by the manufacturer.

As well as being assessed for their resistance to biological colonization using the IBRG laboratory test methods, the paints were subjected to long term exposure to natural weathering/colonization. Under natural colonization, the panels are exposed on north-facing wooden racks, at least 1 m above ground level, inclined at 45°, to accelerate weathering effects and to increase the catchment of algal cells, fungal spores and dirt. This follows long established practice in the exposure of test panels to weathering effects. Panels are monitored for biological colonization at six monthly intervals for up to five years.

Table 18.3 *Products used in the evaluation of the laboratory methods.*

Product code	Description	Expected field performance*
A	Smooth, waterborne, acrylic binder	good
B	Smooth, waterborne, non-acrylic binder	fair
C	Smooth, waterborne, non-acrylic binder	poor
D	Smooth, solvent-borne, acrylic binder	good
E	Smooth, solvent-borne, pliolite binder	good
F	Fine textured, water-based non-acrylic binder	good
G	Fine textured, water-based non-acrylic binder	poor
H	Coarse textured, water-based non-acrylic binder	good

* The terms (good, fair and poor) are an indication of the paint's relative performance in maintaining its condition during the normal lifetime of the film (five to seven years for the smooth emulsion, seven to ten years for the fine textured emulsion and for around ten years the amylate rubber-based products).

18.5.1   Laboratory evaluation

The results of the laboratory trial after 12 weeks' exposure of the treated panels are presented in Table 18.4. Only panels painted with products B, G and H remained free from either algal or fungal growths. In addition to these products, panels of products A and E were also free from algal colonization, but not fungal growths. It was noted that on the panels free from algal colonization brown staining appeared which past experience at BRE indicates debris from dead algal cells. Ranking the products on the

Table 18.4 *Extent of biological colonization on test panels after 12 weeks incubation under laboratory conditions or three years exposure to natural weathering.*

Product code	Laboratory algal rating	Laboratory fungal rating	Exterior exposure rating
A	0	1	0
B	0	0	0
C	5	5	2^3
D	4^3	3	1
E	0	2	0^1
F	4^5	5	2
G	0	0	0^1
H	0	0	0^1
Control	5	5	3

Superscripts indicate rating of individual panel which differs from other replicates.

basis of their resistance to algal and other biological growths in the laboratory test revealed that the best performer was product G and the worst was the control and product C.

In the laboratory trials, the texture of the finish did not appear to influence the degree of colonization of the paint film. However, the panels were positively inoculated in the laboratory and, in the case of the algal test, exposed horizontally, which would minimize the influence of surface texture. In practical situations, surface texture may well be more important as attachment by algal cells and other material is likely to be governed in part by the texture of the surface finish.

However, criteria such as resistance to chalking and cracking used to predict field performance (Table 18.3) do not appear to correlate with the extent of algal or fungal colonization in the laboratory. For example, product G was rated as best in the laboratory against microorganisms but was considered to have a 'poor' in-service performance as judged by physical performance indicators. Therefore, when assessing the likely field performance of paint products it is essential to determine the susceptibility of the paint to micro-organisms in addition to its ability to maintain its physical integrity.

Neither the carrier nor binder type appeared to be significant in determining whether a paint supported algal growth, since in this study both waterborne and solvent-borne paints were susceptible, irrespective of the presence of acrylic or non-acrylic binders. One other possible reason for the differing responses of the paints to biological colonization is their ability to resist water penetration and thus eliminate or reduce the moisture source required by these organisms. Davies and Bassi (1994) determined the water permeability for a range of masonry coatings. They found that synthetic rubber resin products had a mean water permeability of 0.11 kg m^{-2} h$^{-\frac{1}{2}}$, smooth exterior emulsions had a mean of 0.15 kg m^{-2} h$^{-\frac{1}{2}}$ and textured exterior emulsions had the highest permeability at 0.24 kg m^{-2} h$^{-\frac{1}{2}}$. These authors also found a similar ranking of products when the percentage water absorption was determined in accordance with BS 6477 (1987) Appendix F. Of the three smooth emulsions tested (products A, B and C), which are expected to have a moderate water permeability, only one showed algal colonization while the other two remained free from algal growth but were colonized to widely differing degrees by fungi. This inconsistency of response was also observed with the two paints that could be classified along with the textured exterior emulsions as having a potentially high water vapour permeability (products F and G). Where one product supported heavy algal and fungal growth (product F), the other (product G) remained free from colonization. It is therefore concluded that those paints which failed to prevent algal or fungal colonization had a film biocide that was either ineffective or the spectrum of activity of the biocide did not cover the full range of organisms. Assessments in these present trials were only performed on unweathered painted panels when the paints can be considered as in their most resistant state. Even in this state, three of the eight commercial products tested were heavily or severely colonized by algae, thus providing an early indication of potentially poor relative performance in-service.

In the laboratory studies there was little difference between the replicate panels suggesting that the method can produce consistent results. Results were also remarkably consistent between laboratories using this method in a series of inter-laboratory co-operative experiments carried out under the auspices of the IBRG (IBRG, 1990). The vermiculite-bed test therefore offers an effective rapid screening test for exterior coatings under controlled conditions without the risks of variability induced when using natural weathering exposure.

18.5.2 Exterior exposure

Interim results obtained after three years exposure to natural weathering are consistent with those obtained in the laboratory (Table 18.4), that is, those products which showed signs of algal and fungal growth under laboratory conditions also suffered greatest biological attack during the field trial. Two of the products showed minor colonization on one of the three replicates in the field trial but were free from any growths in the laboratory. This minor difference may be the result of weathering effects on the panels during the outdoor trial compared to the laboratory trial in which only assessed unweathered products.

The results from this interim comparison indicate that the laboratory method can give a good predictive indication of likely field performance of masonry coatings but results from the field trials indicate that artificial weathering prior to biological exposure would need to be included as routine in the laboratory trial.

References

Allsopp, C. and Allsopp, D. (1983) An updated survey of commercial products used to protect materials against biodeterioration. *International Biodeterioration Bulletin, 19*, 99–145.

Bravery, A.F. (1992) Preservation in the construction industry. In *Principles and Practice of Disinfection, Preservation and Sterilisation*, 2nd edition (ed. Russell, A. D., Hugo, W.B. and Ayliffe, G.A.J.). Blackwell Scientific Publications, London.

Bravery, A.F., Barry, S. and Worley, W. (1983) An alternative method for testing the mould resistance of paint films. *Journal of the Oil and Colour Chemists Association*, 39–43.

Building Research Establishment (1992) *Control of lichens, moulds and similar growth. Digest 370*. Building Research Establishment, Garston, Watford, UK.

Davies, H. and Bassi, R.S. (1994) The water vapour permeability of masonry coatings: a comparison of BS 3177: 1959 and the draft EN test method for water vapour permeability. *Surface Coatings International, 77*, 386–93.

Drisko, R.W. and Crilly, J.B. (1974) Control of algal growth on paints at tropical locations. *Journal of Paint Technology 46*, 48–55.

Gillatt, J.W. (1991) The need for antifungal and antiagal additives in high performance surface coatings. *Surface Coatings International, 74*, 197–203.

Grant, C. (1982) Fouling of terrestrial substrates by algae and implications for control – a review. *International Biodeterioration Bulletin 18*, 57–65.

Hale, S.C. and Springle, W.R. (1986) *Evaluation of biocidal masonry coatings and guide to paint film biocides*. Paint Research Association, Teddington, UK.

International Biodeterioration Research Group (1990) Minutes of the 37th meeting of the International Biodeterioration Research Group Paints Project Group held 8th March 1990 at St. Peter Port, Guernsey, Channel Islands. *Report No. IBRG/P90/03*, IBRG.

Springle, W.R. (1975) Testing biocidal paints. *Some Methods for Microbiological Assay* (ed. Board, R.G. and Lovelock, D.W.), Academic Press, London, 191–201.

Acknowledgements

This work at BRE was carried out under sponsorship of the Department of the Environment's Construction Support Directorate. The authors would like to thank Mr. J. Boxall, CTTC, BRE for providing the descriptions of the products examined and Mr. G. Rothwell, formerly of the Organic Material Division, BRE for providing the field performance ratings.

19 Review of dynamic crack-bridging tests

R.Bassi

19.1 Introduction

A crack-bridging test is undertaken to determine a coating's ability to accommodate movement of cracks in concrete, due to load and temperature changes in a concrete structure, such as a car park. There are two types of test: static and dynamic. The static test is a one-cycle test which will give an indication of the maximum crack width which can be accommodated by the coating. The dynamic test will give information on the performance of a coating over an active crack.

There are nine national crack-bridging standards in Europe, each with a different testing regime and pass/fail criteria. All these national standards are to be replaced with a single European Standard.

This chapter gives an overview of existing national standards for crack-bridging in Europe and North America, the current position on the European standard test method for a crack-bridging test and a brief summary of research into the topic.

19.2 National standards for crack-bridging tests

Carbonation andlor chlorides (as found in de-icing salts) are the main causes of corrosion of the reinforcement in concrete. Consequently concrete, where appropriate, must be protected from both carbonation and ingress of chlorides. Surface treatments are applied to concrete, with or without surface cracks, to act as barriers to the ingress of carbon dioxide, liquid water and chlorides. One of the important properties of these surface treatments, if they have been applied over cracked concrete, is their crack-bridging ability, particularly if the crack is active.

Crack-bridging tests may be conducted statically, or dynamically by applying either compressive or tensile forces to a membrane bonded to a concrete slab in which a crack has been induced. Test conditions vary in the way that the crack is induced and in the specimen design. Requirements for the width of crack opening, the number of test cycles and the temperature of the test also vary between test methods. Require-ments for the test methods in Europe are tabulated in Table 19.1. The pass criteria for all the tests is no rupture at the end of the test period. All these tests will be replaced by a European Standard for static and dynamic crack-bridging for coatings in Europe.

Table 19.1 *Comparison of crack-bridging requirements.*

Country /test mode		Requirement
Austria	dynamic	0.5–2.0 mm crack opening for 1000 cycles at –20°C at 1 cycle/ second
Belgium	static	Determine crack width at rupture with 1 tonne load. Sample condition 7 days at 50°C, 24 hours at 0°C
		0–0.6 mm crack opening at 0°C for 20,000 cycles at 1 cycle per second
Finland (liquid coatings)	static	Load applied 0.5 mm/min. Samples conditioned 91 days at 70°C then tested at –35°C and –25°C
		Membrane subjected to a crack opening of 1.2 mm for 5 minutes at –30°C
France	static	Membrane subjected to a crack opening of 1.0 mm for 5 minutes at +20°C then 0.7 mm for 5 minutes at –10°C
	dynamic	0.5–1.5 mm crack opening for 200 cycles at 20°C at 25 mm/hour then static test at 10°C with 2.0 mm crack opening
Germany	static (resins)	Membrane subjected to 1.0 mm crack width which is maintained by glueing plates to block. Held 7 days at 70°C then crack opened a further 1.0 mm
	dynamic (resins)	0.1–0.4 mm crack opening for 1000 cycles at –20°C at 0.1 Hz then static test
	static (bitumen sheets)	Crack width of 1.0 mm held for 60 seconds at 23°C
	dynamic (bitumen sheets)	0.1 5–0.25 mm crack opening at 0.1 Hz for 100,000 cycles at –20°C, then static test, then open crack until rupture
Luxembourg	dynamic	0–0.2mm crack opening for 1000 cycles at 10°C then 0.1–1.0 mm for 1000 cycles at 23°C
Sweden	dynamic	0.5–0.7 mm crack opening for 1000 cycles at –20°C at 1 Hz repeated for 500 cycles after thermal shock (150°C), chloride immersion for 10 days, 70°C for 21 days and freeze thaw cycling for 7 days
Switzerland	dynamic	0.25–0.5 mm crack opening for 10 cycles, 0.5–2.0 mm for 100 cycles, tested at –10°C or higher temperatures to room temperature if rupture occurs
United Kingdom*	dynamic and static	0.1–1.0 mm for 100 cycles at –10°C, +23°C, +40°C, (separate tests) then held 24 hours at 1.0 mm each test, then chloride transmission test

* provisional draft method

19.3   Draft European Standard for dynamic and static crack-bridging tests

The latest draft requires that tests are carried out in triplicate. It does not state the design of the specimen, or the roughness of the surface. The draft specifies the mortar and concrete mixes that can be used and that the preferred crack widening rate for the static crack-bridging test should be 0.1 mm per minute. Also, the crack should be induced manually or mechanically in the test specimen at 23°C prior to testing.

Four classes have been agreed for the static crack-bridging test and are listed below.

	Temperature (°C)	Crack width (μ)
Class 1	23	>100
Class 2	–10	>250
Class 3	–10	> 1250
Class 4	–10	>2500

For the dynamic test, the proposed crack-opening cycle should follow the movements shown in Figure 19. 1 a and b and Table 19.2. The proposed pass/fail criteria for the dynamic crack-bridging test is based on the German requirements.

19. 4   BRE dynamic and static crack-bridging test

The dynamic and static crack-bridging test developed at BRE is an example of a test method that complies with the draft European Standard (draft EN 1062-7) and is described below.

19.4.1   Principle

A coated concrete test specimen is rigidly attached to the base and crosshead of a tensile testing machine. The desired movement profile, according to Table 19.2 and Figure 19.1 is programmed into the testing machine. Repeated cycles of the movement profile are imposed on the specimen, which cracks beneath the coating, until a predetermined number of cycles is completed. The coating is monitored during the period of cycling for any holes or ruptures, in which case it is deemed to have failed at the relevant number of cycles.

19.4.2   Testing equipment

A tensile testing machine with the cross head controlled by computer is employed. The computer control is such that sine waves up to 1 Hz and amplitudes of 0.5 mm can be accurately followed. The testing machine should be fitted with devices that eliminate backlash errors during reversible cycling tests.

Software control needs to allow:

Table 19.2 *Classification and test conditions for dynamic crack-bridging test.*

Class	Test conditions
B 0	$w_o = 0.15$ mm $w_u = 0.10$ mm trapezoid $RW = 100$ $f = 0.01$ Hz $w = 0.05$ mm
B 1	$w_o = 0.15$ mm $w_u = 0.10$ mm trapezoid $RW = 100$ $f = 0.01$ Hz $w = 0.05$ mm
B 2.1	$w_o = 0.25$ mm $w_u = 0.10$ mm trapezoid $RW = 1000$ $f = 0.03$ Hz $w = 0.15$ mm
B 2.2	As above, and $w_L = \pm 0.05$ sinus $RW = 20{,}000$ $f = 1$ Hz
B 3.1	$w_o = 0.50$ mm $w_u = 0.20$ mm trapezoid $RW = 1000$ $f = 0.03$ Hz $w = 0.30$ mm
B 3.2	As above, and $w_L = \pm 0.05$ sinus $RW = 20{,}000$ $f = 1$ Hz

Key: f = frequency; w_L = load-dependent crack movement; RW = number of crack cycles; w_o = maximum crack width; w = change in crack width; w_u = minimum crack width.

- zeroing of load measurements;
- the imposition of a small compressive force;
- control of the crosshead to maintain zero force during clamping operations; and
- control of the crosshead to achieve each of the classes given in Table 19.2.

The tensile testing machine should also be fitted with a thermal cabinet which allows testing at the required temperature. It should include a glass viewing panel fitted with defrost heaters to allow visual inspection of the test specimen.

An image archiving system is also required to allow visual detection of cracks to an accuracy of 1 0 cycles.

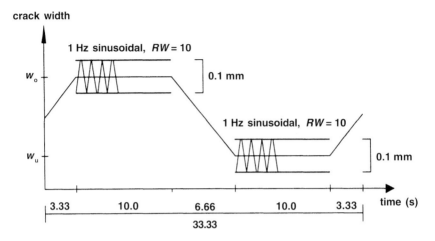

(a) Change of crack width as a function of time for classes B2.2 and B3.2. 1000 crack cycles as a trapezoidal function using 0.03 Hz, with superimosed crack cycles as a sinusoidal function using 1 Hz.

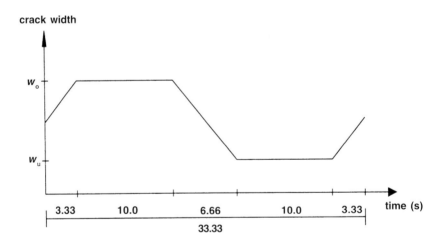

(b) Change of crack width as a function of time for classes B0, B1, B2.1 and B3.1. 1000 crack cycles as a tyrapezoidal function using 0.03 Hz.

Figure 19.1 *Crack width profiles for the draft European dynamic crack-bridging test (cf. Table 19.1).*

19.4.3 Sample preparation for dynamic and static crack-bridging test

The specimen design used for both tests is shown in Figure 19.2. The mortar mix and casting procedure used for the specimen is in accordance with EN 196-1. The notches in the middle of the specimens (see Figure 19.2) act as stress raisers to ensure that the crack propagates between the notches across the specimens. The plastic insert used in the specimens also aids in propagating a straight crack between the two notches of the specimen. This reduces the load required to crack the specimen during testing. Mild

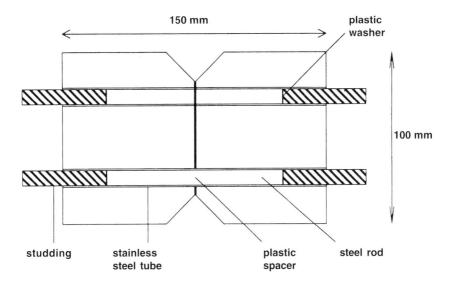

aerial cross-section of sample

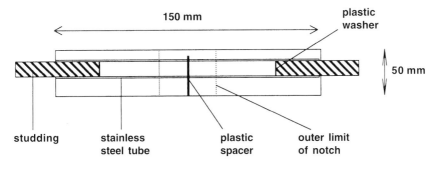

side view of sample

Figure 19.2 *Specimen design used for dynamic and static crack-bridging test.*

Table 19.3 *Coatings investigated at the Kajamia Insitute.*

	Coating type
Multi-layer	acrylic rubber
	chloroprene rubber
	silicone rubber
Single layer	acrylic resin

steel runners shown in Figure 19.2 minimize the flexural movement of the samples during testing. Steel runners are glued to the stainless steel tube and are used to grip the sample in the tensiometer.

19.5 Research into the crack-bridging ability of surface treatments

19.5.1 Investigating the crack-bridging ability of acrylic-based waterproofing system

Polyurethane elastomer is used in Japan as liquid-applied roofing membrane. Since the acrylic rubber can be sprayed, it is also used to waterproof external concrete walls. External concrete walls have joints which crack due to shrinkage and rain enters through these cracks. Liquid-applied roofing membranes are applied to the walls to prevent ingress of water. However, the Japanese industrial standards do not have any guidelines for the application of acrylic rubbers to walls; consequently Iwia of the Kajima Institute of Construction Technology set up a programme to investigate the crack-bridging properties of these elastomeric coatings. Several types of elastomeric waterproofing wall coatings were investigated, as shown in Table 19.3.

The static and dynamic crack-bridging test was undertaken at –10, 0 and 20°C, with the load applied at 5 mm per minute. The substrate used was an asbestos cement board (250 × 180 × 8 mm) with a notch on the face opposite the test face. Dynamic crack-bridging tests were performed on the specimens using crack widths between 0.12 and 4.0 mm. Iwai concluded that the crack-bridging ability of a coating was related to the dry film thickness of the coating. The thicker the coating, the better the crack-bridging ability of the elastomeric coating.

19.5.2 Investigating the crack-bridging ability of acrylic coatings

Swamy and Tanikawa (1993) investigated the crack-bridging ability of an acrylic rubber coating. The test used was to subject the coatings to tensile forces by applying a coating over an area of 100 × 200 mm on a slate board (150 × 250 × 5 mm) tested in tension, until the coating failed. The thickness of the base coat varied between 0.2 and 2.5 mm, whilst the primer and the topcoat were constant at 0.03 and 0.1 mm respectively. Swamy found that if the base coating thickness was between 0.5 and 1 mm, the crack-bridging ability of a coating was between 2 and 3.5 mm. If the base coat thickness was increased to 2.5 mm, the crack-bridging ability was 10 mm. Swamy also investigated the effect of temperature on the crack-bridging ability of 2 mm thick acrylic rubber coating. The results obtained are shown in Table 19.4.

Table 19.4 *Results of crack-bridging ability of acrylic coatings in relation to temperature (Swamy and Tanikawa, 1993).*

Temperature (°C)	Maximum crack width (mm)
−20	2.3
−10	2.7
20	3.8
60	5.2

19.5.3   Relationships for crack-bridging properties of a single coat

The tests developed by Herold (1988) at BAM to assess the crack-bridging behaviour of coatings on concrete have been incorporated into the ZTV BEL-B and ZTV-SIB regulations introduced by the Federal German Transport Ministry. Herold has derived theoretical relationships for the crack-bridging ability of coatings using equations from Klopfer's two layer theory for one coat systems for aiding in the development and understanding of crack-bridging coatings (Klopfer, 1982). The reader is referred to Herold (1988) for more information on these equations.

19.6   Conclusion

A large number of national tests exist to measure the dynamic and static crack-bridging ability of a surface treatment to concrete. However, the test, specimen, equipment and testing regime differ due to different requirements between countries. This wil change in Europe when a European standard for a dynamic test is developed.

References and bibliography

C.E.B. (1982) Durability of concrete structures. *Bulletio d'Information*, **148**, Comité Euro-International du Beton, Paris.
Herold, C. (1988) *Kunstsoffe* **78**, (7), 631–34.
Iwai, Takatsugu (1985) Crack-bridging properties of elastomeric waterproofing wall coatiungs. KICT Report No. 63. Kajima Institute of Construction Technology, Tokyo.

Klopfer, H. (1982) Eine Theorie der Ribuberbruckung durch Bescliichtungen, Bautenschutz, Bausanicrung **2**, 59–60; 86–92.

Leonhardt, F. (1987) Cracks and crack control in concrete structures. *Proceedings of the International Association for Bridge and Structural Engineering*, **109**, Zurich, Switzerland.

The Concrete Society (1 992) Non-structural cracks in concrete.. Report of a Concrete Society Working Party, *Technical Report No. 22,* Wexham.

The Concrete Society (1 995) The relevance of cracking in concrete to corrosion of reinforcement. Report of a Concrete Society Working Party, *Technical Report No.44,* Wexham.

Swamy, R. and Tanikawa, S. (1993) An external surface coating to protect concrete and steel from aggressive environments, *Materials and Structures,* **26**,465–78.

20 Case studies

This chapter deals with case studies of successful coatings applied to concrete. The information provided is by the companies concerned. It should be noted that the authors do not endorse any of these products.

20.1   Coatings for highway bridges in Ireland

Ten newly-built concrete bridges, two culverts, and a number of retaining walls that form part of the recently constructed M50 Northern Cross Motorway in Ireland have been protected with a four-part coating system designed to resist attack from carbonation and atmospheric gases, as well as water and chloride ingress.

The work is notable because it illustrates Ireland's use of a specification that includes specific and strict criteria in terms of coatings performance for a highway project.

More than 15,000 m^2 of surface area were coated with the Betonflair coating system provided by MC Building Chemicals at Castleblayney in County Monaghan, Ireland. The system is developed for long-term protection of both the concrete and its steel reinforcement.

After surface preparation by high-pressure water washing at approximately 200 bar, a scratch filler or fairing coat (Zentrifix FF02) was applied to fill blow holes and provide a porous-free smooth finish for the remainder of the protection system. Once dry, the surface was saturated with a siloxane-based impregnation material (Emcephob SX) to form a hydrophobic and highly alkali-resistant barrier. The final finish was achieved with one coat of an acrylate-based primer (Betonflair LG) followed by two coats of a coloured, acrylate-based surface sealer (Betonflair CT), all applied by airless spray to a total dry film thickness of 160 μm. The system not only resists carbonation and penetration of de-icing salts that contribute to early deterioration of concrete but also allows the concrete to 'breathe', thereby enabling moisture to escape without any detrimental effect to the applied coating.

The Betonflair system was chosen for this project because of its ability to meet the National Roads Authority specification plus all the specific requirements of the contract.

As required by the M50 contract, the system complied with the 1995 Irish National Roads Authority Specification for Road Works (Part 3, Section 1700). This specification covers the use of silane- or siloxane-based sealers as well as coating systems, which must also have Irish Agrément Board Roads and Bridges Certificates. For siloxane-based sealers, the performance standards included in the specification are based on the German Department of Transport's Technical Test Standards for Surface Protection Systems (TP OS 1990) document, which includes criteria for the minimum content of active material (i.e. siloxane) that must be absorbed by the substrate and for the maximum level of water absorption.

According to the specification, coatings should be based on acrylates (either solvent- or water-borne) and must meet performance requirements for both carbon dioxide and water diffusion resistance, water absorption and bond strength. In addition, the contract called for a specific ultraviolet-resistant, colour-stable, and non-staining neutral colour to blend with the environment, plus an anti-graffiti finish.

The 11 kilometres of new motorway, which took 3½ years to construct, completed the northern section of the Dublin C-Ring – the ring highway around Dublin that links Ireland's primary motorways.

Source: MC Building Chemicals, Castleblayney, County Monaghan, Ireland.

20.2   Bridges spanning Skeidara River, Iceland

Three road bridges comprising concrete piers and a steel superstructure were constructed in 1974 to provide an effective communication network across some of the northern hemisphere's most inhospitable terrain. The Icelandic Road and Bridge Authority sought a protective coating for the exposed steel, which could withstand constant spray from the river and regular blasting from sand storms which often have wind speeds in excess of 100 km/h.

Isoclad – a water-based copolymer compound which provides an effective barrier against moisture, chlorides and aggressive atmospheric chemicals – was specified as it was the only product amongst several anti-corrosive systems tested to meet successfully the demanding test criteria. The product has successfully protected the bridges for over 20 years and, in 1996, the Icelandic authorities confirmed they had such confidence in Isoclad that it was re-specified for application to all three bridges again.

Client: Icelandic Road and Bridge Authority
Source: Liquid Plastics Ltd., Preston, Lancashire

20.3   Bridges complex – Western Gate, Brussels

In Belgium, as in many Western countries, numerous reinforced concrete road bridges are in need of repair. Carbonation, chloride attack, weathering and attack by aggressive atmospheric pollution all combine to create a very hostile environment for unprotected concrete, and deterioration can often result.

After a two year research period and extensive testing at the University of Ghent, the Flemish Ministry of Infrastructure and Environment laid down its requirements for a coating that would provide an effective defence against these elements and thereby extend the design life of the bridges. On the basis of the specification, 11 bridges were treated using Flexcrete Decadex 848 – a fast curing, water-based, anti-carbonation coating which offers exceptional resistance to water penetration and attack by airborne chemicals. Manufactured in accordance with the demands of **BS EN ISO 9001**, Decadex 848 typically offers a life span of well over 15 years as a two coat application.

Client: Flemish Ministry of Infrastructure and Environment
Source: Liquid Plastics Ltd., Preston, Lancashire

20.4   Tahtiniemi Bridge, Finland

The 924-metre span Tahtiniemi Bridge was built as part of the Henola Bypass on the Helsinki-Lahti-Lusi motorway and features 20 intermediate reinforced concrete columns in addition to a cable stayed section with an H-shaped pylon towards the southern side. In order to protect the structure against the harsh weather and aggressive conditions to which it would be exposed, a tough, durable coating was sought which would offer effective protection against carbonation, chloride attack, water penetration and subsequent frost damage.

Having considered a number of alternatives, leading road design specialists, the Finnish Road Know-how Group, specified Flexcrete Decadex 848 for the contract and the application was duly carried out over the summer months. Decadex has a water-based formulation which cures at temperatures as low as 3 °C and forms a totally waterproof membrane that presents an effective barrier to the diffusion of carbon dioxide and chloride ions. Backed by a 30-year international track record, it is highly elastomeric and will not embrittle with age or prolonged exposure to ultraviolet light.

Client: Finnish National Road Administration
Source: Liquid Plastics Ltd., Preston, Lancashire

20.5   Maintaining concrete university buildings

Maintaining the appearance and integrity of concrete buildings, especially in aggressive atmospheric conditions, is a challenge requiring assessment of current conditions and available options in order to select the most appropriate approach. This case study is based on the experience of the Estates Department at the University of Manchester Institute of Science & Technology (UMIST) and describes the background to the strategy put into place for concrete structure maintenance and the results obtained to date.

20.5.1   Background

Much of the estate at UMIST was built in the 1960s and 1970s. The campus is in the centre of Manchester, and many of the buildings are high-rise, multi-storey structures with in situ and precast, exposed white, cement-based concrete.

As a result of the UK Clean Air Act of the 1960s, the Manchester atmosphere is now free of sulphur from coal fires, but for many years these concrete buildings were exposed to acid rain, which attacked the concrete and caused it to deteriorate. Consequently, by

1983, the buildings presented a very poor image due to staining from micro-biological growths that lodged in the roughened surface. In addition, spalling of concrete because of rusting steel reinforcement – another effect of the deterioration caused by acid rain – required barrier protection for pedestrians around several of the buildings.

One building, Chandos Hall, had been repaired with epoxy mortars and coated with polyurethane in 1970. Although the coating performed as predicted, gradually powdering over time, the in situ concrete was in poor condition. The epoxy repairs were loose due to corrosion around the repair edges, and extensive repairs to the concrete were necessary. The concrete was recoated with a similar material, but the work was not successful. Within a few years, large areas of the coating were debonding.

By the early 1980s, polymer-modified cement-based mortars were available for concrete repair. These mortars offer many advantages over epoxy mortars.

- They are cementitious products that recreate an alkaline environment to protect the steel reinforcement, similar to the original concrete.
- They bond to the concrete and do not rely solely on providing a waterproof barrier to protect the steel.
- They are easy to mix and use on site, and some materials can be applied overhead to a thickness of more than 100 mm in one application.

Silane-based concrete coatings were also available, and were being used with success on the continent. Therefore, a concrete maintenance strategy was developed at UMIST based on these materials.

Before developing a remedial treatment strategy, however, it was necessary to establish and understand the problems with the current structures.

20.5.2   Assessment of concrete deterioration

An assessment of the nature and degree of concrete degradation was undertaken by independent analytical chemists, who performed tests to determine the following:

1. Depth of cover to reinforcement (the distance of steel rebar from the outer face of the concrete).
2. Depth of carbonation (the depth of deterioration from the outer face of the concrete as a result of penetration by carbon dioxide and moisture).
3. Chloride percentage of concrete and chloride ion content by weight of the cement (which indicate the risk of corrosion to the steel rebar).
4. Sulphate penetration (depth of deterioration from the outer face of the concrete as a result of sulphate attack).
5. Cement content (the amount of cement in the concrete mixture).
6. Alkali-silicate reaction (which indicates the presence of siliceous aggregates that cause expansive cracking within the concrete).

20.5.3   Test results

The following results were obtained from tests performed on the Chemistry Building complex in 1986.

1. Depth of cover to reinforcement: the results ranged from 5–80 mm; 84% of the samples were below 50 mm (design cover) and 50% of the samples were below 35 mm. The results were unacceptable because 84% of the samples were below the minimum design cover, which is the same as the depth of cover to reinforcement.
2. Depth of carbonation: the results ranged from 2–6 mm; the average depth was 2.5 mm, which was acceptable, because the depth of carbonation should be less than the depth of cover.
3. Chloride ion content by weight of cement: the results were
   0–0.4 (low risk), 70%;
   0.4–1.0 (medium risk), 16%;
   above 1.0 (high risk), 14%.
The results were acceptable because the high risk category accounted for only 14%.
4. Sulphate penetration: the results generally were only about 3 mm, which was acceptable because the sulphate penetration should be less than the depth of cover. One reading was 10 mm. It is possible to extrapolate the progress of the deterioration for unprotected concrete. This indicates the penetration of 10 mm would increase to 13 mm by the year 2015.
5. Cement content: the result was as predicted for white concrete, which means the concrete contained the correct amount of cement.
6. Alkali-silicate reaction: there was no evidence of expansive gel formation in the petrographic samples, which means the aggregates in the concrete were stable.

From these results, it was established that lack of cover was the main problem and calcium chloride content was a secondary factor. Carbonation and sulphate penetration were only minor concerns.

20.5.4   Options to solve problems

Following this analysis, the various options available to the maintenance department to solve or manage the problem of concrete deterioration were considered. These options included demolition, overcladding, and the use of protective coating materials.

Demolition

One way to solve a problem building is simply to demolish it. This solution is expected to be used soon on the former headquarters of the Department of Environment at Marsham Street in London because the cost of repairs exceeds the cost of redevelopment.

Another example of demolition involved the high-rise flats built in the 1960s in Hulme and owned by Manchester City Council. They were demolished as much for poor social engineering as for insoluble structural problems. The requirement to keep concrete warm and dry was not met because the underfloor electric heating was too expensive for the tenants to use. Instead, they resorted to other, less effective heating methods, which forced moisture into the structure.

Perhaps more unusual is the case of the University of Salford, where the Chemistry Research Tower was demolished after it was deemed to be surplus to requirements following cuts in 1981. The reasons given for its demolition were poor insulation, falling mosaic, and lift problems.

Overcladding

This remedy involves installation of a sheath of metal or other construction material over the deteriorated concrete. However, overcladding should not be used simply to mask defects. Any defects should first be solved, so that overcladding is used as a cosmetic remedy rather than a structural one.

The following are some considerations in the use of overcladding.

- Problems can occur with condensation and subsequent deterioration in the void between the overcladding and the original concrete.
- Cladding material can be heavy, so it must be decided whether the building structure or foundations can handle the additional weight.
- Installation can be disruptive to a facility that remains in operation while the work is being done.

An unusual problem with overcladding occurred about 1992 at Knowsley Heights, a residential tower block in Liverpool, where a void between the cladding material and the original structure acted as a chimney when a skip at the base of the block caught fire. The result was extensive damage to the tower block.

Protective coatings

In the mid-1980s, concrete problems in high-rise buildings were commonplace, and the best advice then was that a concrete repair system should include protection of any undamaged concrete.

The following types of protective coating materials were available for this purpose.

- Polyurethane – this coating material has average thickness, is slightly flexible but impermeable, and has a durability of 10–15 years.
- Acrylic emulsion – this is an average to relatively thick coating, slightly flexible but permeable, and with a durability of 4–10 years.
- Pigmented silane – this material is relatively thin, inflexible but permeable, and offers a durability of 20–30 years.

20.5.5 Remedial strategy

For UMIST, the demolition and rebuilding option was not feasible on the grounds of cost and temporary loss of facilities. The cost of overcladding was also prohibitive. Since the campus is now required by the Universities Funding Council to maintain its buildings with a 50-year life to avoid depreciation to the value of the estate, the only cost-effective solution was to use protective coatings. Therefore, following an assessment of coatings available in the mid-1980s, the silane-based coating system was chosen. The reasons for its selection were that it had been used successfully for many years on the continent, it provided a life expectancy of 20 years before recoating, it was easy to apply, and it was available in a wide range of colours and shades to replicate the original concrete of the UMIST buildings.

20.5.6   Procedure developed

The maintenance strategy developed was to coat methodically exposed concrete of the UMIST buildings according to the following procedure.
1. Assess concrete deterioration.
2. Clean steel reinforcement to remove all rust (or remove reinforcement that is redundant or near an exposed surface).
3. Protect the reinforcement with a non-water-borne coating.
4. Repair concrete using a polymer-modified mortar system.
5. Clean concrete with high pressure water jet and allow the surface to dry.
6. Apply a biocidal wash to surfaces heavily stained by microbiological growth.
7. Apply the coating system, including
   silane primer;
   first, diluted colour coat (applied while primer is still wet); and
   second colour coat (applied after first and second coats have dried).

20.5.7   Performance in service

Generally, the coatings have performed as predicted. They are scheduled for recoating at 20-year intervals in the UMIST long-term maintenance programme.

At the present time, only the newest of the major multi-storey buildings on campus – the Mathematics and Social Sciences Building built in 1971, remains to be protected.

Localized problems from lack of adhesion and subsequent flaking of the coating have occurred where the concrete surface was not thoroughly prepared and where traces of mould, oil, and/or laitance remained on the face of the concrete. In addition, the coating applied to heavily stained concrete – particularly north-facing elevations with a lack of direct sunlight – did not stop the microbiological growths. These areas now receive a pre-treatment to neutralize the growth prior to application of the coating system.

The coatings retain their colour in wet conditions, which is a cosmetic benefit, and because of the protection the coatings provide, moisture intake by the concrete is greatly reduced. As a result, more than 10 multi-storey buildings at UMIST are being protected and maintained at a fraction of the cost of overcladding.

Client: University of Manchester Institute of Science and Technology
Source: UMIST Estates Department, Manchester

20.6   Unique use of supplier in quality assurance role for concrete repair project

When a building is sited within 100 metres of the North Sea, and is only minutes by car from the North Atlantic, it is exposed to some of the worst weather conditions in the British Isles; an almost daily saturation in salt-laden sea spray, low winter temperatures, snow, sleet, and heavy rainfall. The location is Lerwick in the Shetland Islands, and the building is the Gilbert Bain Hospital.

According to the Shetland Health Board (SHB), there was concern about the energy efficiency of the accommodation block at the hospital. The Common Services Agency in Aberdeen, agents for the SHB, invited PermaRock, a supplier of materials for concrete repair, to visit the site to determine if the block was suitable for external wall insulation.

20.6.1 Condition survey

From the initial site visit, it was apparent that the structure was exhibiting signs of deterioration to the exposed reinforced concrete frame. There was cracking, loss of concrete cover at some locations, and rust staining from corroding reinforcement. The concrete cladding panels, particularly on the upper levels of the north and south-west corners, were bulging out from the surface, with only the brick and block infill panels appearing to be relatively sound.

Some limited research had been carried out on the reinforced concrete frame in 1992 by the Health Board's consultant engineers; of particular interest were the figures on the chloride content of the concrete. Samples taken from the internal faces of the columns in the basement area, where the concrete had been protected from the worst excesses of the weather, had been found to contain chloride levels of about 0.2% by weight of cement. These high figures indicated that chloride had probably been incorporated into the cement at the initial mixing stage, either through the use of admixtures such as calcium chloride accelerators, or through the use of salt-contaminated sand, or even from salt water.

The survey found that the concrete cover to the steel was generally within the original specification, with only minor deviations. The chloride analyses from the exposed elements of the reinforced concrete frame ranged from 0.46 to 1.46% chloride by weight of cement. It is generally accepted that the corrosion risk to the reinforcement is significantly high if the chloride level is in excess of 0.4% by weight of cement. In this case, the risk of chloride-induced corrosion was very high, and it was concluded that these high levels of chloride were contributing to the corrosion of the reinforcement observed from both the visual inspection and from half-cell potential and corrosion rate measurements.

Carbonation depths were found to vary throughout the structure, up to a maximum of 15 mm. At these depths, the loss of alkalinity of the concrete would not have significantly affected the reinforcement, so carbonation was ruled out as the main cause of the rebar corrosion. However, it was noted that the advancing carbonation front could have caused the release of previously 'bound' chlorides, making them available as corrosion cell initiators. Further condition assessment of the structure revealed defective joints between panels which, with subsequent ingress of salt-laden moisture, had caused the metal ties to corrode. The expansive nature of the corrosion by-products had pushed the panels away from the walls, making it a potentially unstable surface and unsuitable for the direct application of an external wall insulation system.

Finally, to assess the type and level of external insulation required, the original construction details were studied. It was then necessary to determine the existing U values (the rate of heat energy transfer (loss) through an element of a building), the dew point, and potential condensation risks. The U values were found to be in the range 0.786 to 1.379 W m^{-2} K^{-1}, somewhat higher than the current Building Standards (Scotland) Regulations 1990 (as amended) requirement of 0.45 W m^{-2} K^{-1}, and thereby indicated poor thermal efficiency.

20.6.2   Proposed system

Upon completion of the physical survey and laboratory testing, a report was submitted to the client for discussion. This report proposed an external insulation system, which would meet the thermal insulating properties required by the current building regulations and be in line with the client's requirements. This system consisted of incorporating 50 mm of mineral fibre insulant throughout the structure, with a dry dash aggregate finish (render with aggregate cast into it) in two colours to improve the aesthetic appearance of the structure. Pull-out tests had confirmed there was sufficient strength in the walls to carry the additional loading of this system. However, the report stated that necessary structural repairs and modifications needed to be carried out as described below.

- Because the external cladding panel ties in all areas inspected were found to be heavily corroded, all other cladding panels where similar joint failure was evident should be removed.
- An impressed current cathodic protection system, using a conductive coating anode, should be installed, after carrying out any necessary concrete repairs, to provide a permanent control against continued reinforcement corrosion.
- Where permissible, and where the concrete cladding panels were to be removed, the full external insulation system should be installed. Where this was not practical, external rendering should be used.
- The external wall insulation system should be designed to be compatible with the cathodic protection system.

20.6.3   Sole source supplier

The supplier provided all the products for the project, including concrete repair materials, cathodic protection materials, external wall insulation, and external rendering systems. The company was invited by the client to prepare a full set of specifications and budget costs for the project on the basis that it was the client's intention to incorporate the company's whole proposal into the renovation works.

Sole specification status was given to the supplier on the basis of access to full technical knowledge and product support, an understanding of the requirements of the project, and availability of quality assurance monitoring of the project in progress.

The materials supplier was invited to submit the names of suitably qualified contractors to undertake the work, which was no easy task because the lead contractor would require an in-depth knowledge of cathodic protection systems as the key element of the work, together with sufficient experience to manage the concrete repair and installation of external insulation. Concrete Repairs Ltd. was finally selected because it had expertise in all aspects of the work and was also an approved contractor for the supplier's product range.

The client decided to include the supplier in the execution of the project in a quality assurance role, over and above that of materials manufacturer/designer. This represented a new development in contracting, in that it is highly unusual for this type of project to be manufacturer/designer-led or managed.

20.6.4 System installation

The decision to remove the cladding panels at the outset of the works proved to be correct, as the corrosion of the tie system was widespread.

The concrete repair element of the work was undertaken using a concrete repair system accredited by the British Board of Agrément (BBA), specifically designed to meet the repair criteria and to be fully compatible with the cathodic protection system. All the main columns, ring beams, and pre-cast reinforced concrete window surrounds were repaired before the installation of the cathodic protection system and external wall insulation application. The cathodic protection system was designed around the company's Permaguard WB water-based conductive coating anode and its anode ribbon. This carbon fibre ribbon was fixed to the repaired and prepared concrete surfaces with epoxy resin (also supplied by the company) and then overcoated with the conductive coating. The connections to the reinforcing steel were made using a proprietary cathodic connection system. The electric supply to the cathodic protection system consisted of transformer-rectifier units located in a single cabinet in the basement. The transformer-rectifiers supply low voltage (12 volt) direct constant current to the system, monitored periodically from the transformer-rectifier cabinet by interrogation of reference electrodes positioned within the reinforced concrete structure.

The company's wall insulation system (also BBA-certified) was applied to the surfaces which had been prepared by levelling and was then treated with a biocidal/fungicidal wash. The insulant was mineral fibre in the form of rigid, compressed slabs (boards), fixed to the substrate with a cementitious adhesive. The mineral fibre boards were then coated with a bedding mortar, into which was trowelled a coated, alkali-resistant glass-fibre mesh. Mechanical fixing pins were driven through this system in a predetermined pattern to tie the insulation to the substrate. The location and type of fixing pins were selected to prevent interference with the cathodic protection system.

The decorative finish was achieved by applying a second coat of polymer-modified mortar, coloured to the client's choice, and into which natural stone aggregate was cast, the colour and size again to the client's specification.

The project was completed with powder-coated aluminium oversills on the copings and window sills. Several pre-cast reinforced window frames, which were not included in the cathodic protection system, were repaired using concrete repair materials and finished using a colour-matched, anti-carbonation coating.

At a number of locations, notably on the east and west elevations between the upper level windows, structural panels were protected using a two-coat polymer-modified render with a dry dash finish to provide a contrast with the main areas of the external wall insulation system. The exposed areas of cathodically protected reinforced concrete were finished in a colour-matched decorative coating, compatible with the cathodic protection anode system.

The existing brick panels were retained as features, and were cleaned and waterproofed using an alkyl alkoxysiloxane-based product designed to provide water repellence while still allowing the passage of water vapour and remaining invisible on the brick surface.

Client: Shetland Health Board

Source: PermaRock Ltd., Loughborough, Leicestershire, and Concrete Repairs Ltd., Mitcham, Surrey

Appendix

Coating manufacturers

Further information about the suitability of coatings for the protection or decoration of concrete can be obtained from the coating manufacturers in the respective countries. Some manufacturers, such as the Sika group of companies, will supply on an international basis, whereas others tend to be national or regional.

A selection of these is given below for Europe and N. America, in alphabetical order.

Europe

Asturlak
Avda Agricultura, 32
33211 Gidon
Spain
tel: *+34 98 5323866*
fax: *+34 98 5314326*

Flexcrete
P.O. Box 7
Preston
PR1 1EA
England
tel: *+44 (0) 1772 259477*
fax: *+44 (0) 1772 202902*

Flowcrete Group plc
Flowcrete Business Park
Booth Lane
Moston
Sandbach
Cheshire
CW11 3QF
tel: *+44 (0)1270 753000*
fax: *+44 (0)1270 753333*

SGL Alotec Ltd. (Ceilcote)
Millbuck Way
Ettiley Heath
Sandbach
Cheshire
CW11 3AB
England
tel: *+44 (0)1270 761720*
fax: *+44 (0)1270 761697*

Liquid Plastics Ltd.
P.O. Box 7
Preston,
PR1 1EA
England
tel :   *+44 (0)1772 259781*
fax: *+44 (0)1772 882016*

Master Builders NV
Nijverheidsweg 89
3945 Ham
Belgium
tel: *+32 11 34 04 34*
fax: *+32 11 40 13 92*

MBT Ucrete
19 Broad Ground Road
Lakeside
Redditch
B98 8YP
England
tel: *+44 (0) 1527 505100*
fax: *+44 (0) 1527 510299*

Permatex France S.A.S.
ZA Les Bruottées Vignolles
21209 Beaune Cedex
France
tel: *+33 3 80 25 05 85*
fax: *+33 3 80 22 90 96*

Permatex GmbH
Postfach 1447
71657 Vaihingen
Germany
tel: *+49 70 42 1090*
fax: *+49 70 42 109180*

Remmers (UK) Ltd.
Remmers House
14 Victoria Way
Burgess Hill
W. Sussex
RH15 9NF
England
tel: *+44 (0)1444 244144*
fax: *+44 (0)1444 243500*

Ronacrete Ltd.
Ronac House
Selinas Lane
Dagenham
Essex
RM8 1QL
England
tel: *+44 (0)20 8593 7621*
fax: *+44 (0)20 8595 6969*

Sika AG
Tuffenwies 16
8048 Zurich
Switzerland
tel: *+41 1 436 40 40*
fax: *+41 1 436 45 84*

Sika Chemie GmbH
Kornwestheimer Strasse 107
70439 Stuttgart
Germany
tel: *+49 71 1 80 09 090*
fax: *+49 711 80 09 321*
www.sika.com

Stirling Lloyd Group plc
Union Bank
King Street
Knutsford
Cheshire
tel: *+44 (0)1565 633111*
fax: *+44 (0)1565 633555*

N. America

Carboline
350 Hanley Industrial Court
St. Louis
MO 63144
tel: *+ 1 314 644 1000*
fax: *+ 1 314 644 3353*

Ceilcote, a division of SGL Alotec, Inc.
6611 West Snowville Road
Brecksville
Ohio 44141
tel: *+1 877 234 5268*
fax: *+1 440 717 7466*

Chemrex Inc.
89 Valley Park Rd
Shakopee
Minnesota 55379
tel : *+1 952 496 6028*
fax: *+1 952 496 6058*

Dudick Inc.
1818 Miller Parkway
Streetsboro
Ohio 44241
tel: *+1 330 562 1970*
fax: *+1 330 562 7638*
www.dudick.com

Industrial Environmental Coatings Corp.
1831 Blount Road
Pompano Beach
FL 33069
tel: +1 954 978 9355
fax: +1 954 978 3913

Madison Chemical Industries Inc.
490 McGeachie Drive
Milton, Ontario,
L9T 3Y5
Canada
tel: +1 905 878 8863
fax: +1 905 878 1449

Sauereisen
160 Gamma Drive
Pittsburgh
PA 15238
tel: +1 412 963 0303
fax: +1 412 963 7620
www.sauereisen.com

Sika Corporation
201 Polito Avenue
Lyndhurst
NJ 07071
tel: +1 201 933 8800
fax: +1 201 804 1076
www.sikausa.com

Stonhard Inc.
One Park Avenue
Maple Shade
NJ 08052
tel: +1 856 779 7500
fax: +1 856 321 7525
www.stonhard.com

Surtreat International
1360 N. Wood Dale Road
Suite A
Wood Dale
IL 60191
tel: +1 630 616 2757
fax: +1 630 616 9203
www.surtreat.net

Tennant Company
701 N. Lilac Drive
Minneapolis
IN 55422-1452
tel: +1 763 540 1200
fax: +1 763 513 2112
www.tennantco.com

Index